Introduction to the special theory of
RELATIVITY

CLAUDE KACSER

DEPARTMENT OF PHYSICS AND ASTRONOMY

UNIVERSITY OF MARYLAND

PRENTICE-HALL, INC.

ENGLEWOOD CLIFFS, NEW JERSEY

PRENTICE-HALL INTERNATIONAL, INC. *London*
PRENTICE-HALL OF AUSTRALIA, PTY. LTD. *Sydney*
PRENTICE-HALL OF CANADA, LTD. *Toronto*
PRENTICE-HALL OF INDIA (PRIVATE) LTD. *New Delhi*
PRENTICE-HALL OF JAPAN, INC. *Tokyo*

Printed in the United States of America.

Library of Congress Catalog Card Number: 67-16387.

Current printing (last digit): 10 9 8 7 6 5 4 3 2 1

PREFACE

This book has grown out of my belief that the special theory of relativity belongs in every liberal arts physics course, whatever the intended major of the student.

One good reason is that the theory (particularly the application of $E = mc^2$) does greatly affect the real everyday world and form part of its technology. However, for the liberal arts student the main reason for studying the theory is that it is an admirable reminder of the necessity to study "self-evident" concepts with great care, even if they have worked satisfactorily in the past. The job of the scientist, and the attitude of the intelligent layman, is one of questioning. All concepts should be subjected to detailed examination so as to discover their hidden assumptions. One common error is to take a concept which is well understood and which works adequately in one domain, and expect that it will work just as well in another. An example is the idea that "what holds for everyday macroscopic objects must also hold for microscopic, atomic, nuclear, and subnuclear objects; for stars, galaxies, and universes." The developments in modern physics belie that idea.

The theory *in itself* it not inherently difficult; but it may seem difficult since it investigates with great care everyday concepts of space and time, which it ultimately shows to be wrong, meaningless, or misleading. Hence to understand the theory, it is necessary to study it in *depth*. I would stress that the theory is not an intellectual construct of a philosophical type, but is very firmly based on the results of experiment.

Mathematically this study requires no more than an understanding of high school algebra. There are many problems in this book, which the student must do if he is to really understand the subject. The worked examples given also form an integral part of the presentation and should be attempted *before* the student looks at the solutions. After reading the solutions, the student should ask himself which were the key steps in the method and why the solution was performed in the manner given. By so doing, he will learn more readily how to solve problems.

One can cover the material concurrently with the development of the Newtonian concepts; i.e., do Chapters 1 to 4 immediately after Newtonian kinematics, then do Newtonian dynamics, followed by Chapters 5 and 6 and some of Chapter 7; and finally continue with Chapter 7 while doing "modern physics." However, depending on the sophistication of the reader, it is perhaps advisable to wait to introduce the subject until all of Newtonian mechanics has been covered. In a minimum program, the sections denoted by asterisks may be omitted. The appendices require more sophistication than is demanded by the body of the book and are probably only suitable for physics majors and honors engineers.

I am very grateful to Harry Lam and to Harry Zapolsky for reading drafts of various parts of the manuscript; to Jim Woods for many fruitful discussions; to Sandy Wall for his cooperation in class-testing the preliminary edition; and not least to the students involved, who really did the testing. My appreciation goes to Cynthia Eisler, Karen Kundell, and Judith Nilsson for their skill in typing the manuscript, and to N. Maisel for suggesting the cover design. To my wife and daughter, my thanks for their forbearance during the preparation of the manuscript.

C.K.

CONTENTS

APPENDIX A
SPACE-TIME   112

APPENDIX B
EXCERPT FROM EINSTEIN'S "ON THE
ELECTRODYNAMICS OF MOVING BODIES"   127

5
INVARIANCE IN PHYSICS.
RELATIVISTIC MASS   141

HISTORICAL BACKGROUND

In the latter half of the nineteenth century, physics was making great strides forward. Mechanics had been understood since the time of Galileo and Newton, and had been brought to such high development by the work of Lagrange that the planet Neptune was discovered by theoretical analysis of the orbital motion of Uranus.*

Another field, the theory of electricity and magnetism, was fast developing. James Clerk Maxwell had proposed his Equations of Electrodynamics in 1864, which suggested that light was an electromagnetic wave. Heinrich Hertz in 1887 had actually detected electromagnetic waves emitted by an electrical spark generator.† The Maxwell equations worked.

Other branches of physics were also developing, but these are not our present concern. Newtonian mechanics and electromagnetic theory each existed as well-tested codifications of experiment and theory, applicable

*The prediction was made independently by Le Verrier in France and Adams in England. Le Verrier was immediately able to persuade the astronomer Galle to look for the planet, and it was found on the same day that Galle received Le Verrier's letter. Adams had no such luck with the English Astronomer Royal, who had other things to attend to. See M. Grosser, *The Discovery of Neptune* (Cambridge, Mass.: Harvard University Press, 1962).

†In the same series of experiments, he accidentally discovered the photoelectric effect.

in their separate domains. Newtonian mechanics spoke of, or at least implied, absolute space and time (as did Maxwell's theory), but different observers in *constant* relative motion with respect to each other saw basically the same physics. The laws of mechanics were invariant under the transformation which corresponds to looking at an experiment first from the point of view of one observer, and then from that of a second observer moving at a constant velocity with respect to the first observer. (We discuss this further in Chapter 2).

On the other hand, if one applied to Maxwell's equations the same transformation from one observer to another moving at constant velocity with respect to the first, one found that the physics was *not* the same to the two observers. What this implied is that there was a special *absolute* frame of reference in which the laws of electromagnetism had their simplest form. This was not so surprising, since electromagnetism is a wave phenomenon, and waves "must" travel on something. This something was given the name "the ether"; it was taken to be all-pervasive and so constructed that it existed even in vacuum, and such that material objects could pass through it with no friction (otherwise, for instance, the planets would have slowed down over the centuries).

If then a special frame of reference existed for electromagnetic phenomena, one should be able to detect motion *relative* to the "ether." Now the earth moves round the sun at a speed of about 30 km/sec, and heads in different directions in summer and winter. (Of course, one had long ago been converted to a heliocentric view of the solar system.) Hence, at some time in the year the earth should have a speed of at least 30 km/sec relative to the "ether," and this relative motion should be detectable. Michelson and Morley in 1887 performed a very clever experiment to determine the absolute motion of the earth through the "ether." They found *no* effect, however often and whenever the experiment was repeated either by themselves or by other experimenters.

This experimental result threw classical physics into consternation. An enormous amount of effort went into performing other experiments and devising theories. Many of the latter were *ad hoc*—merely constructed to explain away the negative results of the various experiments.* We discuss some of these in more detail in Section 2.6.

---

*A rather full summary is given in W. K. H. Panofsky and Melba Phillips, *Classical Electricity and Magnetism* (Reading, Mass. : Addison-Wesley Publishing Co., 1955). A much fuller historical account is given in Sir Edmund Whittaker, *A History of the Theories of Aether and Electricity;* Vol. II: *The Modern Theories* (London: Thomas Nelson and Sons, 1953; paperback edition, New York: Harper & Row, Publishers, 1960). Some of our quotations are taken from this work (which, however, greatly undervalues Einstein's contributions in the development of the special theory of relativity).

The most satisfactory such theory was that developed by H. A. Lorentz between the years 1895 and 1904, since it was not *ad hoc*. Rather, this theory was based on Maxwell's equations, assuming the existence of an ether. Lorentz *followed through* in detail the changes brought about in these equations when looked at from the point of view of an observer moving with respect to the ether. (Understandably, he used the "standard" coordinate transformations appropriate to such a moving observer.) He found that in materials moving with respect to the ether, the electromagnetic forces became modified in such a way that material rods, if held together by basic electrical forces, would actually contract physically. Since "meter sticks" would suffer the same contraction, an observer moving with his apparatus through the ether would not "observe" this contraction. Lorentz also showed that if *all* mass were due to electromagnetism, the mass of a particle should depend on its velocity through the ether. (Experiments had already demonstrated some such effect for electrons when in motion relative to the laboratory.)

In its experimental consequences the theory of Lorentz as finally developed makes *exactly* the same predictions as the theory due to Einstein. However the **physical** models of the universe underlying the two theories are completely *opposed*. Lorentz believed firmly in the Newtonian concepts of an absolute time and an absolute space. In a sense his space was even more absolute than Newton's, since the frame in which the ether was taken to be at rest was the natural primary frame (in which Maxwell's equations applied in their simplest form). Thus the space and time of Lorentz were Newtonian.* By basing all properties of material bodies upon primary electromagnetic interactions (even so far as to include all mass as being electromagnetic in origin), Lorentz was able to analyze completely the behavior of material objects when moving with respect to the ether. He was then able to demonstrate that *all* objects (including meter sticks) would suffer a *real, physical* contraction when moving through the ether. Further, because of an actual dependence of electromagnetic mass on velocity, clocks would run more slowly when moving through the ether. These effects were believed to be *real* effects, which an "omniscient" being would actually be able to detect using "nonmaterial" meter sticks and clocks. Of course, an ordinary observer would not be able to detect these effects, since his standards would also be affected. In fact, simply by working from the *known* equations of electromagnetism, Lorentz was able to show that these various *real* effects had the remarkable property of "canceling out." In particular, for an

---

*Lorentz himself never gave or used the basic *relativistic* transformation equations which are called by his name. Similarly, Einstein was not aware of the work of Lorentz when Einstein presented these equations, which only later became known as the Lorentz transformation.

observer moving through the ether, the *real* velocity of light would be *different* from that in the absolute frame; but the observer would measure the *same unchanged* value, since his meter sticks and clocks would be affected by the motion! In fact *all* the predictions of Lorentz's theory were such that all *observable* effects depended only on the *relative* motion of different parts of the apparatus; the absolute motion of any part of the apparatus *relative* to the ether could *never* be detected. Nonetheless, the ether existed as a very definite primary frame.

This raises a question, partly metaphysical, which was first really discussed by Henri Poincaré. At first Poincaré had believed in the existence of the absolute ether, even though he agreed with Lorentz that its properties were such that *absolute motion is undetectable in principle.* In 1900, Poincaré went further and asked: "Our ether, does it really exist? I do not believe that more precise observations could ever reveal anything more than *relative* displacements."* By 1904 Poincaré had stated the *second* half of the above as a postulate, the Principle of Relativity; and even went so far as to say that "from all these results there must arise an entirely new kind of dynamics, which will be characterized above all by the rule that no velocity can exceed the velocity of light."*

However, it remained for Einstein to provide this dynamics. Lorentz had a complete theory, but he was a firm "absolutist." Poincaré, on the other hand, could well be called the first "relativist," but he did not have a complete theory. Einstein presented the first full theory of relativity in 1905.† Einstein was not aware of the completed form of Lorentz's theory in its 1904 form, nor probably of Poincaré's statements of 1904.

Although Einstein's paper is called "On the Electrodynamics of Moving Bodies," its first section is a complete discussion and reappraisal of Newton's concepts of absolute space and absolute time. In particular, Einstein contended that the concept of absolute time was *empty* (except perhaps to an omniscient being) unless there was some experiment by which one could detect absolute motion. Einstein argued that no such experiment had been discovered or was, indeed, conceivable. Accordingly he abandoned completely the concept of absolute time, and with it the equally empty concepts of absolute space *and of the ether itself.* Starting completely afresh, Einstein developed a "relativistic" view of space and time. From this, he *then* turned to Maxwell's equations. All his final algebraic formulas were the same as those of Lorentz,‡ but the physical model of the universe underlying them was *completely* different. (Physics

---

*These quotations are taken from the work by Whittaker cited in the footnote on page 2. I am grateful to Thomas Nelson and Sons for permission to reproduce them.

†*Annalen der Physik,* **17,** 891 (1905). A portion of this paper is given in translation in Appendix B to Chapter 4.

‡But see the footnote on p. 3.

in general lies in the words and concepts that dress and interpret the equations, and not in the mathematical symbols themselves.)

It is very possible that Poincaré would himself have presented a complete theory of relativity had Einstein not done so. Lorentz did not see the need, and his theory should be classed as "pre-relativity." To Einstein most deservedly goes the fame for formulating the theory of relativity.

We see that a knowledge of the theory of electromagnetism was essential to Lorentz, and was very useful to Einstein, particularly in his analysis of mass—that is, $E = mc^2$. In the present book, however, we assume *no* knowledge of electricity and magnetism.

We follow Einstein in first analyzing space and time. That part of physics which describes motion purely in terms of space and time is called **kinematics.** You certainly have studied Newtonian kinematics. Nonetheless, we commence with a detailed study of Newtonian kinematics, since one cannot overthrow that which one does not know. We then go on to treat the Lorentz transformation, which is the set of basic formulas of the theory (actually first obtained by J. Larmor); but we obtain the formulas by following the Einstein view of the universe. After presenting some kinematic consequences, we go on to the subject of dynamics; that is, we analyze mass, momentum, force, and energy. After some applications, we very briefly introduce Einstein's General Theory of Relativity. (This starts from the basis of the Special Theory of Relativity, but incorporates gravitation as well.)

2

CLASSICAL KINEMATICS

In this chapter we review certain concepts about space and time, which form the basis of "classical" or pre-relativity theory. (This will be our standard use of the word classical.) These concepts were developed primarily by Galileo and Newton, and are associated with their names in physics textbooks. Many of these concepts will seem self-evident and hardly worthy of discussion—for two reasons:

(i) The concepts seem to apply obviously and directly to everyday life, as observed from your birth to the present.

(ii) They form the basis of all the discussion of space and time that has been taught to you up to now, and hence they are now part of your subconscious.

For both these reasons, which not only apply to you but also applied to all physicists before the bombshell of Einstein's 1905 paper, the concepts of classical kinematics became a "dogma," unquestioned and not to be questioned. As discussed in Chapter 1, classical physics was having problems,* and Lorentz and others had gone a long way towards dealing with them. However these physicists never looked at the fundamental dogma associated with classical kinematics. The dogma was so ingrained that the thought of questioning it never arose. It was Einstein's genius to

*This was also the time of the first soul-searching towards quantum mechanics.

question the self-evident. The special theory of relativity is not *basically* difficult. It may seem hard to come to grips with it and understand it, but the reason is neither mathematical nor conceptual. It is simply that the theory of relativity *apparently* violates common sense; that is, it over-throws the dogma. In actual fact, it does not violate common sense in everyday life at everyday speeds. (How could it and survive, since the dogma works so well in everyday life?) But it poses that threat, and since everyone tends to be basically conservative (that is, fears the unknown), it is much easier to say "this is too hard for me" than to come to grips with it.

In this chapter we review classical kinematics, which we must clearly understand before we can overthrow it. The topics to be discussed in relativity theory are these self-same "classical" concepts. Moreover, the techniques of discussion are very similar in the relativity and classical cases, as are the methods of proof for certain very important results. Hence, even though none of the material here is likely to be new to you, it is essential that you read this chapter with care.

2.1 ABSOLUTE TIME—IS IT SELF-EVIDENT?

In physics we talk about events; for example, the ball was at the point P with coordinates $x = 1$, $y = 2$, $z = 4$ at the time $t = 0$. More concisely, the event E has space coordinates $(1, 2, 4)$ and time coordinate $t = 0$. This description of the unique event is not itself unique. It depends on the origin chosen and upon the scales used in the measurements. Thus the origin of the space and time coordinates must be specified; that is, we must state which point has the coordinates $(0, 0, 0)$, and at what time $t = 0$. Further, we must state, for example, that we are using a standard meter stick and a standard seconds clock. We assume, of course, that all observers are using identical meter sticks and identical ideal clocks.

We thus suppose that all the meter sticks have been compared with each other side by side in pairs.* We also assume that the length of a meter stick does not depend on where it has been, but only upon where it now is, and we test this by comparing the same two meter sticks on two occasions.† Notice that in the comparison the two sticks are placed side by side at essentially the same point, and they are at rest with respect to each other.

Turning next to the clocks, we check that when any two are side by side at relative rest, they mark off the same number of standard intervals

---

*Of course, some standards are more standard than others, so that we allow for effects such as thermal expansion.

†This is a very plausible assumption, except perhaps for magnetic materials.

(e.g., seconds) in any period. The two clocks need *not* be identical, and their rates should be independent of "external" quantities (such as the strength of the earth's gravitational field).* We can readily synchronize all the standard clocks by setting them to read the same time when side by side at rest. However, a clock is different from a meter stick in a very essential way: the time a clock reads is *of necessity* dependent on its past history. That is, a clock sums the individual seconds that have elapsed in its past history, in order to obtain the "present" time. Hence if we consider two *identical* standardized clocks which were once synchronized when side by side and at relative rest, it is not immediately self-evident that they will automatically again be synchronized when brought back together after being separated and taken to various different places. In this question we are not interested in any "straightforward" effects that rapidly accelerated motion may have on the working mechanism of the clock, but rather we are enquiring into whether any "extra" effect can occur. (We shall see in our detailed discussion of the "twin paradox" that such a separation of effects can meaningfully be made.)

To Newton it seemed self-evident that time was "absolute"; that is, all standard clocks once synchronized will remain synchronized forever, independent of their subsequent histories. Thus time is also universal in that a time interval is the same independent of who measures it; one hour in Washington is the same as one hour in New York, and the same as one hour in a jet plane over the Atlantic.

This belief in an absolute time works in everyday life. However, in everyday life two clocks are not set into relative motion of 175,000 miles/sec. To extend a belief in "absolute time" to such a case without previous experimental test may well lead to error. Nonetheless, it is the simplest, most natural assumption to make. It was made by Newton, and it was used without further serious thought by all subsequent pre-relativity physicists. We will pursue its consequences in the remainder of this chapter.

2.2   THE GALILEAN TRANSFORMATION—
SYMMETRY BETWEEN OBSERVERS

We consider a single observer, called *A*, who is provided with standard meter sticks† and clocks. He selects an origin *O* and sets up with his meter sticks a set of coordinate axes along three mutually perpendicular directions *Ox*, *Oy*, and *Oz*. He also synchronizes all his standard clocks to read

---

*But see Chapter 8.

†We use the term "meter stick" as a convenient shorthand for "a standard calibrated rule of unit length," and do not mean to imply that one must necessarily work in the meter-kilogram-second system. The same remark holds with regard to the term "second."

the same time when they are together, and then he places these clocks at many locations in his space. He has now set up a **space-time frame of reference.** Any event E that occurs will be at some point $P \equiv (x, y, z)$ in this coordinate frame and will occur at some definite time t (as measured by a clock *near* the event). This frame is really a four-dimensional set of coordinates since each event $E \equiv (x, y, z, t)$. Notice that two events at the same point $P \equiv (x, y, z)$ but which occur at two different times t_1 and t_2 are considered two *different* events E_1 and E_2. Since we are not used to thinking in four dimensions, it is hard to visualize this completely, at least in geometrical terms.

Often we choose the x direction to be one of special physical significance, and it is therefore useful to show the x and t coordinates in a figure, remembering that y and z ought also to be given. In Fig. 2.1 we show A's method of setting up his frame of reference, and in Fig. 2.2 we

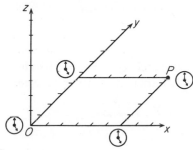

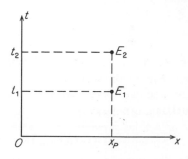

Fig. 2.1 Setting up A's frame of reference. Clocks are shown in various places; also the origin O, and the point P.

Fig. 2.2 The xt section of A's frame of reference. Events E_1 and E_2 are shown, with the same x_P (and also y and z) but different t.

show the (x, t) section of it, with two events E_1 and E_2. By convention throughout this book the t axis is taken as "vertical" rather than horizontal. Do *not* confuse such a plot with the more usual x-versus-t plot.

Suppose another observer B is inside a (rather large) railway train (with large windows) which is moving along A's Ox axis, with a constant velocity V. Suppose B inside the train sets up his frame of reference *in the train*, so that according to B any event is associated with coordinates $(x', y', z', t')_B$. The *same* event according to A will have coordinates $(x, y, z, t)_A$. (The suffixes B and A serve as reminders of the relevant frame.) How are these two descriptions of the same event related?

We assume that by good luck B's origin O' coincided with A's origin O at time $t = 0$, and that at that instant A's clock at O and B's clock at O' (which is at O) both read zero. Furthermore we assume that the directions of A's axes and B's axes coincide.* Then, by using the concept of "absolute" or "universal" time, we see that $t = t'$. Furthermore, we know that B's origin will have coordinates according to A given by $(Vt, 0, 0, t)_A$. This follows from the fact that the train is moving with constant speed V along the Ox axis. Consider Fig. 2.3, and the point P at which an

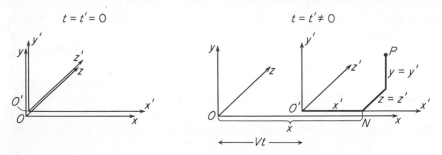

Fig. 2.3 Setting up A's and B's frames of reference, when B is moving at speed V along Ox.

event is occurring at $t = t' \neq 0$. Then from the figure $y = y'$, and similarly $z = z'$. However, x represents the distance ON, x' the distance $O'N$, and we have just seen that $OO' = Vt$. Hence $x' + Vt = x$. Summarizing, we have

$$
\boxed{
\begin{array}{l}
\text{G\scriptsize ALILEAN \normalsize TRANSFORMATION:} \\[4pt]
\begin{array}{lcl}
x' = x - Vt & & x = x' + Vt' \\
y' = y & & y = y' \\
z' = z & \text{and} & z = z' \\
t' = t & & t = t'.
\end{array}
\end{array}
}
\tag{2.1}
$$

Equations (2.1) relate $(x', y', z', t')_B$ to $(x, y, z, t)_A$, and vice versa. They are known as the **Galilean transformation.** We may seem to have been somewhat pedantic in writing $t' = t$ and $t = t'$, but with a purpose. Since the y and z transformations are trivial, there is little loss in going to the (x, t) space shown in Fig. 2.4. We show the transformation both from A's viewpoint, and from B's.

According to B, who likes to think of his train as stationary,† the world and A are moving under him in the $-Ox$ direction. Thus O has coordinates $(-Vt', 0, 0, t')_B$. Except for this minus sign, there is complete symmetry between A's view of B's world, and B's view of A's

---

*These assumptions, made purely for algebraic ease, are totally unnecessary and do not affect the final conclusions.

†B is not a typical train passenger!

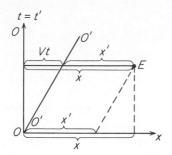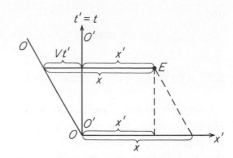

Fig. 2.4 The Galilean transformation in the xt space (left), and also in the $x't'$ space (right).

world. This "symmetry" between the two observers is very important. If B is really on a railway train, it seems clear that A's view of the situation is to be preferred; but in a case where each thinks the other is moving, the transformation equations have no way of singling out the observer who is "really" moving.*

In Eqs. (2.1) the x direction has been specially singled out as being the direction of the train's motion. The general case can readily be considered, and in terms of vectors one easily finds

$$\mathbf{r}' = \mathbf{r} - \mathbf{V}t, \qquad \mathbf{r} = \mathbf{r}' + \mathbf{V}t, \qquad t = t'. \tag{2.2}$$

Example 2.1. Observer B is in a railway carriage which is traveling at a constant velocity of 15 ft/sec due east. Another observer A is at rest w.r.t. the ground (w.r.t. ≡ with respect to). At time $t = t' = 0$, A throws a ball vertically upward w.r.t. the ground, the ball having an initial velocity of 40 ft/sec. Observer B inside the train also observes the ball. Assume that A and B each set up coordinate systems in which the x and x' axes are taken along the east direction, and the y and y' axes are taken vertically. Further assume that the origins are so chosen that at $t = t' = 0$ each of A and B says that the ball is at his origin. What is the trajectory of the ball as seen by A, and as seen by B? Where is the ball at the end of two seconds?

Answer 2.1. The ball has a constant downward acceleration $g = 32$ ft/sec/sec due to gravity. Hence, according to A, its trajectory is given by

$$A \text{ trajectory:} \qquad x = 0, \quad y = 40t - \tfrac{1}{2}(32)t^2.$$

Now according to B, we must have $x' = x - 15t$, $y' = y$, $t' = t$. Hence according to B the trajectory is

$$B \text{ trajectory:} \qquad x' = -15t', \quad y' = 40t' - \tfrac{1}{2}(32)t'^2.$$

At $t = t' = 2$, we have

$$A \text{ position:} \qquad x = 0, \quad y = 80 - 16 \times 4 = 16 \text{ ft}$$

*We cannot resist recommending the film "Frames of Reference" made by P. Hume and D. Ivey (New York: Modern Learning Aids).

and

$$B \text{ position:} \quad x' = -30 \text{ ft}, \quad y' = 16 \text{ ft.}$$

2.3 ADDITION OF VELOCITIES

The Galilean transformation equations (2.1) seem nearly self-evident. However, once they are accepted, a great deal *automatically* follows. It is important to recognize that the really fundamental physics goes into the transformation equations. The rest follows directly by irrefutable logic. We emphasize this point because in the theory of relativity the initial physics goes into changing the Galilean transformation equations. The subsequent deductions in kinematics follow again by the *same* irrefutable logic. Hence, now is the time to question this logic, if ever.

Suppose B in his train is observing a particle which is moving, so that at time t_1' its position is given by (x_1', y_1', z_1'). We can speak of the particle as being at the event X_1, where X_1 has coordinates $X_1 \equiv (x_1', y_1', z_1', t_1')_B$. Similarly, at a slightly later time t_2' let the particle be at the event $X_2 \equiv (x_2', y_2', z_2', t_2')_B$. Then the average velocity of the particle over this time period according to B is given by

$$v_x' = \frac{x_2' - x_1'}{t_2' - t_1'}, \qquad v_y' = \frac{y_2' - y_1'}{t_2' - t_1'}, \qquad v_z' = \frac{z_2' - z_1'}{t_2' - t_1'}.$$

But corresponding to the description of events as given by B there is an equivalent description given by A. That is,

$$X_1 \equiv (x_1, y_1, z_1, t_1)_A = (x_1' + Vt_1', y_1', z_1', t_1')_A$$

and

$$X_2 \equiv (x_2, y_2, z_2, t_2)_A = (x_2' + Vt_2', y_2', z_2', t_2')_A$$

where we have used the Galilean transformation equations (2.1). Further, the average velocity over the period according to A is given by

$$v_x = \frac{x_2 - x_1}{t_2 - t_1} = \frac{(x_2' + Vt_2') - (x_1' + Vt_1')}{t_2' - t_1'} = v_x' + V$$

$$v_y = \frac{y_2 - y_1}{t_2 - t_1} = \frac{y_2' - y_1'}{t_2' - t_1'} \qquad = v_y'$$

and

$$v_z = \frac{z_2 - z_1}{t_2 - t_1} = \frac{z_2' - z_1'}{t_2' - t_1'} \qquad = v_z',$$

that is,

$$v_x = v'_x + V, \qquad v_y = v'_y, \qquad v_z = v'_z.$$ (2.3)

In the limit as $t_2 \rightarrow t_1$ the average velocity approaches the instantaneous velocity. So Eqs. (2.3) also apply to the instantaneous velocity. Now V is simply the velocity of B's frame of reference with respect to that of A, and it is directed along the Ox direction. Hence Eqs. (2.3) can also be written vectorially

$$\mathbf{v}_A = \mathbf{v}_B + \mathbf{V}$$ (2.4)

[see also Eqs. (2.2)], and Eq. (2.4) can be re-expressed in words as follows. "The velocity, $\mathbf{v}_A$, of an object with respect to one observer A, is the vector sum of the velocity $\mathbf{v}_B$ of the object with respect to any other observer B, added to the velocity $\mathbf{V}$ of the observer B with respect to the observer A."*

Equation (2.4) is written from A's viewpoint. From that of B, it is

$$\mathbf{v}_B = \mathbf{v}_A - \mathbf{V}.$$

Since the velocity of A w.r.t. B is $-\mathbf{V}$, there is again symmetry between A and B (w. r. t. $\equiv$ with respect to). This symmetry arises because there are only two events X_1 and X_2, and these determine the "reality." There are then two different but *equivalent* descriptions of these events. (Notice that we find it hard to talk of even one event without using a frame of reference, since without the latter, we cannot really describe the former.)

Example 2.2. (a) Using the same data as in Example 2.1, determine the velocity of the ball at $t = t' = 2$ sec, as observed by A, and as observed by B. Show that they are related by Eq. (2.3).

Answer 2.2. (a) *Calculus method* (or see non-calculus method below). By differentiation of the trajectory equations given in Answer 2.1 we have directly

A velocity: $v_x = \dfrac{dx}{dt} = 0; \quad v_y = \dfrac{dy}{dt} = (40 - 32t) \text{ ft/sec}$

and

B velocity: $v'_x = \dfrac{dx'}{dt'} = -15 \text{ ft/sec}; \quad v'_y = \dfrac{dy'}{dt'} = (40 - 32t') \text{ ft/sec.}$

Hence at $t = t' = 2$ sec

*We give a brief equivalent proof using calculus. We have $x = x' + Vt$, $y = y'$, $z = z'$, $t = t'$. Differentiate each of the first three equations with respect to t, and recall that $v_x \equiv dx/dt$. One then has immediately $v_x = v'_x + V$, $v_y = v'_y$, $v_z = v'_z$.

$$A \text{ velocity:} \quad v_x = 0, \qquad\qquad v_y = -24 \text{ ft/sec}$$
$$B \text{ velocity:} \quad v'_x = -15 \text{ ft/sec}, \quad v'_y = -24 \text{ ft/sec}.$$

We see that $v_y = v'_y$, and that $v_x = v'_x + 15$ ft/sec. But $V = 15$ ft/sec, in the x direction. Hence Eq. (2.3) is indeed satisfied.

(b) *Non-calculus.* Consider the position of the ball at $t = t' = t_1$, and at $t = t' = t_2 = (t_1 + \Delta t)$ sec. Then the trajectory equations give us:

(i) *According to* A:

$$x_2 = 0$$
$$\begin{aligned} y_2 &= 40t_2 - \tfrac{1}{2}(32)t_2^2 \\ &= 40(t_1 + \Delta t) - \tfrac{1}{2}(32)(t_1 + \Delta t)^2 \\ &= [40t_1 - \tfrac{1}{2}(32)t_1^2] + \Delta t[40 - 32t_1] - 16(\Delta t)^2 \end{aligned}$$

and

$$x_1 = 0$$
$$y_1 = 40t_1 - \tfrac{1}{2}(32)t_1^2.$$

Therefore

$$\bar{v}_x = \frac{x_2 - x_1}{t_2 - t_1} = 0$$

and

$$\begin{aligned} \bar{v}_y &= \frac{y_2 - y_1}{t_2 - t_1} = \frac{\Delta t[40 - 32t_1] - 16(\Delta t)^2}{\Delta t} \\ &= 40 - 32t_1 - 16\,\Delta t. \end{aligned}$$

Here $\bar{v}_x$ denotes the *average* x component of velocity over the time interval t_1 to t_2; and similarly for $\bar{v}_y$. Now let Δt become smaller and smaller. Then $\bar{v}_x$ approaches the instantaneous velocity v_x, with a constant value of 0; and $\bar{v}_y$ approaches v_y, with the value $v_y = 40 - 32t_1$. Thus

$$A \text{ velocity:} \quad v_x = 0, \quad v_y = 40 - 32t_1 \text{ ft/sec.}$$

This agrees with the first line of method (a).

(ii) *According to* B: Proceed exactly as in method (b), part (i), but using the trajectory equation according to B. See if you can obtain the second line of method (a). Congratulations, you have just taken your first step in the calculus. The rest of the derivation proceeds as in method (a).

2.4   INVARIANCE OF ACCELERATION; INVARIANCE OF $\mathbf{F} = m\mathbf{a}$

We continue our discussion of the relationship between observations made by A and B, given by the Galilean transformation equations (2.1) [or more generally (2.2)]. In Section 2.3 we considered the motion of one particle, as measured by the two observers, and obtained

$$v_x = v'_x + V$$
$$v_y = v'_y$$
$$v_z = v'_z \tag{2.3'}$$
$$t = t'$$

Inasmuch as these equations apply for any instant of time, they also apply for two instants of time t_1 and t_2. Let the corresponding velocities have suffixes 1 and 2. Then the average acceleration over this time interval as measured by A is given by

$$\bar{a}_x = \frac{v_{x2} - v_{x1}}{t_2 - t_1} = \frac{(v'_{x2} + V) - (v'_{x1} + V)}{t_2 - t_1} = \frac{v'_{x2} - v'_{x1}}{t_2 - t_1} = \bar{a}'_x .$$

Also

$$\bar{a}_y = \bar{a}'_y \quad \text{and} \quad \bar{a}_z = \bar{a}'_z .$$

In the limit of $t_2 \to t_1$ the average accelerations approach the instantaneous accelerations. Hence we see that

$$\begin{aligned} a_x &= a'_x \\ a_y &= a'_y \quad \text{or} \quad \mathbf{a} = \mathbf{a}'. \\ a_z &= a'_z \end{aligned} \tag{2.5}$$

That is, **the acceleration of a particle as measured by observer A is the same as that measured by observer B,** provided only that B and A have a *constant* relative velocity.*

Example 2.3. Using the data of Examples 2.1 and 2.2, prove explicitly that $\mathbf{a} = \mathbf{a}'$ at all times.

Answer 2.3. (a) *Calculus method.* By differentiation of the velocity formulas in Answer 2.2 we have directly

A acceleration: $a_x = \dfrac{dv_x}{dt} = 0, \quad a_y = \dfrac{dv_y}{dt} = -32 \text{ ft/sec/sec}$

B acceleration: $a'_x = \dfrac{dv'_x}{dt'} = 0, \quad a'_y = \dfrac{dv'_y}{dt'} = -32 \text{ ft/sec/sec}.$

Hence $\mathbf{a} = \mathbf{a}'$.

(b) *Non-calculus method.* Be brave and work it out *yourself*, exactly as in Answer 2.2(b).

Comment. In Examples 2.1, 2.2, and 2.3 all of B's equations are identical with those he would calculate if he assumed that (relative to himself) all freely falling bodies have a constant downward acceleration due to gravity of 32 ft/sec/sec, and if he further assumed that the ball started with an

*The result (2.5) can be derived directly from (2.3') by differentiating w.r.t. t, recalling that $\mathbf{a} = d\mathbf{v}/dt$, and that $\mathbf{V} = $ const.

initial velocity having components of 40 ft/sec upwards and −15 ft/sec in the east direction (note the minus sign). Thus, simply by observing the ball, B is unable to tell whether he, B, has a constant horizontal component of velocity; or whether he, B, is at rest and the ball has a constant horizontal component of velocity in the opposite direction. In fact the only thing of which B is certain is the relative velocity of himself and the ball. This relative velocity has a constant horizontal component.

Because all observers in *constant* relative motion w.r.t. each other find the same acceleration **a** for any object, we say that the acceleration is "**invariant**" under the Galilean transformation. Newton's second law says **F** = m**a**.* Since all such observers find the same **a**, they hence all say that the same force is acting on the body. This is very plausible, since one might expect that the force on a body would not depend on the state of motion of the observer. (However, it could well depend on the state of motion of the source of the force! Cf. Chapter 6.) With this assumption of the invariance of forces, we can hence say that Newton's laws of motion are invariant under the Galilean transformation; that is, they make good physics for all observers in *constant* relative motion w.r.t. each other, if they make good physics for one such observer. (This last proviso has to do with the difference between inertial and noninertial frames of reference, and the need for introducing fictitious forces in the latter. We shall not discuss this question in detail.)

2.5 SYNCHRONIZATION OF DISTANT CLOCKS. THE SPEED OF SIGNALS RELATIVE TO THE OBSERVER

By this point the reader is probably nodding his head in agreement (even if somewhat sleepily). We now turn to a subject which should wake him up in alarm.

In Section 2.2, observer A set up a space-time frame of reference, liberally sprinkled with standard clocks at all points. These clocks had originally been synchronized when side by side, and then separated. *How can we test whether these separated clocks are still synchronized?* What in fact does this question mean?

Of course, the first thing to do is to bring one of the distant clocks

*This paragraph can be ignored by those readers who have not yet studied Newton's laws of motion.

back to the base clock and recompare them. In classical mechanics, they certainly ought to agree.*

Since we are discussing pre-relativity kinematics, let us assume that the clocks on recomparison did agree. If time is indeed universal, they *surely* must. *But did the clocks read the same time when separated—before they were brought back together?* Is there in fact a universal "now"? This question is really philosophical, since there is no way of answering it without assuming *something*. Classical physics simply *postulated* that there was a universal "now," associated with a universal time; and at *everyday* speeds classical physics never got into difficulties (though it did get into trouble with certain properties of light).

The reader might well be asking himself why we don't simply send a few signals (such as shouts or flashes of light) from clock P to clock Q, and from Q to P, to sort things out. Naturally, we have to allow for the time it takes for the signal to get from P to Q. And this is where the difficulty arises.

A typical idealized experiment is shown in Fig. 2.5. At time t_{1P} on the clock at P, a signal is sent to Q. It arrives at Q at time t_{2Q} ac-

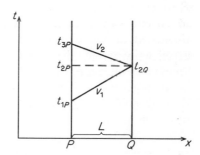

Fig. 2.5 An attempt to test the synchronization of two separated clocks, located at P and Q.

cording to Q's clock. Another signal is immediately sent back to P and arrives at t_{3P} according to P's clock. All the times t_{1P}, t_{2Q}, and t_{3P} are known to both P and Q. Are the clocks synchronized? To answer this question we have to know the speed of the signal on a *one*-way trip between P and Q, and also in the reverse direction between Q and P. Suppose we know these speeds (call them v_1 and v_2); then if the clocks are synchronized we should have

---

*The Special Theory of Relativity actually predicts that at high enough speeds of separation and approach, they will *not* agree! Regrettably the experiment has not yet been performed at suitably large speeds.

$$(t_{2Q} - t_{1P})v_1 = L = (t_{3P} - t_{2Q})v_2$$

where L is the (constant) distance between P and Q. But we do not know v_1 and v_2, since we do *not* yet know how to synchronize clocks at two ends of a measured distance! We are caught in the toils of a logical paradox.

Classical physics avoids the problem by simply *assuming* that clocks, once synchronized when together, remain synchronized when separated. In that case the experiment we have described can be used to measure v_1 and v_2. Once v_1 and v_2 have been measured by this experiment, however, it is then absurd to repeat the *same* measurement to "test whether clocks when separated remain synchronized." Of necessity this experiment must give the answer "yes," but the answer is empty.

The reader might object that really we do know v_1 and v_2, since surely

$$v_1 = v_2 = \bar{v} = \frac{2L}{t_{3P} - t_{1P}}.$$

But this assumes that the speed of the signal is the same going from P to Q as from Q to P. A shout on a windy day can well take longer to go one way than the other, because what is constant for sound is the speed of sound *relative* to the air. So the next question which arises is whether the clocks at P and Q are really at rest w.r.t. the "medium" through which the signals propagate. Our previous experiment, together with the universal time assumption, answers this question by giving us v_1 and v_2. Then the speed V of the "medium" in the direction from P to Q is

$$V = \frac{v_1 - v_2}{2} \quad \text{and} \quad v = \frac{v_1 + v_2}{2} \tag{2.6}$$

where v is the speed of the signal relative to the medium (cf. problem 2.3). Here we should emphasize that Eq. (2.6) is derived by using the Galilean transformation, in particular Eqs. (2.3).

A rather crucial remark is that the observer at P is not surprised at learning that $t_{2Q} \neq \frac{1}{2}(t_{1P} + t_{3P})$—i.e., that $v_1 \neq v_2$. He immediately interprets this as an effect of motion relative to the "medium," and uses it to determine v and V. He would be surprised only if this value of V disagreed with some other measurement of V.

This leads us to the question of whether we can actually measure V in some independent manner. That is, can we test whether P and Q are moving relative to the medium that carries the signals, *without* using the universal time hypothesis? The answer is "yes," and is discussed in the next section.

2.6   THE MICHELSON-MORLEY EXPERIMENT FOR SOUND; FOR LIGHT

We want to test whether we are moving at some speed V relative to some "medium" in which signals propagate at some constant speed v *relative* to the medium. A very clever experiment was devised by Michelson and Morley,* which works for any *wave* propagation (such as sound or light) where interference effects are possible.

The method is indicated in Fig. 2.6. A signal is sent from A to B

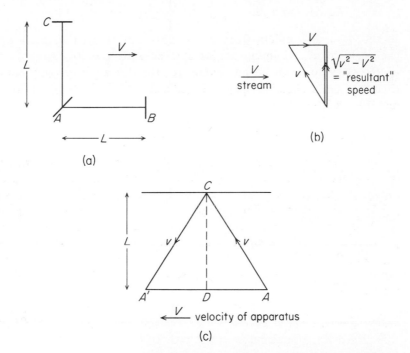

Fig. 2.6 (a) The Michelson-Morley experiment. V is the speed of the medium relative to the apparatus. (b) Swimming "across" a river; effective speed $= \sqrt{v^2 - V^2}$. (c) The transverse beam transit ACA, as seen in the frame of reference of the medium.

*A. A. Michelson and E. W. Morley, *Am. J. Sci.*, **34**, 333 (1887). These investigators invented and used the method for light signals. They were not worried by the question of the universal time hypothesis, but simply did not have clocks which were able to measure the *expected* difference between $(t_{3P} - t_{2Q})$ and $(t_{2Q} - t_{1P})$ with sufficient accuracy to detect any effect, for their case of light signals. An extract of their paper is reprinted in W. F. Magie, *A Source Book in Physics* (Cambridge, Mass.: Harvard University Press, 1963).

and back to A, taking a time t_{ABA}; and another signal is sent from A to C and back to A, taking a time t_{ACA}. The paths AB and AC are at right angles, and the distance $AB = L$ is made the same as the distance AC. Hence if there is no motion of the apparatus through the medium, we expect that $t_{ABA} = t_{ACA} = 2L/v$, where v is the speed of the signal in the medium.

However, suppose the medium has a speed V relative to the apparatus, and let us assume for simplicity that V is in the direction AB. Then, *using the Galilean transformation of velocities*, we have instead

$$t_{ABA} = t_{AB} + t_{BA} = \frac{L}{v + V} + \frac{L}{v - V} = \frac{2Lv}{v^2 - V^2} > \frac{2L}{v}. \qquad (2.7)$$

In fact t_{ACA} also differs from $2L/v$. This can be seen by analogy with the problem of swimming across a river with a swift current, when it is necessary to swim at an angle to the "straight-across" path and therefore one's effective speed is reduced to $\sqrt{v^2 - V^2}$ [cf. problem 2.4 and Fig. 2.6(b)]. Thus

$$t_{ACA} = \frac{2L}{\sqrt{v^2 - V^2}} > \frac{2L}{v}. \qquad (2.8)$$

It is instructive to derive this result also by going into the frame of reference of the medium [cf. Fig. 2.6(c)]. In this frame the apparatus moves to the left at speed V. Thus the transverse signal ACA is emitted from the point A, but by the time t_{AC} has elapsed, A has moved to D, where $DA = Vt_{AC}$. Hence C must be this far *to the left* of the point A at which the signal was emitted. We must also have $AC = vt_{AC}$. But $DA^2 + DC^2 = AC^2$, from which one obtains $t_{AC} = L(v^2 - V^2)^{-1/2}$. Similarly one finds $t'_{CA} = t_{AC}$, so that again we finally obtain (2.8). Thus we find

$$\Delta t \equiv t_{ABA} - t_{ACA} \equiv \frac{2Lv}{v^2 - V^2} - \frac{2L}{\sqrt{v^2 - V^2}} = \frac{2L}{v^2 - V^2}[v - \sqrt{v^2 - V^2}].$$
$$(2.9)$$

Let us put in some typical numbers for the case of sound: Suppose we want to test whether there is a wind of about 10 ft/sec, and we use a length $L = 100$ ft. The speed of sound can be taken to be 1000 ft/sec (for the sake of the illustration). Then if there is no wind, $t_{ABA} = t_{ACA} = 200/1000 = 0.2000$ sec. If there is a wind of 10 ft/sec along AB,

$$t_{ABA} = \frac{200 \times 1000}{1000^2 - 10^2} = 0.20002 \text{ sec}$$

and

$$t_{ACA} = \frac{200}{\sqrt{1000^2 - 10^2}} = 0.20001 \text{ sec.}$$

Thus to detect the effect requires timing accurate to 10^{-5} sec! This is clearly not a simple way to test whether a 10 ft/sec ($\approx$ 7 mph)* wind is blowing. Nonetheless, it *would* work.

One remark concerns our assumption that V was along AB. Since we do not know that there is any relative motion, let alone its direction, this assumption is untenable at first sight. But if we rotate the apparatus, then Δt changes, and we can rotate it until Δt is positive and as large as possible. In this case V is either along AC or along CA. Since (2.9) depends only on V^2, we cannot determine the sign of V. (This result was to be expected; why?)

The Michelson-Morley experiment was actually performed using light signals with $v = 3 \times 10^8$ m/sec $= 3 \times 10^5$ km/sec, in an attempt to see whether the earth was moving through the "ether," this being the official name of the "medium" (which was presumed to exist even in a vacuum) through which light propagates. The speed of the earth around the sun is about 30 km/sec (that is, about two million miles per day), so that sometime during the year one would expect that $V \approx 30$ km/sec.

Two problems then arise. The *fractional* change in $t_{ABA} - t_{ACA}$ is of order V^2/v^2, which becomes 1 part in 10^8; and t_{ABA} itself becomes 10^{-5} sec for a length $L = 3$ km, and 10^{-8} sec for a length of 3 m. Furthermore, apparently the length AB must be equal to that of AC to an accuracy better than 1 part in 10^8. In this form the experiment is clearly impossible even today. However, by using interference effects one can measure *changes* in $\Delta t = t_{ABA} - t_{ACA}$ *direct*ly, and a change of 10^{-15} sec can readily be measured. (This corresponds to half a wavelength of yellow light.) Further, by this means, and by deliberately rotating the apparatus, it is not even necessary to have AB exactly equal to AC in length. The concept of the experiment is really very beautiful, as you will come to realize when you study interferometry. The essential remark is simply that the experiment *can* in fact be performed.

When the experiment was performed, the result was totally unexpected: *there was no effect*. At whatever time of year the experiment was done, the earth was *always* at rest w.r.t. the ether. Could it be that Ptolemy was right after all, and the sun goes round a stationary earth? We cannot interpret this experimental result without knowing independently whether the earth is moving.

The pre-relativity conclusion was that either the earth was in fact stationary, or that the ether was "dragged" along by the earth. The

*The symbol $\approx$ means "approximately equal to."

latter is indeed a plausible explanation but, in fact, both explanations were proved to be untenable by the observed phenomenon of stellar aberration (discussed further in Section 4.3). This effect of stellar aberration could only be understood classically if indeed the speed of the earth relative to the fixed stars was about 30 km/sec *and* if the ether did *not* get dragged along by the earth! (Furthermore, Sir Oliver Lodge was unable to observe any ether drag effects due to a rapidly spinning disc.)

The Michelson-Morley experiment has been performed many times and has always* led to a null result. We hence end up with a contradiction. The earth does move relative to the ether, as shown by stellar aberration, and yet the ether does not get dragged along. Hence a positive effect must be observed in the Michelson-Morley experiment. But no effect was observed.

Naturally a way out was found. G. F. Fitzgerald suggested that in the Michelson-Morley experiment, when the apparatus moved through the ether with speed V along BA, the arm AB was physically "compressed" and hence shortened to a new length $L\sqrt{1 - (V^2/c^2)}$, where c is the velocity of light in the ether. (From now on c will always have this meaning.) This is known as the **Fitzgerald contraction.** Hence t_{ABA} becomes

$$t_{ABA} \rightarrow \frac{L\sqrt{1 - (V^2/c^2)}}{c + v} + \frac{L\sqrt{1 - (V^2/c^2)}}{c - v} = \frac{2L}{\sqrt{c^2 - v^2}} = t_{ACA}.$$

Thus $\Delta t = 0$. This is again a rather beautiful explanation, except that by its very nature it *can neither be tested nor refuted.* The reason is that any meter stick will also suffer the *same* contraction. Hence this explanation leaves us with no way to measure V.

Meanwhile H. A. Lorentz had developed his electromagnetic theory, based on Maxwell's equations. We have briefly discussed this theory in Chapter 1. It *did* lead to a "length-contraction" effect, and also, in its later forms, to a time-dilation effect.† However, even Lorentz's theory suffered from the fact that one assumed that the earth was moving with a definite speed V through the ether, yet nature then

---

*Well, almost always. A positive effect (though much smaller than that to be expected on the basis of 30 km/sec) was consistently found by D. C. Miller [*Rev. Mod. Phys.*, **5**, 203 (1933) and *Nature*, **133**, 162 (1934)]. His results have since been reinterpreted by R. S. Shankland, S. W. McCuskey, F. C. Leone, and G. Kuerti [*Rev. Mod. Phys.*, **27**, 167 (1955)] as arising from temperature gradients in Miller's laboratory which caused that arm which was closer to one particular direction always to be longer than the other arm!

†Much later, Kennedy and Thorndike repeated the Michelson-Morley experiment but deliberately made $L_{AB} \neq L_{AC}$. They again found *no effect*. The time-dilation effect is needed in order to understand this result (see problem 3.16).

conspired to prevent one from *ever* measuring V.* This is disquieting. It remained for Einstein to clear the air.

2.7 SUMMARY

We began this chapter with a review of classical kinematics, which is based on the concept of an absolute time. Once this concept is accepted, the Galilean transformation, the addition of velocities, and the invariance of acceleration all follow by irrefutable logic. (We will use precisely the same logic in our later relativistic relations.)

Sound waves are carried by a detectable material medium, and in a given experiment it is meaningful to ask for the velocity of the sound relative to the medium, and the velocity of the medium relative to the observer. The velocity of sound relative to the observer is the vector sum of these two velocities. The speed of sound relative to the medium is a constant.

If one assumes that light waves are carried by an undetectable but all-pervading ether, then the Michelson-Morley experiment and its extensions apparently show that the ether is dragged along by the earth. But this is incompatible with other experiments. The most direct experimental statement is: **"The velocity of light relative to any observer when measured by that observer is always the same, independent of the state of motion of one observer relative to another."** (This is not exactly what has been proved experimentally, but is a reasonable synthesis thereof.) Notice, however, that this statement really applies only to the *apparent* velocity as determined by an observer.

Thus it is possible to remove the paradoxical nature of the above conclusion by postulating certain properties of the ether. For instance, the Fitzgerald-contraction explanation asserts that motion through the ether "just happens" to cause all material objects to contract along the direction of motion by precisely that correct factor $\sqrt{1 - (V^2/c^2)}$ which cancels out the true effects of relative motion, expected on the basis of the Galilean transformation. Such explanations are workable, but untestable, and hence unappealing. They are, however, forced upon one if one wants to preserve the concept of absolute time inviolate, and still live with the results of the Michelson-Morley experiment.

In summary: **Absolute time plus the experimental results of the Michelson-Morley experiment force us to conclude that if the ether exists, it has properties so arranged that we are prevented from devising any experiment whatsoever which enables us to measure our velocity relative**

*An elegant critique of these theories, in particular that of Lorentz, is given in David Bohm, *The Special Theory of Relativity* (New York: W. A. Benjamin, Inc., 1965).

to the ether. The only alternative is to give up the concept of absolute time which led us to the apparent paradox.

PROBLEMS

(Essential problems are indicated by !, difficult problems by *.)

2.1 An airplane flies at an airspeed of 400 mph towards the northeast relative to the air. It is actually flying in a storm, and the velocity of the air is 100 mph *from* the east. What is the ground velocity of the airplane (magnitude and direction)?

2.2 In problem 2.1, suppose that the pilot wants to travel in a northeast direction *relative* to the ground. What apparent course should he steer, and what will be the plane's effective ground speed?

2.3 Consider the experiment shown in Fig. 2.5, and prove Eq. (2.6).

!2.4 Two swimmers are to have a race in a stream which flows at 3 ft/sec. Each swimmer can swim at 5 ft/sec in still water. Swimmer A is to swim directly upstream a distance of 50 ft, then turn around and swim back to his starting point. Swimmer B is to swim in such a way that he swims directly across the stream, as seen from the bank; he is to swim a distance of 50 ft across the stream, and then turn around and swim back to his starting point. Thus A and B must each swim 100 ft relative to the banks, and so each would take the same time, if there were no current. (a) In what direction must B swim, *relative to the water*, in order to *apparently* swim directly across the stream? (b) What is B's effective speed? (c) How long does B take for the whole trip? (d) How long does A take? (e) Does the result of such a race enable one to test whether there is a current flowing? (f) What would happen if the stream velocity were 6 ft/sec?

*2.5 Consider observers A and B as in Example 2.1, but assume that B and his train have a horizontal acceleration of 16 ft/sec/sec w.r.t. the ground, so that according to A, B's origin is located at A's point $x = \frac{1}{2}(16)t^2$. A again throws the ball vertically as in Example 2.1. (a) What is the relationship between x and x' for a general event (assume $t = t'$)? (b) What is the trajectory of the ball as seen by B? (c) Prove that this is the same trajectory as B would predict if he assumed that he, B, was at rest, but in a region of constant acceleration due to gravity, this acceleration g^* having magnitude $16\sqrt{5}$ ft/sec/sec and directed west of "downwards" at an angle of $\tan^{-1} 1/2$ to the "downwards" direction.

Here by "downwards" we mean the "true" downwards direction as determined by A, outside the train. However, B would find that a plumb line would also lie along the direction of g^*. B would be forced to call this direction downwards, and would simply say that the walls of his railway compartment were not vertical.

3

THE
LORENTZ TRANSFORMATION

In the summary to Chapter 2 we implied that the concept of absolute time is the true cause of the difficulties associated with the negative results of the Michelson-Morley experiment. Actually we did not expect the cautious reader to be convinced by our last remark. In this chapter we first investigate this remark more fully, and we will find that it leads to the overthrow of classical kinematics, and of the Galilean transformation. In their place we are led to the Lorentz transformation, and we go on to consider some of its consequences.

3.1 SYNCHRONIZATION OF DISTANT CLOCKS.
THE SECOND RELATIVITY POSTULATE

In Section 2.1 we raised the question of whether two identical, ideal clocks, when once synchronized, remained synchronized forever. The assumption of "absolute time" assured us that they do. But now we want to test this hypothesis experimentally.

More specifically, consider two such clocks, initially synchronized and both at the same point (or "nearly" at the same point) called O. Suppose we carry one of these clocks to some other point A. Is it still synchronized with the clock at O? This is the same question that we have already briefly discussed in Section 2.5.* We found ourselves caught in a logical vicious circle, and we were able to proceed only by using the universal time hypothesis, together with the Galilean transformation and the addition of velocities, both deductions from the universal time hypothesis. Of course classical physicists did not notice these problems, since absolute time seemed self-evident.

So let us return to the two clocks at O and at A and ask how we can test whether they are synchronized. Our previous method of sending signals from one clock to the other led nowhere, because we needed an *independent* way of determining the speed of the signal on a *one-way* trip. For most signals this speed depends on the specific circumstances (e.g., the air velocity for the case of a shout). However, the (most astonishing) conclusion of the Michelson-Morley experiment was in fact that the velocity of light is a constant for all observers. Even in that experiment, we really only determine the average velocity on a forward-and-back trip, but if this is always constant, it is only reasonable to assume that it has the same value on any one-way trip.† We therefore state the following postulate or physical law:‡

> **Second Relativity Postulate: The speed of light in vacuum is an absolute constant for all observers, independent of the velocity of the light source, or the velocity of the observer.**   (R.2)

We have added to the postulate an extra part that has already been implicit in much of our discussion: namely, that the speed of light is independent of the speed of the source. The speed of a bullet fired from a moving car certainly depends on the speed of the car. On the other hand a shout travels through air at a speed independent of the velocity of the emitter. It is the speed of sound relative to the air on which it is carried that is constant. As long as one thinks of light as a wave propagating through the ether, it is reasonable to believe that what is constant is the speed of light relative to the ether.

On the other hand, another very easy way out of the difficulties of the Michelson-Morley experiment is to say that the velocity of light

---

*It might be well to reread that section before proceeding.

†Any other assumption would go against the idea of the uniformity of space. Furthermore, in many experiments the light effectively travels in one-way trips around a "circuit" of many sides, and never does one find any contradiction with this assumption.

‡We will discuss the First Relativity Postulate in due course! In the second postulate, we implicitly assume that space is homogeneous, isotropic, and uniform.

depends on the velocity of the emitter, or perhaps on that of the last object off which the light was reflected. Then the negative results of the various experiments are to be expected. The most fully developed theory of this type is due to W. Ritz.

Such an idea does go against the whole of the theory of electricity and magnetism, the greatest achievement of which was to demonstrate both theoretically and experimentally that light is an electromagnetic wave.* This theory is a field theory, in which the development of the disturbance propagates step by step, totally independent of the source once the disturbance has been started. Although this is not a good argument against such a hypothesis, the effect would be "out of the frying pan into the fire" as measured by the damage to the whole of classical physics.

The best modern argument against such "emission" theories is provided by an experiment in which one measured the speed of light emitted in the decay of a π°-meson, whose kinetic energy was known.† If one makes use of the relativistic energy-velocity relationship, the π°-mesons had speeds $v_s \geq 0.99975c$, and if one were to use the classical relationship $K.E. = \frac{1}{2}mv^2$, the source speed would have been even greater. If one writes the speed of the emitted light in the form $c' = c + kv_s$, the experimental result was $k = (-0 \pm 13) \times 10^{-5}$. This indicates that the assumption that the speed of light is independent of that of the source is very good indeed.‡

*Thus whenever we use the words "light" or "a light signal" in the future, this is to be understood as including radio waves, radar, microwaves, infra-red radiation, ultraviolet, X-rays and nuclear X-rays. The speed of all these radiations is the same in vacuum, to within the experimental uncertainties; and the Michelson-Morley experiment has been performed with microwave radiation.

†T. Alväger, F. J. M. Farley, J. Kjellman, and I. Wallin, *Phys. Letters*, **12**, 260, E **13**, 359 (1964); also *Arkiv för Fysik* **31**, 145 (1966). In principle, in this experiment the light passed through two detectors A and B, and each detector then sent an electrical radio-frequency signal through a cable to a common timing unit C. It was assumed that the time delay caused by the electrical signal going from A to C was independent of the position of the cable, as long as its length was kept constant; similarly for the signal going from B to C. By commencing with A and B at the same point, these delays could then be effectively eliminated. A quantitative experiment must necessarily make use of such an assumption. A very elegant "yes-no" experiment has been performed by T. A. Filippas and J. G. Fox, *Phys. Rev.* **135**, B 1071 (1964), who used a π° source with velocity $= 0.2c$, and found no effect of the motion of the source. (However, if their data is interpreted quantitatively their value of k is given by $|k| \leq 0.4$, where k is the quantity defined below.)

‡A more thorough description and critique of these "emission" type theories is given by J. G. Fox, *Am. J. Phys.* **33**, 1 (1965). He also discusses a severe practical consideration which makes it, of necessity, very hard to perform such experiments. The case $k = 1$ would lead to results identical in all respects to the Galilean transformation.

Throughout the remainder of this book we will accept the Second Relativity Postulate as a true law of nature, and we will follow wherever it leads. It is a most remarkable law, but no experiment has ever disagreed with any predictions based on this law.

By means of this principle, we can at last answer our reiterated question of how to test whether two clocks, at points P and Q which are far apart, are in fact synchronized. We use precisely the method suggested in Section 2.5, taking our signal to be a pulse of light. The basic method is shown in Fig. 3.1. This is similar to Fig. 2.5, but with the crucial

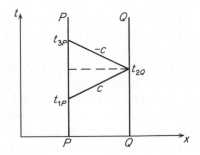

Fig. 3.1 A true test of the synchronization of distant clocks.

difference that now we *know* that $v_1 = v_2 = c$, a universal constant. A *light* signal is emitted from P at time t_{1P} measured on P's clock. It arrives at Q at time t_{2Q} according to Q's clock. Another signal is immediately sent back to P and arrives at t_{3P} according to P's clock. Then, if and only if:

$$t_{2Q} = \tfrac{1}{2}(t_{1P} + t_{3P}): \quad \text{synchronization condition} \tag{3.1}$$

is the clock at Q synchronized with the clock at P. Note that the basis of this condition is the belief that we now *know* how to allow for the time it takes the signal to travel from P to Q, or from Q to P.

By simply repeating this experiment at some later time, one can test whether the clocks at P and Q are in fact at rest relative to each other, as was assumed in drawing Fig. 3.1. How? (Cf. problem 3.1.) If they are at rest, one can go on to prove that if Q is synchronized w.r.t. P, then P is synchronized w.r.t. Q. (Cf. problem 3.2, also 3.3.)

Now that we at last know how to synchronize distant clocks, we should be able to answer our other question, namely: if two clocks are synchronized when at the same point, and are then separated, do they remain synchronized? Is there a universal time? The Theory of Relativity says "no," but the experiment is not presently feasible at suitable speeds. Nonetheless, sufficient other predictions of the theory, in particular that of time dilation in the decay of mu-mesons, have been tested so that nearly all practicing physicists believe in the "lack of universal time." As our development proceeds, you too will become convinced.

3.2 SYNCHRONIZATION OF CLOCKS WHEN IN RELATIVE MOTION

We now turn to one of the crucial deductions of the special theory of relativity. We consider two observers, called A and B, as in Section 2.2, each with an ideal clock. They are in motion at a constant relative velocity V, which we take to be along the x direction. Thus B moves at $+V$ w.r.t. A, and A moves at $-V$ w.r.t. B.

The fact that both A and B say that their relative velocity has the *same* magnitude V is an important theorem, and we hence give a proof of it. We imagine that both A and B are equipped with *identical* relative-velocity measuring kits (e.g., the police "radar" speed-trap kit). Further, we imagine that each of A and B can read both the dial on his own meter and the dial on the other man's meter. Then *if* the dials were to show two different speeds, one of the observers would say, "My stationary equipment shows a larger speed than is shown on the moving equipment." But the other observer would say, "My stationary equipment shows a smaller speed than is shown on the moving equipment." The First Relativity Postulate can be taken as stating that no possible experiment can distinguish between two observers in constant relative motion.* We explicitly assume the validity of this postulate throughout the remainder of this book. Then since the two assumed statements of A and B do distinguish between A and B, we are forced to the theorem in order to avoid a contradiction.

We should emphasize that when we discuss the synchronization of two separated clocks (and we will run into difficulties over this concept), we are of course allowing for the time delay involved in the signaling process. If one receives a light signal at an event 2, at time t_2, which came from an event 1; and if L is the distance between events 1 and 2; then one naturally says that t_2 is later than t_1, and specifically that $t_2 - t_1 = L/c$. This seems straightforward, and even trivial. But it will lead us into great difficulties, which are at the heart of the special theory of relativity.

To whet the reader's appetite for the hard work ahead, we discuss an example due to Einstein. Consider a long train moving with constant velocity V along a track. Two lightning flashes strike the train, one at each end, and each leaves a mark on the train and also on the track at

*This is a loose way of stating the First Relativity Postulate. We state it more precisely in Section 5.1, but will already use it here, and later, in the above sense.

the same instant. Let the front mark on the train be labeled F′, and that on the track F ; similarly let R′ and R denote the marks on the train and on the track of the rear lightning flash. Suppose that one observer B is on the train and at its midpoint; that is, B is midway between F′ and R′. And suppose another observer A is at rest on the railway track at the midpoint of FR. Each of the observers A and B sees each of the lightning flashes by the light which is transmitted from the flashes toward the observers. Each then corrects for the time delay introduced by the signal transmission time, and asks whether the two lightning flashes were synchronous. We *assume* that the stationary observer A does find that the two flashes were synchronous,* and we ask whether B finds them to be synchronous also.

In Fig. 3.2(a) we show the arrival of the two flashes in the frame of reference of the observer A, in which *by assumption* they are synchronous. At this instant F and F′ are coincident, as are R and R′. Hence at *this* instant, so are A and B.

In Fig. 3.2(b) we show the situation in the frame of reference of A, at the later instant at which the two signals from FF′ and RR′ reach A

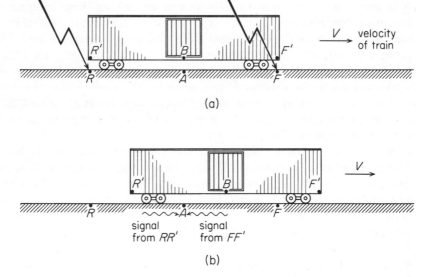

(a)

(b)

Fig. 3.2 The lightning flash experiment: (a) the configuration according to the stationary observer A,
at the common instant at which each lightning flash
strikes; (b) the configuration according to A, at the
instant when A receives the (coincident) light signals from F and R.

*This is a physical condition that is being imposed on the lightning flashes, and is *not* open to possible doubt.

simultaneously. Since A is midway between F and R, he knows the the signal time delay is the same for each of the signals. For naturally he uses the Second Relativity Postulate and assumes that each of the two signals travels at the same constant speed c.

But in Fig. 3.2(b) we also see that B is now to the right of A, and that B had already received the signal from FF' at some earlier instant; and yet the signal from RR' has still to catch up with B! Thus B will surely find that the signal from FF' reaches him before the signal from RR'. But B now says, "I am equidistant from F' and R'. Hence, since the speed of each of the light signals is constant and equal to c (relative to myself), it follows that the front lightning flash struck *before* the rear flash."

It is easy to see that the reason A and B come to this disagreement is that *each* uses the *same* speed c as the speed of the light signals when they attempt to calculate the signal transmission delay. In pre-relativity or Galilean physics, if the speed of each signal had been c relative to the stationary observer A, then relative to B the signal $F'B$ would have a larger speed $c + V$, and the signal $R'B$ would have a smaller speed $c - V$. Thus B would of course say that the signal from F' should reach him before the signal from R'. (Recall that B is equidistant from F' and R'.) But in fact detailed calculations then show that B *would* find that the lightning flashes were synchronous, so that B would agree with A concerning the simultaneity of the two lightning flashes. This is as it must be, since the Galilean transformation and its consequence, the addition of velocities, both make use of the concept of an absolute time. However, its consequence is in contradiction with the Second Relativity Postulate.

The moral of this example is that the Second Relativity Postulate is in contradiction with the concept of an absolute time. However, so is the result of the Michelson-Morley experiment. We will accept the Second Relativity Postulate throughout the rest of this book. We now leave Einstein's example, but still assume that distant clocks can be meaningfully synchronized according to condition (3.1) when they are relatively at rest.

We now return to our two observers A and B in relative motion. We suppose that B carries out our standard synchronization experiment, as is shown in Fig. 3.3, *from the viewpoint of B*. In this figure, B is shown at a fixed point, while A is moving to the left with speed V. The lines AA and BB represent the trajectories of A and B in the (x, t) space. Such a trajectory [properly in the four-dimensional $(\mathbf{r}, t)$ space] is called the **world line** of the particle.

The light signals travel with speed c. We call the *event* (i.e. the space-time point) at which B sends the first signal event 1, the event at which A receives the first signal and retransmits it event 2, and the final reception by B event 3. Let t_{B1} and t_{B3} be the times of events 1 and 3 according to B's clock, and let t_{A2} be the time of event 2 according to

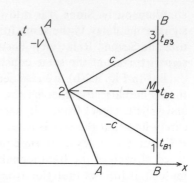

Fig. 3.3 Synchronization of A's clock, *from the viewpoint of B.*

A's clock. Then B says that A's clock is synchronized with his if $t_{A2} = t_{B2} \equiv \frac{1}{2}(t_{B1} + t_{B3})$. Here t_{B2} is the midpoint in time between t_{B1} and t_{B3}, *as measured on B's clock*, and corresponds to event M, midway between events 1 and 3, each of these occurring at the same space point. Naturally B insists that A adjust his clock to ensure that $t_{A2} = t_{B2}$.

So far we have considered B's point of view. But let us now consider the *same* experiment from A's point of view. Remember that we have been unable to find any experiment which enables us to tell which of two observers A and B is "really" moving, as long as they are in constant relative motion. Hence A can consider the same experiment from his point of view, in which he considers himself to be at rest, and B to be moving with constant velocity **V** in the $+x$ direction. **The physics as seen from A's viewpoint must be as good physics as that seen from B's viewpoint.***

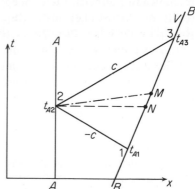

Fig. 3.4 The same experiment as that in Fig. 3.3, but seen from A's viewpoint.

*This again is a loose form of the First Relativity Postulate.

We show the three events 1, 2, 3 from A's point of view in Fig 3.4. By the Second Relativity Postulate the speed of the light signals from 1 to 2 and from 2 to 3 are *again* equal to c, so that lines 12 and 23 have opposite slopes. In this figure we have introduced a fifth event N, synchronous with event 2 according to A. It is clear from the geometry of the figure that N is not the midpoint of the line element 13, which corresponds to M.* Clearly, in fact, N occurs before M. **Thus B says that events M and 2 are synchronous, while A says that events 2 and N are synchronous, yet event N occurs before event M.**

How did we get into this paradox? We were bound to do so once both A and B considered that the light signals traveled at the same speed c with respect to *each* of them. If we had used the Galilean transformation of velocities, and if in fact B had been at rest w.r.t. the ether, then in Fig. 3.4 the line 12 should correspond to a speed $c - V$, and the line 23 to a speed $c + V$. It then turns out that N is the midpoint of 13, so that there is no paradox (cf. problem 3.4).†

We were forced into the paradox once we had accepted the results of the Michelson-Morley experiment at face value, as expressed in the Second Relativity Postulate. We have found that time is relative. **Two events which are simultaneous w.r.t. one observer are not simultaneous w.r.t. another observer who is moving at a constant speed w.r.t. the first observer.**‡

To A, it is absurd that B wants to say that the time between events 1 and 2 should be the same as the time between events 2 and 3. To A it is obvious that $t_2 - t_1$ should be less than $t_3 - t_2$, since B is moving away from A, and hence the distance that the first light signal had to travel from B to A is less than the distance the second light signal had to travel from A to B. Thus A *knows* that the event 2 should occur somewhat earlier than the time $\frac{1}{2}(t_1 + t_3)$.

Since the meaning of the phrase "the time of an event" is becoming somewhat uncertain, we show on Fig. 3.4 the times of events 1, 2, and 3, as measured by A or observers at rest w.r.t. A who are synchronized w.r.t. A. The (infinite) set of these observers are the basis of A's space-time frame of reference (cf. Section 2.2). Thus we define the times t_{A1}, t_{A2}, and

---

*That M remains at the midpoint of 13 even when seen from A's viewpoint is a consequence of the assumed linearity of space and time. The space-time intervals $1M$ and $M3$ are identical from B's viewpoint, and hence must also be identical from that of A.

†Of course no paradox could arise. We would prove that a universal time did exist, but our proof would use the Galilean transformation, which assumes that a universal time does exist.

‡Naturally we must qualify this somewhat. The geometry of Fig. 3.4 can and will be analyzed by us shortly. It turns out that the size of the effect depends on V/c. Since $c = 3 \times 10^8$ m/sec $= 186,000$ miles/sec, V must be quite large for a measurable effect to occur. No effects should be, nor are, observable in everyday life.

t_{A3} as being the times of events 1, 2, and 3 according to A. Similarly we define t_{AM} and t_{AN}. Then our previous remark should properly be stated as, "A knows that t_{A2} should be less than $\frac{1}{2}(t_{A1} + t_{A3})$." By construction, $t_{AN} = t_{A2}$, and $t_{AM} = \frac{1}{2}(t_{A1} + t_{A3})$. Thus $t_{AM} > t_{A2}$, or **"according to A event M happens later than event 2."**

Yet B insists to A that event M occurred at the same time as event 2—that is, $t_{BM} = t_{B2}$. Furthermore (cf. Fig 3.5), **B insists that all events anywhere on the line $2M$ (even when extended) occur at the same time** (cf. problem 3.5).

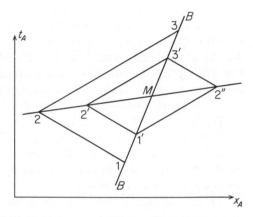

Fig. 3.5 The generalization of Fig. 3.4, from A's viewpoint.

Notice that A and B are not arguing about the actuality of what events occur, in that A will accept Fig. 3.4 and Fig. 3.5 and agree with B that M *is* the mid-instant in time between event 1 and event 2. He is only arguing (as you probably are) about whether the clock at 2 should be forced to agree with the clock reading at M. A says, "I am obviously at rest, and B is moving. B doesn't know this, and being egocentric, B is insisting that I synchronize my clock to agree with his crazy view of things, cf. Fig. 3.3, in which I am moving and he is at rest. But of course I know I am at rest" (perhaps because A is a little egocentric).*

After a long and heated argument, A says to B, "You are apparently a fool, but if we are going to communicate at all, I had better get used to your conventions. I'll just retranslate them into my sense." Thus A realizes that B will insist that all events along the line $2M$ occur at the same time t_{BM} (though A knows they occur at different times t_A).

*On a more mundane level, B is simply asserting his right to use a frame of reference at rest w.r.t. himself. Our whole subsequent discussion, while phrased in terms of psychological egocentricity, does of course have physical content. See also the end of Section 3.3.

Now A has already managed to live with the fact that B says that all events along the line 13 occur at the same point x_B. A says that events along the line 13 have different x_A and different t_A, but agrees that $x_A - Vt_A = $ const. Up to now A and B have believed that $t_A = t_B$ for any event, but they are getting more than a little worried about this. In fact (see the Appendix to this chapter, Section 3.8) it is not difficult to show that the line $2M$ in Fig. 3.4 has the form

$$t_A - \frac{x_A V}{c^2} = \text{const.} \tag{3.2}$$

We hence see that A and B should pair the statements

$$x_B = \text{const.} \iff x_A - Vt_A = \text{const.}' \tag{3.3}$$

and similarly

$$t_B = \text{const.}'' \iff t_A - \frac{x_A V}{c^2} = \text{const.}''' \tag{3.4}$$

(The various primes indicate that each constant may have a different value.) In the "old" days we would have extended (3.3) to

$$x_B = x_A - Vt_A.$$

However, it now seems wiser to be more cautious and write

$$x_B = p(x_A - Vt_A) \tag{3.5}$$

and similarly

$$t_B = q(t_A - \frac{x_A V}{c^2}). \tag{3.6}$$

[Equations (3.5) and (3.6) are conjectures, based on linearity. See also problem 3.8.] In (3.5) and (3.6) p and q are scale functions and must not depend on (x_A, t_A) or (x_B, t_B), but they can depend on V and c. We will determine them very soon.*

So far B has done all the experimenting. But A can attempt to justify his point of view by sending a signal to B, who then retransmits it immediately back to A. A's aim is to synchronize all clocks w.r.t. his frame of reference (cf. problem 3.6). If one draws his experiment from his point of view, one obtains the exact analogue of Fig. 3.3, call it Fig. 3.3'; while if one draws his experiment from B's point of view, one obtains the exact analogue of Fig. 3.4, call it Fig. 3.4'. From this

---

*In Equations (3.5) and (3.6) we have made the simplifying assumption of a common origin—that is, $x_A = 0$, $t_A = 0 \iff x_B = 0$, $t_B = 0$. What this means is simply that, by design or good fortune, at the instant when A and B were at the same point, *both* their clocks read zero. This assumption is exactly equivalent to the one we made in Section 2.2, and the same footnote applies. Again we have assumed that both take their x axes parallel, and similarly their y and z axes.

second experiment, its associated figures, and the argument that B will now make, one immediately sees that there is complete symmetry between observers A and B. The boot is now on the other foot, and B must resign himself to saying, "I, B, am obviously at rest, but A is insisting that he is at rest, and hence that I should use his coordinates x_A and t_A. His idea that fixed t_A corresponds to a fixed time is of course wrong, since in fact his line of fixed t_A is a sloping line in my Fig. 3.4′ given by

$$t_B + \frac{x_B V}{c^2} = \text{const."} \tag{3.2′}$$

In fact we see that B will come to the conclusion that if he is to communicate with the egocentric A, he should use

$$x_A = p(x_B + V t_B) \tag{3.5′}$$

and

$$x_B = q\left(t_B + \frac{x_B V}{c^2}\right). \tag{3.6′}$$

Here (cf. problem 3.7) p and q are *precisely* the same scale functions as in (3.5) and (3.6). In fact they can be functions only of V^2 and c.

We hence see that there is *complete symmetry* between A and B. Each decides that the other is wrong and is making the *same* foolish egocentric mistake. Each realizes he will have to learn to live with the other's foolishness, and in order to do so each needs a translating key. These keys are provided in Eqs. (3.5) and (3.6), and (3.5′) and (3.6′). The symmetry is complete between A and B except for a straightforward minus sign in front of V (cf. p. 29). This simply corresponds to the fact that B is moving away from A to the right, while A is moving away from B to the left. Since the choice of the "positive" direction is arbitrary, none of the real physics can depend on the sign of V (cf. problem 3.7).

This section is probably one of the most important in the whole book. It is essential that you understand it fully and also that you do all the problems 3.1 through 3.8 before you read any further. We hence give a summary.

When two observers A and B are in relative motion with constant relative velocity V, they disagree over the problem of synchronizing their clocks. A's method is obviously foolish to B, and B's method is obviously foolish to A. The cause of the difficulty is that *each* assumes that light has the same speed c, as demonstrated by the Michelson-Morley experiment. Looking specifically at Fig. 3.4, it is clear to A that event M, the mid-instant in time between events 1 and 3, should occur later than events 2 and N. This is because A says that the distance that the light signal must go

from event 1 to event 2 is less than the distance on the return trip from event 2 to event 3, since B is moving. On the other hand B says that A is moving, so that the distances for the two trips 12 and 23 are of course the same (cf. Fig. 3.3). Thus B insists that all events on the line joining events 2 and M are simultaneous, while A knows (from his Fig. 3.4) that this line has a slope. That is, according to A, different events along this line have different times t_A, associated with their positions x_A in such a way that $t_A - (Vx_A/c^2) = $ const.

The situation is actually symmetric between A and B. In order for them to communicate, each realizes that he will have to translate his own (correct) coordinates into the other observer' s (wrong) language. These "translation" equations are provided in Eqs. (3.5) and (3.6), and (3.5′) and (3.6′). (Of course we have yet to determine p and q.)

[Note. The proof that the line $2M$ in Fig. 3.4 has the form $t_A - (Vx_A/c^2) = $ const. is given in the Appendix to this chapter, Section 3.8. The proof is based on trigonometry, and is not essential to the understanding of the rest of this book. (In fact we will later give another proof of the Lorentz transformations.) What is essential is simply a realization that the line $2M$ *is* sloping, and an understanding of why this *must* be the case. Read NO further until you are absolutely clear on this point.]

A final remark has to do with clocks in relative motion but separated only in a direction *perpendicular* to their relative motion, at the *moment* under discussion. One can readily prove (cf. problem 3.9) that if A finds B's clock to be synchronized w.r.t. his (A's) clock at that moment, then B finds A's clock to be synchronized w.r.t. his (B's) clock at that moment. Thus no extra difficulty occurs, over and above that already discussed due to a separation along the direction of relative motion.

3.3   THE LORENTZ TRANSFORMATION

In the previous discussion, each of the two observers A and B claimed that the other's definition of time was incorrect. In fact each of the two observers attempted to define the time at a distant point as if he himself were at rest. Further, each used the synchronization condition of Section 3.1, which was discussed there for clocks relatively at *rest* w.r.t. each other.

In fact each of them is attempting to set up his *own* space-time frame of reference, similar to those discussed in Section 2.2. Thus, observer A constructs his space-time frame of reference by placing clocks at many locations in space, all of the clocks being at rest relative to A, and all being synchronized w.r.t. the clock that A has at his own location. In distinction to Section 2.2, this synchronization does not make use of the universal time hypothesis, but tests and adjusts the clocks, using Eq. (3.1), *after* they are in their final positions, all relatively at rest. We call the time on any such A-synchronized clock the time t. Furthermore, A sets up a frame of space coordinates (x, y, z), using standard meter sticks. For convenience we assume he takes his origin to be at his own location, and his x axis along the direction of motion of B.

Similarly B sets up his space-time frame of reference, with clocks all relatively at rest w.r.t. B, and all synchronized using the synchronization condition of Eq. (3.1), but now based on B's clock. We call the readings on B's set of clocks t'. Similarly B sets up a frame of space coordinates (x', y', z') using standard meter sticks, and for convenience we assume he takes his origin to be at his own location, and his x', y', and z' axes parallel to those of A. Finally we assume that their time origins are so chosen that the event Ω, which corresponds to A and B being at the same point, has coordinates $(0, 0, 0, 0)$ according to *each* of A and B.

We now have two separate space-time frames of reference (x, y, z, t) and (x', y', z', t'), very similar to those considered in Section 2.2. But now $t' \neq t$, since we use the (relativistic) synchronization condition Eq. (3.1).

In the previous section we used the coordinates x_A and t_A, and x_B and t_B. It is clear that

$$x = x_A, \quad t = t_A; \quad x' = x_B, \quad t' = t_B$$

and hence that the "translation" Eqs. (3.5) and (3.6), and (3.5') and (3.6') become

$$x' = p(x - Vt), \qquad x = p(x' + Vt')$$
$$t' = q\left(t - \frac{Vx}{c^2}\right), \qquad t = q\left(t' + \frac{Vx'}{c^2}\right).$$

We do not as yet know p and q. Here, of course, (x', t') and (x, t) refer to the *same* event.

Before proceeding to determine p and q, let us ask whether A and B should have any difficulty about their y and z coordinates; that is, can we immediately write $y = y'$, and $z = z'$? The answer is "yes." For suppose this were not the case, and recall that both A and B use the same standard meter sticks, originally compared when at rest w.r.t. each other. Consider two sets of these meter sticks directed parallel to the y axis, and hence parallel to the y' axis; the A set at rest w.r.t. A, and the B set at rest w.r.t. B.* Then if $y' \neq y$, this implies that at the instant one of the B-set meter sticks passes one of the A-set sticks,

---

*That the y and y' axes are parallel is not self-evident, and it can best be proved by considering the yz plane. By linearity, this must transform into some unique plane. Since only the x' axis is specially determined, the only possible plane is perpendicular to the x' axis.

one of these two sticks is actually shorter than the other. Let us assume that, according to A, the B stick which is moving w.r.t. A is actually shorter than the stick which is at rest w.r.t. A. Then, by the symmetry between observers and the first principle of relativity (cf. p. 29 and the footnote) B must say that the stick which is moving w.r.t. him is shorter than his stationary stick. That is, B says that A's stick is shorter than B's stick; while A says that B's stick is shorter than A's stick. But they are each looking at the *same* two sticks, which are parallel to each other, at the same instant of time as measured by *each* of A and B, at the moment at which they are side by side at essentially the same point (cf. problem 3.9).* Either A's stick is shorter than B's, or B's stick is shorter than A's; but both *cannot* be the case simultaneously. Thus in fact $y = y'$, and $z = z'$. In words, **the apparent length of a rod is independent of any constant motion of an observer in a direction transverse to the rod.** Hence we now have

$$x' = p(x - Vt) \qquad\qquad x = p(x' + Vt')$$
$$y' = y \qquad\qquad y = y'$$
$$z' = z \qquad (3.7) \qquad z = z' \qquad (3.7')$$
$$t' = q\left(t - \frac{Vx}{c^2}\right) \qquad\qquad t = q\left(t' + \frac{Vx'}{c^2}\right)$$

as the complete set of transformations between the two descriptions of the *same* space-time event.

All we now need is to obtain p and q. This is straightforward. For the two sets of transformation equations (3.7) and (3.7') must be compatible with each other, or another argument will arise. Hence we can substitute from Eq. (3.7') into Eq. (3.7) and obtain

$$x' = p[x - Vt] = p\left[p(x' + Vt') - Vq\left(t' + \frac{Vx'}{c^2}\right)\right]$$
$$= \left(p^2 - \frac{pqV^2}{c^2}\right) x' + (p^2 V - Vpq)t' \qquad (3.8a)$$

and

$$t' = q\left[t - \frac{Vx}{c^2}\right] = q\left[q\left(t' + \frac{Vx'}{c^2}\right) - \frac{Vp(x' + Vt')}{c^2}\right]$$
$$= \left(\frac{q^2 V}{c^2} - \frac{qpV}{c^2}\right) x' + \left(q^2 - \frac{V^2 pq}{c^2}\right) t' \qquad (3.8b)$$

These equations are algebraic *identities*, and must hold for *all* x' and

*This situation is very different from the one where A and B compare meter sticks lying along the x axis. In that case *each* of A and B say that the other's meter stick is the shorter, but the reason for this apparent paradox is that A and B are unable to agree on the proper moment to view the *two* ends of the meter sticks (cf. Section 3.5).

t'. Thus, in Eq. (3.8a) we see that the t' coefficient must vanish, and hence that $p = q$. Then, again in (3.8a), the x' coefficient gives us that

$$1 = p^2 - \frac{pqV^2}{c^2} = p^2\left(1 - \frac{V^2}{c^2}\right)$$

or

$$p = \frac{1}{\sqrt{1 - \left(\frac{V^2}{c^2}\right)}}. \tag{3.9}$$

These results, when substituted into Eq. (3.8b), lead to an identity, so that we have a completely consistent set of equations.* We remark that, in Eq. (3.9), the positive square root must be taken, since both A and B want their *positive x* axes to point in the same direction. We therefore have obtained the complete set of transformation equations, which is known as the **Lorentz transformation:**

$$x' = \frac{1}{\sqrt{1 - \left(\frac{V^2}{c^2}\right)}}(x - Vt)$$

$$y' = y$$
$$z' = z \tag{3.10}$$

$$t' = \frac{1}{\sqrt{1 - \left(\frac{V^2}{c^2}\right)}}\left(t - \frac{Vx}{c^2}\right)$$

and

$$x = \frac{1}{\sqrt{1 - \left(\frac{V^2}{c^2}\right)}}(x' + Vt')$$

$$y = y'$$
$$z = z' \tag{3.11}$$

$$t = \frac{1}{\sqrt{1 - \left(\frac{V^2}{c^2}\right)}}\left(t' + \frac{Vx'}{c^2}\right).$$

the form $[1 - (V^2/c^2)]^{-1/2}$ arises so frequently that it is given a special symbol

---

*In fact, if we had not assumed that A's velocity w.r.t. B was $-V$, but simply $-V'$, and had inserted p' and q' in B's part of Eq. (3.7), we would have proved that $V = V'$. We prefer to prove this directly by imposing symmetry between A and B (cf. the discussion at the beginning of Section 3.2).

$$\gamma = \frac{1}{\sqrt{1 - \left(\frac{V^2}{c^2}\right)}} \geq 1. \tag{3.12}$$

With this substitution, the final form is given by:

LORENTZ TRANSFORMATION:

$$x' = \gamma(x - Vt) \quad \text{and} \quad x = \gamma(x' + Vt')$$
$$y' = y \qquad\qquad\qquad y = y'$$
$$z' = z \qquad\qquad\qquad z = z'$$
$$t' = \gamma\left(t - \frac{Vx}{c^2}\right) \qquad t = \gamma\left(t' + \frac{Vx'}{c^2}\right). \tag{3.13}$$

These equations replace the "classical" Galilean transformation of Chapter 2, Eqs. (2.1). Since classical physics does work in everyday life, it is essential that, for small V, the Lorentz transformation collapse to the Galilean transformation. For small V, we see that $\gamma \to 1$; further the term $Vx/c^2 \ll t$, provided $x/t \ll c$.* We see that the characteristic relativistic speed is the velocity of light c. All velocities should be compared to this (very large) velocity in order to test whether any relativistic effects are likely to occur. If all velocities are much smaller than c, classical physics is a good approximation. Thus in everyday life the use of a universal time, and of the Galilean transformation, is in fact completely justified.

Example 3.1. Consider the two observers A and B, moving with a relative velocity $V = 0.6c = 1.8 \times 10^8$m/sec $\approx 112{,}000$ miles/sec, in the x direction. As usual, the origins of coordinates "happen" to coincide at the time $t = t' = 0$. A observes a rocket which passes through his origin at $t = 0$ and goes in the x direction at a constant velocity of $0.4c$. Determine the trajectory of the rocket as measured by A, and as measured by B.

Answer 3.1. According to A, we must have $x = (0.4)ct$, $y = 0$, $z = 0$. According to B, the typical event (x, y, z, t) on the trajectory must be re-expressed in terms of x', y', z', and t' using Eq. (3.13). Here $V = 0.6c$, and hence

$$\gamma = \frac{1}{\sqrt{1 - (V^2/c^2)}} = \frac{1}{\sqrt{1 - (0.6)^2}} = \frac{1}{\sqrt{0.64}} = \frac{1}{\sqrt{0.8}} = 1.2.$$

Hence

$$x' = (1.2)[(0.4)ct - (0.6)ct] = -(0.24)ct$$
$$y' = 0$$

*The symbols $\gg$ and $\ll$ mean "much greater than" and "much less than."

$$z' = 0$$

$$t' = (1.2)[t - (0.6)(0.4)t] = (1.2)(0.76)t = (0.912)t.$$

Hence

$$x' = \frac{-0.24}{0.912} ct' \approx -(0.263)ct'.$$

Comment. The result $t' \neq t$ is, of course, to be expected. But we notice that the speed of the rocket according to B is $\approx -0.263c$, which differs from the expected Galilean result of $-(0.6)c + (0.4)c = -0.2c$. The theory of relativity does indeed have remarkable real consequences.

Example 3.2. Reconsider Examples 2.1 (p. 11), 2.2 (p. 13), and 2.3 (p. 15), but now make use of the Lorentz transformation to relate observer B on the train to observer A.

Answer 3.2. (i) The trajectory according to A must still be given by

$$A \text{ trajectory:} \quad x = 0, \quad y = 40t - \tfrac{1}{2}(32)t^2.$$

But now, according to B, we must have

$$x' = \gamma(x - Vt), \quad y' = y, \quad t' = \gamma\left(t - \frac{Vx}{c^2}\right)$$

or more usefully, though equivalently

$$x = \gamma(x' + Vt'), \quad y = y', \quad t = \gamma\left(t' + \frac{Vx'}{c^2}\right),$$

where $\gamma = [1 - (V^2/c^2)]^{-1/2}$, $V = 15$ ft/sec, and $c = 9.84 \times 10^8$ ft/sec. Thus γ is very close to unity. However, for the sake of the example, let us keep γ. (We could have considered a larger V, such as $V = 0.6c$; cf. Example 3.1). Then by substitution

$$x = 0 = \gamma(x' + Vt') \quad \text{or} \quad x' = -Vt'.$$

Hence $t = \gamma[t' + (Vx'/c^2)] = \gamma[t' - (V^2t'/c^2)] = \gamma^{-1}t'$. Therefore, substituting for t in y

$$y = y' = 40(\gamma^{-1}t') - \tfrac{1}{2}(32)(\gamma^{-1}t')^2.$$

Hence

$$B \text{ trajectory:} \quad x' = -Vt', \quad y' = 40\gamma^{-1}t' - \tfrac{1}{2}(32)\gamma^{-2}t'^2.$$

Note that we had to eliminate t, so that B's trajectory is expressed only in terms of x', y', and t'.

We now ask where the ball is at the end of 2 sec. However, this is not a complete specification in the special theory of relativity, since $t = 2$ sec implies $t' = 2\gamma$ sec; while $t' = 2$ sec implies $t = 2\gamma^{-1}$ sec. Throughout the following, we will consider the event corresponding to $t = 2$ sec. Then $t' = 2\gamma$ sec and

$$x' = -V(2\gamma) = -2\gamma V = -30\gamma \text{ ft}$$

$$y' = 40(\gamma^{-1}\gamma^2) = \tfrac{1}{2}(32)\,(\gamma^{-1}\gamma^2)^2$$
$$= 40(2) - \tfrac{1}{2}(32)(2)^2 = 16 \text{ ft.}$$

Thus $y' = y$, as it must at a particular event, even though the dependence of y' on t' is different from the dependence of y on t. In summary,

A position; $x = 0$, $y = 16$ ft

B position: $x' = -30\gamma$ ft, $y' = y = 16$ ft

(cf. pp. 11 and 12). Notice that all A's results are necessarily the same as in the classical case.

(ii) Next we consider the velocities. Again the velocity according to A must be the same as in the classical case. However, when we consider B we have

B velocity: $v'_x = \dfrac{dx'}{dt'} = -V = -15$ ft/sec

$$v'_y = \frac{dy'}{dt'} = 40\gamma^{-1} - (32)\gamma^{-2}t'.$$

[Note. The non-calculus derivation of this and subsequent results proceeds exactly as in Answers 2.2 and 2.3. Even if you have not met calculus before, you should be able to obtain all these results yourself.]
Then at $t = 2$ sec, $t' = 2\gamma^{-1}$ sec, so that

B velocity: $v'_x = -15$ ft/sec, $v'_y = -24\gamma^{-1}$ ft/sec.

In this case v'_x agrees with the classical result, but v'_y differs from it (cf. p. 14).

(iii) Finally, considering the accelerations, we have

B acceleration: $a'_x = \dfrac{dv'_x}{dt'} = 0$, $a'_y = \dfrac{dv'_y}{dt'} = -32\gamma^{-2}$ ft/sec^2.

Thus a'_y again differs from the classical result (cf. p. 15).

Comment. This example shows that if we know the trajectory of a particle according to A, then by using the Lorentz transformation we can obtain the trajectory according to B, in which x', y' and z' are expressed in terms of t'. In these B coordinates, we can then obtain the velocity and acceleration according to B, in the normal way. However, when we come to evaluate them, we must be careful to distinguish between t and t'; and even then we find some surprising results. While we can always proceed via the trajectory equations, it is in fact useful to have a set of transformation equations for the velocity and for the acceleration. These will be given in due course.

We show the Lorentz transformation in Fig. 3.6, drawn from A's point of view. Notice that B says that all events along the line RP happen at the same time t', and that all events along the line SP occur at the same point x'. We have a set of *oblique* coordinate axes for B, when drawn from A's point of view. The reason that B's t' axis has a slope

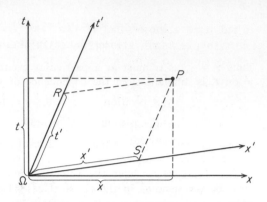

Fig. 3.6 The Lorentz transformation from A's viewpoint, showing the *two* sets of axes and coordinates for the same event P.

is simply that it corresponds to $x' = 0$—that is, to B's spatial origin which is moving at speed $+V$ w.r.t. A's coordinates. Similarly B's x' axis corresponds to $t' = 0$, and we saw in Section 3.2 that $t' = 0 \longrightarrow t - (Vx/c^2) = 0$.*† An important warning should be given with reference to Fig 3.6, namely that the scales along the oblique axes are *not* the same as those along the rectangular axes. This is due to the factors of γ in the Lorentz transformation. Hence Fig. 3.6 is useful for visualization, but all detailed predictions are best carried out algebraically.

Naturally (cf. problem 3.10) if one looks at the Lorentz transformation from B's point of view, one obtains an exactly analogous set of oblique axes except for the interchange of right and left. This must be the case, since our *entire* discussion has preserved a complete symmetry between the two observers A and B. Thus also the scale-factor effects are symmetric beween A and B.

The Lorentz transformation is the keystone of the special theory of relativity. We therefore recapitulate the main steps in our derivation. Commencing with the Michelson-Morley experiment, we were led to the Second Relativity Postulate, which states that the velocity of light is a universal constant. This forced us into the realization that different observers A and B would disagree over the question of whether two events at different places occurred at the same time (cf. Section 3.2). However, there remained a basic symmetry between A's view of B's foolishness, and B's view of A's foolishness. This general symmetry between the viewpoints of different observers is very basic, and we ex-

*The symbol $\longrightarrow$ means "implies that."

†Note that the x' axis is taken along the line $t' = 0$, and the t' axis along the line $x' = 0$. This is similar to the case of an (x, y) plot in which the x axis is taken along the line $y = 0$, and vice versa.

alted it to a loose form of the First Relativity Postulate. (We will discuss this in much greater detail in Section 5.1.) In order for A and B to continue to communicate, they "agreed to disagree" in their coordinates, but were forced to make use of a "translation" scheme [Eqs. (3.5) and (3.6), and (3.5′) and (3.6′)]. This scheme incorporated their knowledge that each was moving away from the other with constant speed V, and also their detailed analysis of the cause of their disagreement over the concept of time. This knowledge, together with a further application of the First Relativity Postulate, completely determined the final form of the Lorentz transformation.

We emphasize that the above derivation could not have been carried out by a philosopher locked up in an ivory tower with no windows. The experimental results of the Michelson-Morley experiment are essential input. Thus one can easily imagine a world in which a positive result would be obtained in that experiment. In that world the ether would exist. A special frame of reference would be singled out which is at rest w.r.t. the ether, and in which the velocity of light is indeed c. There would be a universal time, and absolute motion would be detectable w.r.t. the ether.

Granting that the Michelson-Morley experiment was crucial, the skeptic can still argue that A and B need not have "agreed to disagree," particularly in the precise form to which we have been led. That is, the Lorentz transformation and all subsequent deductions that we will make are not forced upon us. We could continue to use the Galilean transformation. But then the results of other experiments (which will be discussed) would be most unlikely to agree with our theory. The Lorentz transformation and deductions from it do agree with all present *experimental* knowledge.

3.4* LIGHT-SPHERE DERIVATION OF THE LORENTZ TRANSFORMATION

The Lorentz transformation is so basic to the whole special theory of relativity that it is worthwhile to give more than one derivation. The one we are about to give is very common, and is *apparently* more direct than the one we have given. It is certainly the most convenient one to use in order to derive the equations in a hurry, but its very ease tends to hide the true physics of the Lorentz transformation. The previous derivation is similar to Einstein's own derivation, which also commences with a discussion of simultaneity, and is given in Appendix B to Chapter 4.

*This section may be omitted.

We look for a transformation between (x, y, z, t) and (x', y', z', t') with the properties that

(i) It is linear. That is, a single event transforms into a single event. This also ensures that a straight line in the (x, y, z, t) coordinates transforms into a straight line in the (x', y', z', t') coordinates, and that similar intervals transform into similar intervals (e.g, the intervals $1M$ and $M3$ in Figs. 3.2 and 3.3).

(ii) B's spatial origin moves away from A's spatial origin along the x direction with constant velocity $\mathbf{V}$.

(iii) The speed of light has the same constant value, c, for both sets of coordinates.

These conditions are each very physical. If we argue, as in Section 3.3, that $y' = y$ and $z' = z$, then condition (i) implies

$$x' = kx + lt, \qquad t' = mx + \text{n}t,$$

where k, l, m, and n are independent of x and t. [Here we have assumed for simplicity that the space-time event $\Omega = (0, 0, 0, 0)$ has the same coordinates in both systems.] Next, condition (ii) means that $x' = 0$ corresponds to $x = Vt$. This leads to $0 = kVt + lt$, or $l = -kV$, and therefore

$$x' = k(x - Vt), \quad y' = y, \quad z' = z, \quad t' = mx + nt. \tag{3.14}$$

Finally, we consider condition (iii). The event $\Omega \equiv (0, 0, 0, 0)$ occurs at the spatial origin for each of the two observers A and B, at the time $t = t' = 0$. Let a flash of light be emitted from this common origin at $t = t' = 0$. At some later time t, let it have reached the point (x, y, z) according to A. Then necessarily

$$x^2 + y^2 + z^2 = c^2 t^2.$$

Suppose the *same* event has coordinates (x', y', z', t') according to B. Then also

$$x'^2 + y'^2 + z'^2 = c^2 t'^2$$

That is

$$x^2 + y^2 + z^2 - c^2 t^2 = 0 \longrightarrow x'^2 + y'^2 + z'^2 - c^2 t'^2 = 0. \tag{3.15}$$

Now under the linear transformation (3.14), the homogeneous quadratic form $Q = x^2 + y^2 + z^2 - c^2 t^2$ must go into some homogeneous quadratic form $Q'(x', y', z', t')$, such that $Q = Q'$. Further from Eq. (3.15) we see that *if* $Q = 0$, then the result $Q' = 0$ must imply that $x'^2 + y'^2 + z'^2 - c^2 t'^2 = 0$. It follows that Q' must contain this quadratic form as a *factor*. Hence from (3.15) and the linear nature of the transformation, we are led to the much stronger condition that

$$x^2 + y^2 + z^2 - c^2 t^2 = \lambda^2(x'^2 + y'^2 + z'^2 - c^2 t'^2). \tag{3.16}$$

Here λ is a constant, independent of x, y, z, or t, or x', y', z', or t'. It corresponds to a scale factor, and could depend on V. However, if we substitute (3.14) directly into the right-hand side of (3.16), we see that the terms $\lambda^2(y'^2 + z'^2)$ go directly into $\lambda^2(y^2 + z^2)$, and no other terms containing y and z occur. Since the left-hand side of (3.16) only contains y and z in the form $y^2 + z^2$, it follows that $\lambda^2 = 1$. Hence we see that (3.16) becomes

$$x^2 + y^2 + z^2 - c^2 t^2 \equiv x'^2 + y'^2 + z'^2 - c^2 t'^2. \tag{3.17}$$

This is an identity, for *all* x, y, z, and t.*

If we now substitute (3.14) into (3.17) and demand that this be an *identity*, we obtain

$$x^2 - c^2 t^2 \equiv x'^2 - c^2 t'^2 \equiv k^2(x - Vt)^2 - c^2(mx + nt)^2$$
$$\equiv x^2(k^2 - m^2 c^2) - 2xt(k^2 V + c^2 mn) + t^2(k^2 V^2 - n^2 c^2).$$

Since this is an identity, we can equate the *coefficients* of x^2, xt, and t^2 *separately*, which gives the three equations

$$k^2 - m^2 c^2 = 1$$
$$k^2 V + c^2 mn = 0$$

and

$$-k^2 V^2 + n^2 c^2 = c^2.$$

These equations can be solved straightforwardly, and lead directly to the Lorentz transformation.

We emphasize that Eq. (3.17)'s being an *identity* followed from the assumed linearity of the transformation equations, and it is more than we need simply to maintain the postulated constancy of the speed of light. In fact it enables one to develop a complete geometry of Lorentz transformations in a four-dimensional space-time. This was first developed by H. Minkowski, and takes a particularly elegant form (at least formally) by the introduction of a new coordinate ict, where $i = \sqrt{-1}$. We will not pursue this further here, but see Appendix A of Chapter 4.

3.5 LENGTH CONTRACTION

We are now ready to apply the Lorentz transformation to some physical examples, and to make predictions. (Up to now, all we we have done

---

*We remark that the argument from (3.15) leading to (3.17) is not self-evident. Several "proofs" go directly from (3.15) to (3.17). Such a procedure is incomplete.

is construct a theory which is compatible with the Michelson-Morley experiment.) The first effect we consider is that of length contraction.

Consider the operations involved in measuring the length of a rod. If the rod is at rest w.r.t. our frame of reference, then its two ends correspond to two *fixed* points in this frame. Hence we can locate the two ends separately at our leisure, and then measure off the number of standard meters between these two points, again at our leisure.

On the other hand, if the rod is moving w.r.t. our frame of reference, it is essential that we locate two marks *at rest in our frame* which correspond to the two ends of the moving rod at the *same instant of time*. We can subsequently measure the distance between these two marks at our leisure, since they are at rest. But it is essential that we make the two marks at the same instant of time, *according to us*.

It is clear that this really needs two observers, both stationary w.r.t. ourselves, who by good fortune are located at the two ends of the *moving* rod at the instant of time referred to. This is an example of the general fact that when we speak of "an observer" or "an observation" we really must make use of a whole set of observers, all relatively at rest in a particular space-time frame of reference, and all of whose clocks are synchronized w.r.t. each other. That observer (call him P) who is adjacent to a space-time event E is then the one who really makes the observation of that event; that is, he determines the space-time coordinates of the event E. Once these coordinates are determined and recorded, this information can be transmitted to any other observer (say Q) in the same frame of reference, and one can then loosely speak of the latter observer Q as having observed the event E. In this sense, the "observation" by the distant observer Q does *not* involve Q's directly observing the event E, either visually or otherwise. Thus no problem arises due to a possible time delay in the transmission of information from E to Q. Nearly always, when we speak of the observation of an event E by an observer Q who is not at the event E, we really imply the existence of another observer P who by good fortune is at the event E, and who is at rest w.r.t. Q. This use of the word "observation" is not the normal everyday usage, but is nearly universal in discussing the theory of relativity. Thus, **by "an observer" we really mean an infinite set of observers spread throughout space, all relatively at rest, and all of whose clocks are synchronized w.r.t. each other.** Their individual local observations are then later collected together and analyzed by "the observer."

From our discussion of the measurement of the length of a moving rod, to be carried out by marking the location of its two ends at the same instant of time, it immediately follows that the measurement of the length of a moving rod involves a synchronization experiment. Since time is now relative, it is not completely surprising that the length of an object is a subject for the special theory of relativity. (See also problem 3.12.)

Let us analyze this question in detail. Suppose the rod is at rest w.r.t. the observer B, and observer A is attempting to measure the length of the rod. There is no problem about the length of the rod if it is perpendicular to the relative velocity V, since then both ends of the rod can be located at the *same* instant of time both as defined by A, and as defined by B (cf. the discussion at the end of Section 3.2). We used this result implicitly in Section 3.3 when we proved that $y = y'$ and $z = z'$.

We therefore consider a rod at rest w.r.t. B and located so that its two ends are permanently at the space points $(0, 0, 0)_B$ and $(L_0, 0, 0)_B$.* Naturally the time according to B is irrelevant. We show this in Fig. 3.7, where one end of the rod is always located somewhere along the line ΩW, and the other end is always located somewhere along the line

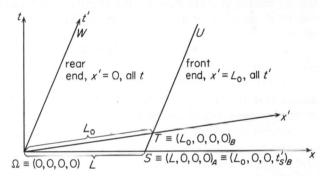

Fig. 3.7 The length contraction effect.

STU. **According to A, at the instant when one end is at Ω, the other end at the *same* instant is at S. On the other hand B says that at the instant one end is at Ω, the other end at the same instant (but according to B) is at T.**

This is the basic reason for the length-contraction effect. According to A, at $t = 0$ the two ends of the rod are respectively at $(0, 0, 0)_A$ and at $(L, 0, 0)_A$. That is, the event $S \equiv (L, 0, 0)_A$ corresponds to one end of the rod. (We will refer to this as the front end in future.) But according to B, the front end of the rod is always at $(L_0, 0, 0)_B$. Let us call t'_S the time of the event S, according to B. From the figure we already see that $t'_S < 0$. We now have two equivalent descriptions of the event S, namely

*We remark that B knows the rod has length L_0 because he has measured it with a meter stick at rest relative to the rod, and hence while both are at rest relative to B.

$$S \equiv (L, 0, 0, 0)_A \equiv (L_0, 0, 0, t'_S)_B \tag{3.18}$$

These two descriptions must necessarily be related by the Lorentz transformation (3.13). Hence, using $x' = \gamma(x - Vt)$, we immediately obtain $L_0 = \gamma L$, or;

> LENGTH CONTRACTION:
>
> $$L = \gamma^{-1}L_0 = \sqrt{1 - \frac{V^2}{c^2}}\, L_0 \tag{3.19}$$

Similarly, using $t = \gamma[t' + (Vx'/c^2)]$, we find that $t'_S = -VL_0/c^2$. This in fact shows why L is apparently shorter than L_0. According to B, A has located the rear end of the rod at the instant $t' = 0$, but has located the front end at the *earlier* instant $t'_S = -VL_0/c^2$. Since the rod is moving to the right, this means that the front end has not yet reached the "correct" location. Hence of course A says that the rod is shorter than B knows it to be.

A, on the other hand, claims that B has made a similar type of error in locating the front end of the rod at the event T, while the rear end was located at Ω. Since T occurs later than Ω, *according to A*, A explains that this is why B believes the rod to have a length L_0 which is greater than the "true length" L.

Notice, however, that while A and B each believe that the other is making a mistake, the argument is again one of *interpretation*. Both A and B agree that the front end of the rod was once at the event S, and some time later at the event T. The argument is simply on the question of which of these two events should be related to the other end's being at the event Ω.

In this discussion, the symmetry between A and B seems to have been violated. This is true, but there is *no* symmetry, since the rod is at rest w.r.t. B, but moving w.r.t. A. The full symmetry is restored when B comes to consider a rod which is at rest w.r.t. A (cf. problem 3.11). In both cases, the final conclusion is: **that observer who is moving w.r.t. a rod in the direction of the rod believes the rod to be shorter than does an observer who is at rest w.r.t. the rod.** The ratio of the lengths is given by Eq. (3.19).

This length contraction was first postulated by G. F. Fitzgerald as a "mechanical" effect due to "friction," or dragging, caused by motion through the ether. H. A. Lorentz (who suggested this independently) was able to construct a complete, "mechanistic" theory by assuming the reality of the ether, and by assuming that all forces were ultimately electromagnetic in origin. Since effects also occur for measuring rods themselves, Lorentz's theory did preserve the "apparent" symmetry between observers, even though the theory was firmly based on an absolute frame of reference. Thus while Lorentz's theory gives the same results as the formulation due to Einstein, the underlying physics of the two theories are completely opposed.

The effect is known as the Lorentz-Fitzgerald contraction, or more commonly as the **Fitzgerald contraction.**

Example 3.3. Consider the length-contraction experiment of Fig. 3.7. The derivation used in the text considered the event S. Show how one can obtain the same result by considering the event T.

Answer 3.3. Let the event T have coordinates $(x_T, 0, 0, t_T)_A$ according to A. Then at this time t_T, the rear end of the rod should have $x_{rear} = Vt_T$. Hence A must demand that $x_T - x_{rear} = L$, or $x_T - Vt_T = L$. But by the Lorentz transformation applied to the event $T \equiv (L_0, 0, 0, 0)_B$, we have

$$x_T = \gamma(x_T' + Vt_T') = \gamma L_0, \qquad t_T = \gamma\left(t_T' + \frac{Vx_T'}{c^2}\right) = \frac{\gamma V L_0}{c^2}.$$

Hence A demands that

$$L = x_T - Vt_T = \gamma L_0 - \frac{V\gamma V L_0}{c^2} = \gamma^{-1}L_0.$$

(Note that x_T does not equal L!)

Example 3.4. A rod of length l' is at rest w.r.t. the frame of reference S', and makes an angle θ' w.r.t. the x' axis. Determine the length and orientation of the rod as seen in the frame S (which as usual is moving with constant velocity V w.r.t. the S' frame along the *negative* x direction).

Answer 3.4. We call the two ends of the rod P and Q, and suppose these are located at $P \equiv (0, 0, 0, t')_{S'}$ and $Q \equiv (a', b', 0, t')_{S'}$ in the S' coordinates. Here $a' = l'\cos\theta'$, $b' = l'\sin\theta'$. [There is no loss of generality in taking the rod to lie in the (x', y') plane.] Then, using the Lorentz transformation, we find

$$P \equiv (\gamma Vt', 0, 0, \gamma t')_S$$

$$Q \equiv \left(\gamma a' + \gamma Vt', b', 0, \gamma t' + \frac{\gamma Va'}{c^2}\right)_S$$

with $\gamma = [1 - (V^2/c^2)]^{-1/2}$. We observe that *if P and Q have the same t', they have different t.* This is the crux of all such problems, since we must assume that P and Q are observed in the frame S at the same time t. Hence we consider P and Q separately.

For P, we set $\gamma t' = t$; then we find

$$P \equiv (Vt, 0, 0, t)_S.$$

For Q, we cleverly set $\gamma t' + (\gamma V a'/c^2) = t$; then we find

$$Q \equiv (Vt + \gamma^{-1}a,'\, b, 0, t)_S.$$

Thus indeed the rod moves with velocity V w.r.t. S. However, we see that while $b = \Delta y = b' = \Delta y'$, $a = \Delta x = \gamma^{-1}a' \neq \Delta x'$. (This is just the x length-contraction effect, and could really have been written down straight away.) Hence

$$l = \sqrt{\gamma^{-2}a'^2 + b'^2} = l'\sqrt{\gamma^{-2}\cos^2\theta' + \sin^2\theta'}$$

and

$$\theta = \tan^{-1}\left(\frac{b'}{\gamma^{-1}a'}\right) = \tan^{-1}(\gamma\,\tan\,\theta').$$

Comment. This result shows that the concept of a "rigid" rod is not relativistically invariant. More precisely, a draftsman's triangle set at θ' in one frame of reference indicates an angle θ in another frame! We will find several other indications that the concept of a "rigid" rod is in contradiction with the theory of relativity (see, for instance, problem 4.25). The reason can be traced back to the fact that *by definition* a rigid rod must move as an entity when it is pushed at one end. Hence the other end of the rod starts moving at the same instant as the end that is pushed. But this is equivalent to sending a signal from one end to the other at infinite speed. Such a signal is in contradiction with the theory of relativity.

There is one most interesting experimental verification of the length-contraction effect. Mu-mesons (symbol μ) are elementary particles that decay into an electron e, an electron antineutrino ($\bar{\nu}_e$), and a mu-neutrino (ν_μ); that is, $\mu \to e + \bar{\nu}_e + \nu_\mu$. The *mean* lifetime of a mu-meson before it decays is 2.2×10^{-6} sec. Mu-mesons are produced by primary cosmic rays at the top of the earth's atmosphere, with speeds up to about $0.99c$. (As we will later "prove" on the basis of the special theory of relativity, the maximun possible speed for any particle is c.) On the average therefore the mu-meson should decay after traveling a distance $\approx (2.2 \times 10^{-6}\text{ sec}) \times (3 \times 10^8\text{ m/sec}) \approx 660$ meters. In fact, rather more than one per cent of the mesons produced at the top of the atmosphere reach ground level before decaying, having traveled typically 20 km. Using the standard exponential decay law, one would expect the fraction surviving to be e^{-30}. How can even one per cent arrive?

Let us look at the experiment from the viewpoint of the mu-meson. The meson sees the 20 km of atmosphere rushing up to and past itself at a speed $\approx 0.99c$. Hence, by the length-contraction effect, the meson believes that the atmosphere has a length of only

$$20\text{ km} \cdot \sqrt{1 - \frac{V^2}{c^2}} = 20\text{ km} \cdot \sqrt{1 - (0.99)^2} = 2.8\text{ km}.$$

While 2.8 km is still ≈ 4.2 times greater than 660 meters, one does expect approximately the fraction $e^{-4.2} \approx 0.013$ of the mesons to live the necessary 4.2 mean lifetimes before decaying, and hence this fraction will indeed reach the earth's surface. Detailed numerical data from such experiments agree exactly with this explanation.*

The same experimental fact can also be interpreted from the viewpoint of time dilation. We discuss this in the next section. The two explanations are equivalent, since it is the lack of a universal time which leads to the length contraction effect.

We cannot leave the subject of the Fitzgerald contraction without briefly discussing the question of the visual appearance of rapidly moving objects. It turns out that the Fitzgerald contraction would *not* be seen as a contraction by an observer *looking* at a fast-moving object, or taking a photograph of it. The reason is that the light reaching the eye (or the camera) at one instant of time has left different parts of the object at *different* times. This experiment should be contrasted with that implied in the technical definition of an observation as discussed on p. 48. It is for the latter that the Fitzgerald contraction occurs.

The experiment of actually looking at an object was first analyzed as recently as 1959 by J. Terrell.† A readable account of this effect is given by V. F. Weisskopf.‡ If we restrict ourselves to objects which subtend small angles to the viewer, it turns out that instead of being contracted, such an object is rotated as seen by the viewer, so that one can see the side face of the object.§ In fact, a camera in the observer's frame and one in the rest frame of the object will take *different* photographs, even when each photograph is taken with the lens of the camera at the *same* point at the instant the shutter is opened. This most paradoxical conclusion can easily be understood if one realizes that the film in one of the two cameras is moving while the light continues to travel between the shutter and the film. In fact, the whole effect is closely related to that of stellar aberration, which we discuss further in Section 4.3.

*See, for instance, F. Friedman, D. Frisch, and J. Smith, *Am. J. Phys.*, **31**, 342 (1960). The same authors have also made a film, "Time Dilation, An Experiment with Mu-mesons" (Watertown, Mass.: Educational Services Inc.). In actual fact one measures the fraction of mesons which have not decayed as a *function* of distance traveled.

†*Phys. Rev.*, **116**, 1041 (1959).

‡*Physics Today*, **13**, 24 (1960). This is reprinted in the volume Special Relativity Theory—Selected Reprints, referred to in the footnote on p. 69.

§Recently G. D. Scott and M. R. Viner, *Am. J. Phys.*, **33**, 534 (1965), have emphasized that, when one views large objects moving at relativistic speeds, one does see some *distortion*; this distortion is a visible consequence of the Fitzgerald contraction.

3.6 TIME DILATION

We turn now to the final basic kinematic effect which is implicit in the Lorentz transformation, namely that of time dilation. This effect is somewhat more complex to understand than that of length contraction, since there is no simple classical explanation analogous to that of locating the two ends of a moving rod at two different times. A relativistic explanation will be given in Section 4.1.

We consider a standard clock at rest w.r.t. B, and hence moving with constant velocity V w.r.t. A. According to B, the clock ticks once a second. How many ticks per second does it make according to A (and the set of all observers who are at rest w.r.t. A)? The pre-relativity answer is, of course, one tick per second. But now we are aware of the dangers of the universal time hypothesis, so we proceed more carefully, using the Lorentz transformation as our bulwark.

The method of analysis in all such problems is always the same. **Describe the key parts of any experiment in terms of space-time events. Specify these events as completely as possible in terms of space-time coordinates as assigned by both the "moving" observer and the "stationary" observer. Relate these two equivalent descriptions of the same events by means of the Lorentz transformation. Take what comes out of the algebra, and interpret the result.**

Let us follow these rules. The clock is at rest w.r.t. B, and there is no loss of generality if we take it to be located at B's spatial origin. Furthermore let us assume it makes one tick at time $t' = 0$, and the next at time $t' = 1$. Hence two events are:

the first tick: $\Omega \equiv (0, 0, 0, 0)_B$

and

the second tick: $T \equiv (0, 0, 0, 1)_B$

We show these two events in Fig. 3.8. Both observers agree that the first tick occurred at the event Ω. However, according to A the second tick occurs the same time as the event R, while according to B the second tick occurs at the same time as the event S. This disagreement is the cause of the effect we are considering. But what is the effect?

Always, in such problems, one should trust in the Lorentz transformation. We know the coordinates of the event T in B's frame of reference. Hence we can immediately obtain them in A's frame. In particular

$$t_T = \gamma\left(t'_T - \frac{Vx'_T}{c^2}\right) = \gamma > 1.$$

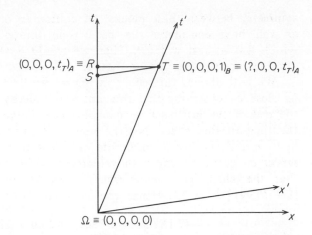

Fig. 3.8 The time dilation effect.

Hence, according to A, the time that has elapsed between the two ticks is not one second, but a *longer* time, γ seconds. If B uses his clock to time the duration of a certain sequence of events *which all happen at the same point in his (B's) frame, A* will see the sequence of events moving w.r.t. him (A), and will find that the duration of the sequence was longer by the factor $\gamma = [1 - (V^2/c^2)]^{-1/2}$ than the duration according to B.

We call the duration of a time interval between events, measured by a clock that is present at both events, and furthermore at rest w.r.t. those events, the **proper time interval.*** Customarily this is denoted by τ (Greek *tau*). Our conclusion is: **an observer who is moving at a constant velocity V w.r.t. a sequence of events finds that the time duration, t, of the sequence is greater by the factor γ than the proper time interval τ measured by a clock present at each event (and also at rest w.r.t. the sequence of events).** That is:

TIME DILATION:

$$t = \gamma\tau = \frac{1}{\sqrt{1 - (V^2/c^2)}}\,\tau. \tag{3.20}$$

Notice that we have been very careful to distinguish between the clock in the rest frame of the sequence of events, and a clock moving at constant velocity V w.r.t. the rest-frame clock. Hence there is no

---

*For simplicity we never consider the possibility that the clock was accelerated between the two events, even though it was present at each event. Hence our use of "proper time" is a *restricted* definition.

symmetry between these clocks. Of course, in our derivation we could as well have considered the basic time interval to occur at a point which was at rest w.r.t. A. Then we would have found that B would say the interval was longer than it was according to A.

We will discuss this effect in more detail in Section 4.1. Here let us close by observing that the mu-meson decay paradox discussed at the end of the last section can also be viewed as a confirmation of the time-dilation effect. For the mu-meson is essentially a clock which *in its rest frame* has a mean life of 2.2×10^{-6} sec. However, an observer on earth moving with velocity $\approx 0.99c$ w.r.t. this clock claims that the clock goes *more slowly* than it ought by a factor $\gamma = [1 - (0.99)^2]^{-1/2} \approx 7.1$. Hence the mean life becomes extended to

$$\approx (7.1)(2.2 \times 10^{-6} \text{ sec}) \approx 15.6 \times 10^{-6} \text{ sec}$$

as measured by the earth-based observer. In this time the mu-meson can travel $\approx (7.1)(660\text{m}) \approx 4.7$ km. Hence in order to travel 20 km according to the earth-based observer, we again find that the mu-meson need only live ≈ 4.2 mean lives before decaying.

This explanation is in fact completely equivalent to the previous one, based on length contraction. The number of mean lifetimes τ_0 required to travel a distance D at a speed V is given by the length-contraction explanation as

$$\frac{D_{\text{effective}}}{V\tau_0} = \frac{\gamma^{-1}D}{V\tau_0} .$$

On the time-dilation explanation this is given by

$$\frac{D}{V\tau_{\text{effective}}} = \frac{D}{V\gamma\tau_0} .$$

These two results are the same, as of course they must be. The reason is that we are simply viewing the same experiment from two different frames of reference, namely the rest frame of the mu-meson, and the earth-based frame. The fraction of those mesons originally produced which reach the earth is a *number* which cannot change for different observers.*

*It is worth pointing out that nearly all high-energy physics experiments which involve unstable particles make use of the time-dilation effect. Beams of unstable particles are made to travel laboratory distances which are much greater than would correspond to their lifetime when at rest, even if they were traveling at the speed of light. The fact that such experiments are performed successfully is itself a test of the special theory of relativity, which is always used in the design of such experiments; and the experiments always work as planned (at least in this respect).

3.7 SUMMARY

This can be rather brief, since various sections have had their own summary. From the negative results of the Michelson-Morley experiment, we were led to the (very surprising) Second Relativity Postulate. This states that the velocity of light is an absolute constant, independent of the motion of the source or the receiver. This postulate gave us a method of synchronizing distant clocks. As long as the two clocks are at rest w.r.t. each other, then if one clock is synchronized with the other, the other clock is synchronized with the first. However, once the two clocks are in relative motion, this is no longer the case. Each observer attached to his own clock finds that the other observer is making a mistake. The magnitude of the effect depends on the distance between the two clocks, so that **space and time become interrelated**. The detailed relationship is fully determined in terms of c and V, the relative velocity of the two clocks. Time is no longer universal. The basic cause for this lies in using the *same* speed of light for each observer.

In order to keep communication going, each observer realizes he must translate his (correct) coordinates in terms of the other observer's (incorrect) coordinates. There is a basic symmetry between the two observers, which we raise to the level of a law of physics, the First Relativity Postulate. This symmetry, together with the detailed analysis of the disagreement over synchronization, is sufficient to determine the complete relationship between the two sets of space-time coordinates. The relationship is called the Lorentz transformation. All kinematic consequences of the special theory of relativity can be derived from this. We considered the effects of length contraction and of time dilation in detail. The former has a fairly direct "explanation." In Section 4.1 we "explain" time dilation.

3.8 APPENDIX

We refer to the discussion associated with Fig. 3.4, and wish to prove that the line $2M$ has the form $t - (Vx/c^2) = $ const. For this derivation it is desirable to work with the variable $r = ct$ instead of the variable t. Then both x and r are measured in the *same* units (e.g., meters in the MKS system), though x refers to space and r to time. We thus label the "vertical" axis of Fig. 3.4 by r ($= ct$), and the "horizontal" axis by x.

In these units, Fig. 3.4 becomes as shown in Fig. 3.9, in which are shown the same world lines AA and BB as before, as well as the various other lines of that figure. Thus again M is the midpoint of the line 13. However in these

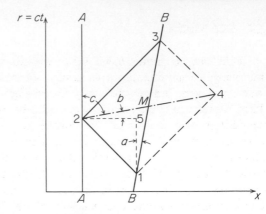

Fig. 3.9 Figure 3.4 redrawn in the $(r = ct, x)$ space.

units the light signals 12 and 23 have a particularly simple geometrical form,
for they have *unit* slope, i.e.

$$\frac{\Delta r}{\Delta x} = \frac{\Delta(ct)}{\Delta x} = c \frac{\Delta t}{\Delta x} = c \left(\frac{\Delta x}{\Delta t}\right)^{-1} = \frac{c}{c} = 1$$

for the light signal 23; and $\Delta r / \Delta x = -1$ for the signal 12. Hence also the
angle 123 is a right angle.

For convenience we construct the lines 25 and 15 as shown, and also we
complete the *rectangle* 1234. Then M, which by definition is the midpoint of
the diagonal 13, is *also* the midpoint of the diagonal 24; and since 1234 is a
rectangle, we also see that the angle 413 is equal to the angle 324. Further, the
angle 415 is equal to the angle 325. Hence, since angle 315 = (angle 415) −
(angle 413), and angle 425 = (angle 325) − (angle 324), we see that angle
315 *equals* angle 425; or that angle a = angle b, where these are as shown in
Fig. 3.9. Thus angle $c = 90° − a$, where c is also as shown.

When we convert this result into words having physical significance, it
says that the angle a that B's world line BB makes with the r (= ct) axis is the
complementary angle to the angle c that B's line of constant time $2M$ makes
with the r (= ct) axis. Now the line BB corresponds to a speed of V, and
hence in the (x, r) coordinates we see that the line BB has slope w.r.t. the
"vertical" r (= ct) axis of

$$\frac{\Delta x}{\Delta r}\bigg|_{BB} = \tan a = \frac{\Delta x}{\Delta(ct)} = \frac{1}{c}\frac{\Delta x}{\Delta t} = \frac{V}{c}.$$

On the other hand, in the (x, r) coordinates we see that the line $2M$ has slope
w.r.t. the r axis of

$$\frac{\Delta x}{\Delta r}\bigg|_{2M} = \frac{\Delta x}{\Delta(ct)}\bigg|_{2M} = \tan c = \tan(90° − a) = \cot a = \frac{1}{\tan a} = \frac{c}{V}.$$

Hence in the more usual (x, t) coordinates, we see that the line $2M$ has slope

$$\frac{\Delta x}{\Delta t}\bigg|_{2M} = \frac{c^2}{V}.$$

Thus $\Delta t = (V/c^2)\,\Delta x$, or $t - (Vx/c^2) = $ const. This is the result we set out to prove.*

The use of the variable $r\,(= ct)$ instead of t is really a rather natural choice. For then r and x have the same dimensions, so that they are more comparable. (This does *not* mean they are equivalent.) In these variables many of the formulas of the special theory of relativity become very simple. Further, velocities are then measured relative to the speed of light. Thus if we set $\beta = V/c$, then $\Delta x/\Delta r = \beta$. In these variables the Lorentz transformation Eq. (3.13) becomes

$$x' = \gamma(x - \beta r), \qquad r' = \gamma(r - \beta x), \qquad \text{with } \gamma = \sqrt{1 - \beta^2}. \quad (3.21)$$

It follows that the Lorentz transformation figure shown in Fig. 3.6 also becomes very symmetrical between r and x. In particular the angle between the x and x' axes becomes equal to the angle between the r and r' axes.

PROBLEMS

(Essential problems are indicated by !, difficult problems by *.)

!3.1 [Refer to the paragraph following Eq. (3.1), p. 28.] Devise an experiment to test whether two clocks P and Q are at rest w.r.t. each other. You may assume each of them has a constant velocity. Show the details of this experiment in a space-time diagram.

!3.2 Consider two identical clocks A and B *relatively at rest* but separated. Prove that if A is synchronized with respect to B, then B is synchronized with respect to A, on our operational definition.

!3.3 Consider three identical clocks A, B, and C, all relatively at rest but separated. Prove that if A and B are synchronized, and then C is synchronized with A, then in fact C is also synchronized with B, on our operational definition.

*An algebraic proof using the (x, t) coordinates can also readily be given. For let event $1 \equiv (x_1, t_1)$, event $2 \equiv (x_1 - l, t_1 + l/c)$ and event $3 \equiv [x_1 - l + m, t_1 + (l/c) + (m/c)]$. But event 3 is connected to event 1 by the world line of B, which has speed V. Hence $(x_3 - x_1) = V(t_3 - t_1)$ or $m - l = V(m + l)/c$. Finally since M is the midpoint of 13, it has coordinates

$$(x_M, t_M) = [\tfrac{1}{2}(x_3 + x_1), \tfrac{1}{2}(t_3 + t_1)] = [x_1 + \tfrac{1}{2}(m - l), t_1 + \tfrac{1}{2}(l + m)/c],$$

so that the line $2M$ has a slope

$$\frac{\Delta x}{\Delta t}\bigg|_{2M} = \frac{x_M - x_2}{t_M - t_2} = \frac{\tfrac{1}{2}(m + l)}{\tfrac{1}{2}(m - l)/c} = \frac{c^2}{V}.$$

Question: Justify the choice of coordinates for events 2 and 3.

!3.4 Draw the analogue of Fig. 3.4, assuming the Galilean transformation of velocity. Show that M and N then *do* coincide if B is truly at rest. Discuss the physical significance of this result.

!3.5 In Fig. 3.5 the line $11'M3'3$ represents the world line of B as seen by A. At event 1, B transmits a light signal to the event 2, which is reflected and returns to B at event 3. M is midway in time between events 1 and 3. A similar experiment "connects" events $1'$, $2'$, and $3'$. If the event $2'$ is on the line $2M$ (as drawn), prove that M is indeed also the mid-instant of the interval $1'3'$. Similarly, for the experiment "connecting" events $1'$, $2''$, and $3'$, prove that the event $2''$ is also on the line $2M$. Discuss the physical significance of these results. [Hint: Various lines in the figure are parallel, since they correspond to velocities of $+c$ or $-c$. Find some similar triangles.]

!3.6 [Refer to the paragraph above Eq. (3.2'), p. 36.] Consider the experiment described in the text which A is to perform, and draw this experiment in a Fig. 3.3', in which A is "clearly" at rest. Also draw a Fig. 3.4', showing the *same* experiment, but drawn from the point of view of B. Hence obtain Eq. (3.2').

!3.7 By considering the Fig. (3.4') which you constructed in problem 3.6, prove that B will decide that $x_A = p(x_B + Vt_B)$, $t_A = q[t_B + (x_B V/c^2)]$; that is, prove Eqs. (3.5') and (3.6'). Prove that p and q are the *same* quantities as already introduced in Eqs. (3.5) and (3.6). Note that p and q can hence only depend on V^2 and c.

!3.8 Suppose we try the "naive" choice $p = 1$, $q = 1$ in (3.5) and (3.6). Solve these equations for x and t. Do you get equations similar to (3.5') and (3.6'), with $p = q = 1$? If not, one has a method for determining whether A is really at rest (if your equations are found to hold experimentally), or whether B is at rest (if the primed equations are found to hold). Since *no experiment* has been found which can determine absolute motion, we had better keep p and q arbitrary functions of V and c.

3.9 Show that there is no difficulty involved in synchronizing two separated clocks which are moving "side by side" in a direction perpendicular to the line joining the clocks. Go on to consider two clocks and observers A and B in *constant* relative motion, but separated only in a direction *perpendicular* to their relative motion, at the moment under discussion. Prove that if A finds B's clock to be synchronized w.r.t. A's clock at that moment, then B finds A's clock to be synchronized with B's clock at that moment. Hence show that we do not need to generalize Eq. (3.6) to include a possible y or z dependence (cf. the discussion in the final paragraph of Section 3.2).

! 3.10 Draw the figure equivalent to Fig. 3.6, but which shows the Lorentz transformation from B's point of view.

3.11 Consider a rod of length L_0, at rest w.r.t. observer A and lying along the x axis. Consider the operations B must make to determine its apparent length L', and prove that $L' = L = \gamma^{-1} L_0$.

3.12 Another way to determine the length of a rod moving along its length is to measure the time T it takes to pass a fixed point. Then $L = VT$ where V is the velocity of the rod. Show that if A uses this method to determine the length of B's rod he again finds $L = \gamma^{-1} L_0$ (cf. Section 3.5).

3.13 Consider the derivation of the Lorentz transformation given in Section 3.4. The conditions (i) and (ii) are independent of the result of the interpretation of the Michelson-Morley experiment, and hence should apply in *any* universe. If we further demand a symmetry between the observers, we can set $x = k(x' + Vt')$. Show that this equation together with Eq. (3.14) leads to the *unique* class of transformations

$$x' = k(x - Vt), \qquad t' = k\left[t - \frac{(1 - k^{-2})x}{V}\right].$$

Notice that $k = 1$ corresponds to the Galilean transformation; and that $k = \gamma = [1 - (V^2/c^2)]^{-1/2}$ gives the Lorentz transformation. Of course, c is not as yet defined, and in this context is simply that finite speed which is the same to both observers. The Galilean transformation corresponds to this invariant speed being infinite.

3.14 How fast must a rocket travel w.r.t. the laboratory so that its "measured" length is half its proper length? In that case, how long is one of its seconds?

3.15 In the discussion of Section 3.4, *each* observer sees spherical light waves. Consider the spatial surface $x^2 + y^2 + z^2 = R^2$, and transform this surface into B's coordinates. Contrast your result with that of Section 3.4, and explain in detail how it does come about that a light wave is indeed spherical to all observers.

3.16 *The Kennedy-Thorndike Experiment.* An important generalization of the Michelson-Morley experiment was performed by Kennedy and Thorndike. They modified the apparatus of Fig. 2.6(a) by making the lengths of the two arms different, with $AB = L_1$, and $AC = L_2$. Once again, as the equipment was rotated, *no* change in the interference pattern was observed. (a) Assume only the Fitzgerald contraction, and calculate Δt_1, the transit time difference between the two signals when arm AB is along V; and similarly calculate Δt_2, when AC is along V. (b) Hence show that the experimental observation suggests that interference patterns (and other local phenomena) do not depend on time intervals Δt as measured or calculated by an observer who is moving w.r.t. the apparatus, but can depend only on *proper* time intervals $\Delta \tau$, measured or calculated in the frame of reference of the equipment. (c) Show that the observation $\Delta \tau_1 = \Delta \tau_2$ demands the validity of the time dilation effect, $t = \gamma \tau$ [cf. Eq. (3.20)].

4

SOME KINEMATIC
RELATIVISTIC EFFECTS

In the previous chapter we derived the Lorentz transformation and the two basic kinematic relativistic effects, namely length contraction and time dilation. All other kinematic effects can be deduced in terms of these two. However, it is often more direct to use the Lorentz transformation for each specific problem. In this chapter we discuss various such effects, but start with a treatment of the "light clock." This "explains" the cause of the time-dilation effect.

4.1 THE LIGHT CLOCK

We consider an idealized clock which uses a light pulse as its basic mechanism. Straightforward analysis will show that this clock does undergo "time-dilation" effects when seen by an observer moving w.r.t. the clock. From this it follows that *all* clocks, whatever their mechanism, must suffer time dilation. This most powerful corollary can be deduced by using simply the First Relativity Postulate, which says that all observers in constant relative motion w.r.t. each other see the same physics. Put differently, it is impossible by any experiment to determine one's state of *absolute* motion.

We are now ready to describe our admittedly somewhat artificial clock. It consists of a rod of length *l*, with a mirror at one end. At the other is a source which emits a sharp pulse of light when it is triggered by receiving such a pulse (cf. Fig. 4.1). The clock is started by emitting a single pulse from the source. This pulse travels along the rod to the mirror, and is reflected back to the receiver, instantaneously causing the source to emit another pulse, and so on. Each time the source emits a pulse, it also makes

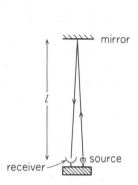

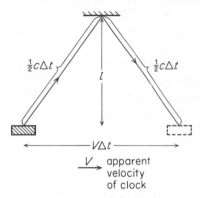

Fig. 4.1 The light clock, as seen in its rest frame, that of observer *B*. (The receiver and source are, in fact, nearly coincident.)

Fig. 4.2 The light clock as seen by an observer *A* moving with velocity *V* w.r.t. the clock.

a "tick" and activates a counter. By counting the number of ticks during a time interval, we can actually measure the duration of the interval in terms of our basic unit of time. This unit of time is given by $2l/c = \Delta\tau$.*

To an observer *B* at rest w. r. t. this clock, it certainly "ticks" at a constant rate, which we relate to the proper time as measured by this clock. Let us now consider this clock from the point of view of an observer *A* who is moving at a constant velocity *V* w. r. t. the clock, in a direction *perpendicular* to the rod. His view of one cycle of the clock is shown in Fig. 4.2. Recall that there is no length contraction perpendicular to the relative motion. To the moving observer the light must travel a greater distance than 2*l*. Since the speed of light according to him is again *c*, it follows that the time Δt required for one tick is greater than $\Delta\tau$. By using the Pythagorean theorem one readily sees from Fig. 4.2 that

*We remark that since *c* is a universal constant, then the three quantities "the standard meter," "the standard second," and "the velocity of light" are interrelated. Any two of them can be taken as primary standards, leaving the third to be measured experimentally. A proposal has been made to use *c* and a standard of length (actually a spectral wavelength) as the primary standards. If the derived standard of proper time were then found to vary with time, it would still be possible to test whether *c* were indeed constant over time.

$$\tfrac{1}{4} V^2 \, \Delta t^2 + l^2 = \tfrac{1}{4} c^2 \, \Delta t^2.$$

Hence

$$\Delta t = \frac{2l}{c} \frac{1}{\sqrt{1 - (V^2/c^2)}} = \gamma \, \Delta\tau. \tag{4.1}$$

Thus, for this particular relative motion, the observer A moving w.r.t. the clock *calculates* that the unit of time on the moving clock is Δt. However, the observer B in the rest frame of the clock calculates that the unit of time is $\Delta\tau$, with $\Delta t = \gamma \, \Delta\tau$. Hence if the clock makes n ticks, the observer in the rest frame of the clock says that a time $n \, \Delta\tau$ has elapsed, but the moving observer says a time $n\gamma \, \Delta t$ has elapsed.* **The ratio of the two determinations of the elapsed time is $\gamma \, (\geq 1)$, the moving observer finding that more time has elapsed than is found by the observer in the rest frame of the clock.** If the motion is not perpendicular to the rod, the analysis is more involved since a length contraction also occurs, but the same result is found.

This in fact is a special case of the more general statement that **this result must hold true for all clocks, whatever their mechanism or orientation, provided the clocks are such that their mechanism does not depend on the outside world.** (This last proviso excludes pendulum clocks, but includes balance-wheel clocks.) For first we observe that if B has two different clocks which keep the same time *according to B*, then they also keep the same time according to A, since this only has to do with the relative number of "ticks" counted by each clock during the same interval. Now suppose that B has two different clocks which are adjusted at some moment to go at the same rate. Then as long as they are kept together and at rest w.r.t. B, they must go on "ticking" together forever according to B, even if B is accelerated so that he acquires a velocity V relative to A. For otherwise B would have a way of detecting his "absolute" velocity, and hence we would violate the two relativity postulates. (For instance, B could use his "other" clock to measure the speed of light in his light clock, and find that this had changed from its usual value.)

The above reasoning and conclusion is a good example of the power of the First Relativity Postulate. We remark that in using this postulate, which is equivalent to the statement that absolute motion can never be detected, nothing is said or implied about motion relative to an essential part of the environment. Thus, since a pendulum clock works by interacting with the gravitational field of the earth, it is certainly possible for a pendulum clock which is moving rapidly w.r.t. the earth to behave dif-

---

*Note well the reciprocal relationship between the size of the unit and the number of units. 200 cents = \$2. This point is straightforward, but easily overlooked.

ferently from a light clock or a balance-wheel clock in these circumstances (cf. problem 4.23).*

Example 4.1. Our derivation of Eq. (4.1) was performed from the point of view of A, who *moves* w.r.t. the light clock. It gave $(\Delta t)_A = \gamma(\Delta t')_B = \gamma\Delta\tau$. Consider the *same* experiment from the point of view of B, and explain what mistake A "nominally" made.

Answer 4.1. B says: "Let the light pulse be sent out at the event S, and received at the event R. These two events occur at the same *spatial* location, and are separated by a (correct) time interval $\Delta t' \equiv \Delta\tau$. However, A is moving and so he *necessarily* observes the time t_S of event S on one clock C_S, and the time t_R of event R on *another* clock C_R. I, B, of course admit that these clocks *actually* then *read* the times t_S and t_R (because I saw them), and that $(\Delta t)_A \equiv t_R - t_S = \gamma(\Delta t')_B = \gamma \Delta\tau$. However this is not the correct time interval that A should use, since I know that A's two clocks C_S and C_R are not properly synchronized. I know this because A "synchronized" them by the standard method, which however ignored the common motion of A, C_S, and C_R. In fact this lack of synchronization is given by the form $t' + Vx'/c^2 =$ const. [cf. Eq. (3.2′), and the analogue of Fig. 3.6; cf. problem 3.10]. Now clock C_S is $V(\Delta\tau)$ to the left of C_R (B's time, of course), so that A has *improperly* set C_S ahead of C_R by an amount $\delta t = V(V \Delta\tau)/c^2$. This δt should hence be added to $(\Delta t)_A$ to obtain the adjusted time interval $\widehat{\Delta t} = (\Delta t)_A + \delta t = \gamma \Delta\tau + V^2 \Delta\tau/c^2 = \gamma^{-1} \Delta\tau < \Delta\tau$. This result *seems* to tell me that the adjusted time interval as measured by A's clocks is shorter than the true time interval $\Delta\tau$. This must mean that A's clocks run *slow* by the factor $\gamma > 1$. But of course this is exactly what they do, since if I analyze one of A's light clocks, I immediately work out that each to-and-fro motion takes a time $(\Delta t) = \gamma l/c = \gamma \Delta\tau$, so that A's clocks do run slow by the factor γ; that is, the adjusted A time intervals should be given by $(\widehat{\Delta t})_A = \gamma^{-1} (\Delta t)_B$."

Comment. In this example we see how A looking at B can say that $(\Delta t)_B = \gamma^{-1}(\Delta t)_A$ [cf. Eq. (4.1)]; and yet B looking at A can say that $(\widehat{\Delta t})_A = \gamma^{-1}(\Delta t)_B$. The fact that $(\Delta t)_A$ is an "adjusted" time looks unsymmetric, but recall that the original $(\Delta t)_B$ is really similarly adjusted. Thus, *as always*, there is complete symmetry.

We have now demonstrated the "mechanism" of the time-dilation effect, at least for the case of a light clock. As usual, A's view of the time dilation of a light clock which is at rest w.r.t. B is identical with B's view of the time dilation of a light clock which is at rest w.r.t. A. Hence again the effect cannot be considered as a real mechanical effect due to absolute motion. Rather it is one of interpretation involving the determination of the time of a distant event. Time is no longer absolute. Or rather, there

---

*In fact, Einstein's General Theory of Relativity tells us how it ought to behave. This is outside the scope of this book, but see Chapter 8.

is no absolute way of determining the time interval between events. While we have given the mu-meson decay "paradox" as an example of time dilation, it should be emphasized that the mesons were "timed" in their *motion* between two different spatial locations (the top and the bottom of the atmosphere). From the point of view of an observer attached to the mu-meson, the meson mean decay lifetime is exactly what it ought to be, 2.2×10^{-6} sec. (It would be the lifetime of a meson at rest on the earth's surface that would seem to be dilated.)

It follows that time dilation as so far discussed, with the basic symmetry between the two observers, is more an effect of interpretation than a real effect, in the sense that at some stage in the discussion the time at a distant spatial point must be determined in an *ad hoc* (not to say egocentric) manner. In the next section we turn to a "real" effect which is a consequence of time dilation, but in which the symmetry between the two observers must therefore have been destroyed.

4.2   THE TWIN PARADOX

This is a well-known if sometimes misunderstood prediction of the special theory of relativity. Briefly, it can be paraphrased as follows.

Consider twins A and B living on the earth. Let twin B go on a voyage into space at very high speed, and then come back again to earth. Assuming that B's metabolism is unaffected by the (short) periods of (rather large) acceleration needed to start off, to turn around, and to land again on the earth, B will have aged less than the stay-at-home A when they meet again.

In this experiment the two clocks start at the same space-time event, and are later recompared when *together* again, at another space-time event. What is compared is the number of "ticks" (or heartbeats) that the two clocks have made in the intervening period. Hence the effect which is predicted is a *real* effect, and the question of interpretation does *not* arise (except perhaps in a later philosophical sense).

However it might then seem that the predicted effect violates the first relativity postulate. For one might argue (incorrectly) that from B's point of view, it is the stay-at-home A who is "really" going on the round trip, and hence he, A, should be the younger when he "returns" from the trip to meet B again. Thus from the symmetry between observers one might deduce that both twins should have aged the same amount. This argument is the reason the effect is known as a "paradox." In fact the argument is false, and there is *no* paradox. (There never is when something is understood.) This follows because actually there is *no* symmetry between the stay-at-home A and the space traveler B. B can tell unambiguously that he has gone on the trip, since he has undergone three periods of acceleration. During those periods, he was "pushed back" into his seat in the rocket, and his rocket ship did *not* constitute an inertial frame.* *A*, on the other hand, remained throughout in a nonaccelerated or inertial frame (if we ignore the small effects due to the motion of the earth about the sun, and the rotation of the earth).

This explanation can in turn be misunderstood by saying, "Of course, if you mean that things go haywire during the accelerations, that is quite likely, though I would expect them to age *B* prematurely." This is not the meaning of the prediction. While the accelerations are crucial in breaking the symmetry between *A* and *B*, yet the prediction is *not* concerned with what happens to *B*'s heartbeats, or even the working mechanism of any clock, during the periods of acceleration. In fact it is straightforward to devise two experiments in such a way that the possible effects on the clocks during the acceleration can be subtracted out. We show this by a numerical example.

Suppose that, according to *A*, *B* accelerates from rest to a velocity $= 0.8c = 149{,}000$ miles/sec in 1 year ($\approx 3 \times 10^7$ sec) and travels for 1 year at this constant velocity (covering about 4.5×10^{12} miles). *B* then decelerates and reverses his velocity to $-0.8c$ in a further 1 year, travels for 1 year at this constant velocity, and finally takes 1 year to decelerate to rest, finding himself back at *A*'s position. According to *A*, *B* has been away 5 years. We cannot tell what time *B* will say his trip took, since most of it occurred as accelerations. But suppose another space traveler *C* also takes a somewhat similar trip, in which, again according to *A*, *C* accelerates from rest to $0.8c$ in 1 year, then travels for 11 years at this velocity before turning around in 1 year, then travels back at the same speed for another 11 years, finally decelerating in 1 year and meeting *A* again. *C*'s trip took 25 years according to *A*, or 20 years longer than *B*'s trip. If *B* and *C* used the same clocks to determine the time durations of each of their trips, the clocks should have undergone the same "acceleration-period" effects.† Hence we can ask, "What is the difference between the recorded duration of *C*'s trip according to *C*'s clock, and the recorded duration of *B*'s trip according to *B*'s clock?" The *incorrect* answer, based on a misunderstanding of the first relativity postulate, would be 20 years. The answer according to the special theory of relativity would be 12 years,

---

*By performing experiments only at low speeds relative to himself, he would have discovered that Newton's laws did not hold without the introduction of fictitious forces. This violation of Newton's laws has nothing to do with our later discussion of the modifications that must be made to Newton's laws due to relativistic effects.

†According to the general theory of relativity, one must also be careful about gravitational effects. We can assume that all parts of the various trips take place in a region of constant gravitational potential, in which case no extra effect will arise.

so that C would be 8 years younger than he ought to have been in comparison with B.*

The prediction of the special theory of relativity is based on the time-dilation effect—that is, upon $t = \gamma\tau$ [cf. Eq. (3.20)]. If the space traveler believes his outward trip at velocity V lasted a time τ_1, then τ_1 is the *proper time* of this interval, and an observer moving at velocity V with respect to the space traveler will find that the elapsed time is $t_1 = \gamma\tau_1$. Similarly on the return trip $t_2 = \gamma\tau_2$, where $\gamma = [1 - (V^2/c^2)]^{-1/2}$. Hence $t = t_1 + t_2 = \gamma\tau$ where $\tau = \tau_1 + \tau_2$; or $\tau = \gamma^{-1}t$. In our example, $V/c = 0.8$, therefore $\gamma = \frac{5}{3}$, $\gamma^{-1} = \frac{3}{5}$.

In this calculation, the stay-at-home clock also measures a proper time, but it is a different proper time from the *sum* of the two proper times that the traveler measures. Since B measures the *sum* of two intervals, it would be totally wrong to consider A's time as the proper time, and "dilate" it to get B's trip duration. [See in particular problem 4.16, part (a). In that frame the time of R is dilated by γ compared with the time PR as measured by A. But B's trip time is still shorter by γ^{-1} compared with A's trip time.]

The "twin-paradox" effect has not yet been demonstrated experimentally. A somewhat similar experiment could perhaps be performed in which unstable particles such as mu-mesons are made to travel in a circle at high speed, so that they keep returning to the same point. It is confidently expected that the number surviving after any time would be greater than if the mesons were at rest, owing to the time-dilation effect. An analogue of this latter experiment has been performed, and did find the predicted results.

In that experiment, one "clock" was placed on the rim of a turn-table which was rotating, and its rate was compared with that of another "clock" located at the center of the turn-table. The experiment used the Mössbauer effect, and detected an effect over a range of γ from 1 up to $\gamma = 1 + 6 \times 10^{-15}$.† This experiment is closely related to the twin paradox; it also demonstrates that one can use the time dilation effect as predicted by the special theory for the instantaneous rate of a clock, even if it is accelerated, *provided* that the acceleration does not produce dynamical stresses in the clock. (This excludes mechanical clocks.)

---

*We might remark that to save these 8 years C (and also B) has undergone accelerations that last one year each, of magnitudes of the order of g, where g is the acceleration due to gravity. Such an acceleration is not large, but to keep it up for a year might be difficult.

†H. J. Hay, J. P. Schiffer, T. E. Cranshaw, and P. A. Egelstaff, *Phys. Rev. Letters*, **4**, 165 (1960). The clock consisted of atoms of Fe^{57}.

Although no direct "twin-paradox" experiments have been performed, there are numerous tests of time dilation (cf. Section 3.6). If it were not for time dilation, most present-day elementary-particle experiments could not be performed. It is hard to see how time dilation can be a true experimental effect, and yet there be no twin-paradox effect. Of course time dilation is a symmetric effect, while the twin-paradox effect is necessarily asymmetric. But once one has understood that this lack of symmetry is indeed real (and can, for instance, be detected in the stomach of the traveler), then the twin-paradox effect becomes a "necessary" consequence of time dilation. In this sense it has been abundantly tested.

We remark that while the effect is most useful for traveling to distant stars, yet the space traveler does not really experience life for any longer than his usual life span. Thus a traveler can go on a round trip to a star which is 99 light years away at a speed of $0.99c$, and take 200 years for the trip. To him the trip takes 200 γ^{-1} years ≈ 28 years, the star approaching and receding from him at $0.99c$, but he considers that the outward distance covered is (14 years) $(0.99c) \approx 14$ light years, so that there is nothing paradoxical to him. But he correspondingly only has 28 years' worth of thoughts, heartbeats, meals, etc., and *not* the longevitist's dream of 200 years' worth. He does return to earth 200 years later being only 28 years older, but he has not really "lived" 200 years. (We of course have ignored the brief acceleration periods here.)

We return to the twin paradox in Section 4.8, and again briefly in Chapter 8. A very extensive treatment is provided in *Special Relativity Theory—Selected Reprints.**

4.3 ADDITION OF VELOCITIES

We now turn to an effect that involves both length and time, namely the addition of velocities.† In Chapter 2 (particularly Section

---

*Published for the A.A.P.T. by the A.I.P., and available at a price of $2.00 from the American Institute of Physics, 335 East 45th St., New York, New York, 10017.

†This should more properly be called "transformation" or "compounding" of velocities. In classical physics one loosely uses the phrase "addition of velocities" to treat relative motion, and since one finds that the result satisfies the axioms of addition (reflexivity, commutativity, and associativity), the term is justified *a posteriori*. In relativity theory these axioms turn out *not* to be satisfied. Certain "paradoxical" results of this section seem even more so owing to the misuse of the term "addition." However, another phrase would only beg the question, by attempting to conceal the fact that in classical physics the result is indeed addition.

2.3) we saw how the standard addition-of-velocities theorem followed directly from the Galilean transformation. The latter has now been replaced by the Lorentz transformation, and hence we must start afresh. The method of derivation is precisely as in Section 2.3.

We consider the motion of a particle as seen by the two observers A and B, B moving at a constant speed V along the x axis w. r. t. A. B measures a certain (instantaneous) velocity $(v'_x, v'_y, v'_z)_B$ when the particle is at some space-time event. What velocity $(v_x, v_y, v_z)_A$ does A determine for the particle when it is located at the *same* space-time event? (Of course A and B give different space-time coordinates for this same event.)

We proceed as in Section 2.3. Let the particle be initially at the event X_1

$$X_1 \equiv (x_1, y_1, z_1, t_1)_A = (x'_1, y'_1, z'_1, t'_1)_B,$$

and slightly later at the event X_2

$$X_2 \equiv (x_2, y_2, z_2, t_2)_A = (x'_2, y'_2, z'_2, t'_2)_B.$$

But

$$x = \gamma(x' + Vt'), \quad y = y', \quad z = z', \quad t = \gamma\left(t' + \frac{Vx'}{c^2}\right). \qquad (4.2)$$

Hence if we define $\Delta x = x_2 - x_1$, $\Delta x' = x'_2 - x'_1$, etc., we see that

$$\left. \begin{aligned} \Delta x = (x_2 - x_1) &= \gamma(x'_2 + Vt'_2) - \gamma(x'_1 + Vt'_1) \\ &= \gamma(\Delta x' + V\,\Delta t') = \gamma\left(\frac{\Delta x'}{\Delta t'} + V\right)\Delta t' \\ \Delta y &= \Delta y' \\ \Delta z &= \Delta z' \end{aligned} \right\} \qquad (4.3)$$

and

$$\Delta t = \gamma\left(\Delta t' + \frac{V\,\Delta x'}{c^2}\right) = \gamma\left(1 + \frac{V}{c^2}\frac{\Delta x'}{\Delta t'}\right)\Delta t'. \qquad (4.4)$$

These equations are more involved than in the classical case, the most important difference being Eq. (4.4). We observe that

$$\frac{\Delta x}{\Delta t} = v_x, \qquad \frac{\Delta x'}{\Delta t'} = v'_x, \qquad \text{and so on.} \qquad (4.5)$$

These properly are the *average* velocity components. Let us divide each equation in (4.3) by Eq. (4.4), and use the definitions Eq. (4.5). We obtain directly

Relativistic velocity addition:

$$v_x = \frac{v_x' + V}{1 + (v_x' V/c^2)}$$

$$v_y = \frac{v_y'}{\gamma[1 + (v_x' V/c^2)]} \qquad \text{with } \gamma = \left(1 - \frac{V^2}{c^2}\right)^{-1/2} \qquad (4.6)$$

$$v_z = \frac{v_z'}{\gamma[1 + (v_x' V/c^2)]}$$

While the above was derived for the average velocities, it is easy to take the limit $\Delta t \to 0$, $\Delta t' \to 0$, in which case we obtain the instantaneous velocities. Hence the result also holds for the instantaneous velocities (cf. problem 4.4). Notice the lack of symmetry between V and v' in (4.6). Clearly, "adding" V to v' does *not* give the same result as adding v' to V (cf. the footnote on p. 69).

It is straightforward to obtain the primed velocities in terms of the unprimed velocities, either by solving Eqs. (4.6) or by working from the inverse of Eqs. (4.3) (cf. problem 4.6). One finds

$$v_x' = \frac{v_x - V}{1 - (v_x V/c^2)}$$

$$v_y' = \frac{v_y}{\gamma[1 - (v_x V/c^2)]} \qquad \text{with } \gamma = \left(1 - \frac{V^2}{c^2}\right)^{-1/2} \qquad \left.\right\} \qquad (4.7)$$

$$v_z' = \frac{v_z}{\gamma[1 - (v_x V/c^2)]}$$

Equations (4.6) should be compared with Eqs. (2.3). In each case (v_x', v_y', v_z') are the velocity components of a particle as measured by an observer B, and (v_x, v_y, v_z) are the components as measured by an observer A. Furthermore B is moving in the positive x direction with velocity V w.r.t. A. The equations are complicated, and the different velocity components behave differently. Nevertheless, certain remarks can be made:

(i) In the limit that *all* speeds are small compared with the speed of light, these results "collapse" onto the classical results. (It is not enough simply to make $|V| \ll c$, as is readily seen by taking $v_x' = c$.)

(ii) The y and z components of velocity, which are *transverse* to the relative velocity, are nonetheless different for the two observers, even though transverse lengths are invariant. The reason is that velocity involves both length *and* time, hence the time-dilation effect is also involved. Since in general neither A nor B is in the proper frame of the particle, this effect is *not* simply given by the usual factor $t = \gamma\tau$.

(iii) **Addition of parallel velocities:** Consider the special case $v'_y = v'_z = 0$. Then $v_y = v_z = 0$, and we find

> **Addition of parallel velocities:**
>
> $$v = \frac{v' + V}{1 + (v'V/c^2)}.$$ (4.8)

Here v, v', and V are all parallel velocities, and Eq. (4.8) refers to their magnitudes. If V and v' are both positive, v is *less* than their algebraic sum. That is, parallel velocities do *not* add according to the laws of arithmetic.* Of course, if both v and V are much smaller than c, the relativistic correction is negligible. Let us compute some examples.

Example 4.2 A man is in a car traveling at 30 mph. He throws a ball in the direction of travel, at a velocity of 30 mph relative to the car. What is the velocity of the ball relative to the ground?

Answer 4.2 We apply Eq. (4.8) and recall that

$$c = 186,000 \text{ miles per second} \approx 6.7 \times 10^8 \text{ mph.}$$

Then $v' = 30$, $V = 30$, $c = 6.7 \times 10^8$, so that

$$v = \frac{30 + 30}{1 + [(30)(30)/(6.7 \times 10^8)^2]} = \frac{60}{1 + (2 \times 15^{-15})}$$

$$= 59.999,999,999,999,88 \text{ mph.}$$

Hardly a large effect!

Example 4.3. A man is in a rocket ship traveling at $0.9c$ relative to an observer on earth. He fires a proton in the direction of travel at a velocity of $0.9c$ relative to the rocket ship. What is the velocity of the proton relative to the observer on earth?

Answer 4.3. This time we have $v' = V = 0.9c$, so that

$$v = \frac{0.9c + 0.9c}{1 + (0.9)^2} = \frac{1.80c}{1.81} = 0.995c.$$

In this case relativity leads to a very noticeable modification of the classical result (which would be $1.8c$).

*Why should they? What is imperative is only that they add according to some law. Velocities have to do with physics, not pure mathematics. Another example showing the difference between mathematics and physics is the fact that the sum of the angles in a triangle on the surface of the earth can have any value greater than 180°. Only for a triangle of zero area does the sum equal 180°. (Of course, spherical trigonometry does allow for this effect.)

Example 4.4. A man in a rocket ship traveling at speed V w.r.t. an outside observer fires a beam of light in the direction of travel, at a velocity c relative to the rocket ship. What is the speed of the light relative to the outside observer?

Answer 4.4. Now $v' = c$, $V = V$. Hence

$$v = \frac{c + V}{1 + (cV/c^2)} = c.$$

That is, the velocity of the light is also c according to the outside observer. This is as it must be, since the Lorentz transformation was constructed precisely to ensure that this would be the case!

Pursuing Examples 4.3 and 4.4, we can readily prove that the results of adding two parallel velocities each less than or equal to c is always less than or equal to c. For

$$c - v = c - \frac{v' + V}{1 + (v'V/c^2)}$$

$$= \frac{c}{1 + (v'V/c^2)} \left(1 - \frac{v'}{c} - \frac{V}{c} + \frac{v'V}{c^2} \right)$$

$$= \frac{c}{1 + (v'V/c^2)} \left(1 - \frac{v'}{c} \right) \left(1 - \frac{V}{c} \right). \tag{4.9}$$

Hence our result is proved.*

Equation (4.9) has some other unusual features. We see that adding one velocity larger than c to one which is smaller than c leads to a result which is larger than c; but adding two velocities both larger than c leads to a velocity which is less than c! These results are amusing but of no significance physically, since we will later "prove" that no physical object can travel faster than the speed of light. In fact for $|V| > c$, the Lorentz transformation itself becomes meaningless, since γ is then imaginary.

We return to a further discussion of the general addition of velocities, Eqs. (4.6).

(iv) For the special case when $v'_x = 0$, that is, when the motion of the particle w.r.t. B is perpendicular to the relative motion of A and B, we find:

*At several points in our discussion we have assumed that both v' and V are positive. All our equations hold independently of the signs of v' and V, and the modifications necessary in our discussion for negative v' or V are straightforward.

VELOCITY ADDITION WITH $v'_x = 0$:

$$v_x = V$$

$$v_y = \frac{v'_y}{\gamma} \qquad \text{with } \gamma = \left(1 - \frac{V^2}{c^2}\right)^{-1/2} \qquad (4.10)$$

$$v_z = \frac{v'_z}{\gamma}.$$

In this case the result is fairly straightforward, and the appearance of the factor of γ^{-1} in v_y and v_z can be directly linked to the time-dilation effect.

(v) For the general case, we can rewrite Eqs. (4.6) in vector notation as

$$\mathbf{v} = \frac{1}{1 + [(\mathbf{V}\cdot\mathbf{v'})/c^2]}\left\{\mathbf{V}\left[1 - \frac{(\mathbf{v'}\cdot\mathbf{V})}{V^2}\left(\frac{1}{\gamma} - 1\right)\right] + \frac{1}{\gamma}\mathbf{v'}\right\}. \qquad (4.11)$$

This equation is quite unwieldy and is not suitable for computations. However, it does exhibit the general "addition" of two velocities $\mathbf{v'}$ and $\mathbf{V}$. It is the analogue of Eq. (2.4). Notice that it is *not* symmetric in $\mathbf{v'}$ and $\mathbf{V}$.

(vi) A final remark is in order concerning the meaning of the velocity addition formulas. What they enable us to determine is the velocity v_A of a particle w.r.t. one observer A, when we know the velocity $\mathbf{V}$ of another observer B w.r.t. A, and the velocity $\mathbf{v'_B}$ of the same particle w.r.t. the *second* observer B, *as measured by B*. Each of the three quantities $\mathbf{v}_A$, $\mathbf{V}$, and $\mathbf{v'_B}$ has a *physical* meaning as the true velocity of some point or particle relative to some stated observer. Thus the law of addition of velocities is a statement about the relationship of these three *physically meaningful* quantities.

This is totally different from a breakdown by observer A of the velocity v_A into separate parts or components. For instance, in Example 4.3 above we had $v'_B = V = 0.9c$, $v_A = 0.995c$. Observer A can take v_A and break it down as $0.995c = 0.4975c + 0.4975c$ according to arithmetic, saying in effect, "A speed of $0.995c$ relative to myself is the sum of a speed of $0.4975c$ relative to myself 'plus' a speed of $0.4975c$ relative to myself." This is not a statement about physical quantities, since "plus" does not mean anything very physical in the context. Similarly A can say, "A velocity of $(1/\sqrt{2})c$ in a northeast direction relative to myself is the vector sum of a velocity component of $0.5c$ in the north direction relative to myself 'plus' a velocity component of $0.5c$ in the east direction relative to myself." But this does *not* mean that if A sees an observer B traveling in a rocket ship with a velocity of $0.5c$ in the east direction relative to A; and B sees a particle traveling with a velocity of $0.5c$ in the north direction relative to B, then A sees the particle traveling at $(1/\sqrt{2})c$ in a northeast direction relative to A.

4.4 THE FIZEAU EXPERIMENT*

We now turn to the experimental verification of the relativistic addition of velocities. For the case when $v' = c$, we have already mentioned a very accurate test performed by T. Alväger et al. (cf. p. 27). In this experiment a source, moving in the laboratory with speed $v_s \geq 0.99975c$, emitted light whose laboratory speed c' was found to be given by $c' = c + k v_s$, with $k = (0 \pm 1.3) \times 10^{-4}$. This is clearly compatible with $c' = c$. Other experiments have been performed in which one measures the speed of the light emitted by an electron-positron pair undergoing annihilation.

A test when neither velocity is c is provided in the Fizeau experiment, first performed in 1851. We have so far talked only of the velocity of light in a *vacuum*, and it is only the velocity in a vacuum which is a universal constant according to the second relativity postulate. The velocity of light in a material medium such as glass or water is given by c/μ, where μ is called the refractive index. Suppose then that light is made to travel through water, which is in turn flowing with a speed V in the laboratory. What is the speed of the light which will be measured in the laboratory?

According to the special theory of relativity, the answer is directly given by Eq. (4.8). For c/μ is the speed of the light relative to the water, as measured by an observer who is at rest w.r.t. the water,† and V is the speed of the water relative to the laboratory observer. Hence we predict

$$v = \frac{(c/\mu) + V}{1 + [V/(\mu c)]}.$$

Since V is always very small w.r.t. c, we can expand this by the binomial theorem‡ and obtain

$$v \approx \left[\left(\frac{c}{\mu}\right) + V\right]\left[1 - \frac{V}{\mu c} + \cdots\right] = \frac{c}{\mu} + V(1 - \mu^{-2}) + \cdots \quad (4.12)$$

where the "$+ \cdots$" indicates higher-order terms in V/c. We see that the light is "dragged" along by the water, but not to the full extent

---

*This section may be omitted.

†The fact that the water is moving cannot affect this conclusion, by the First Relativity Postulate.

‡$(1 + x)^a = 1 + ax + (1/2)a(a - 1)x^2 + \cdots$ for $|x| < 1$.

of V. The Galilean transformation gives $v = (c/\mu) + V$, while various other predictions were also devised on the basis of pre-relativity electrodynamics.

In order to measure this effect for a water speed of the order of 10 m/sec, it is again necessary to use an interference method, particularly if we want to distinguish between the Galilean and relativity predictions.

The actually experimental arrangement is shown in Fig. 4.3. Water flows at a known speed in the U-shaped tube as shown. Light from a

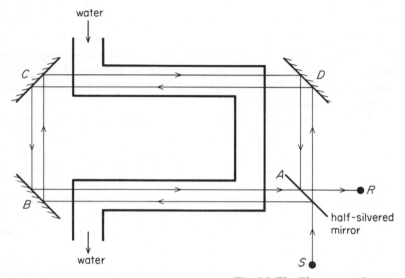

Fig. 4.3 The Fizeau experiment.

point source S hits a "half-silvered" mirror A so that part of the beam is reflected to B, then to C and D and back to A where part is reflected to R; while the other part of the light first passes through the mirror to D, then to C and B and A and finally to R. By interference methods it is possible to measure the relative time delay between the circuit $ABCDA$ and the circuit $ADCBA$, if one starts with the water at rest, and slowly increases its speed to V, watching the interference fringes all the while. The experiment was first performed by Fizeau in 1851, long before the theory of relativity was invented. The results disagreed with the Galilean prediction, but the ingenuity of physicists was soon able to provide an "electrodynamic-theory" explanation. The theory of relativity has the advantage that its explanation is not *ad hoc*, but fits into the basic structure of the theory. The experiments confirm the relativity prediction completely, though of course V is very nonrelativistic, while c/μ is comparable to c. Hence this is not the most general test. In particular the terms of order V^2 in (4.12) are too small to be observable, so that predictions that differ only in such terms cannot be ruled out experimentally.

4.5 SIMULTANEITY AND CAUSALITY*

Even before we had derived the Lorentz transformation we had found (in Section 3.2) that two events which were simultaneous according to one observer occurred at different times according to a second observer moving with velocity V w.r.t. the first observer. Here we want to investigate this further, particularly with respect to the meaning of the term "now" or "the present instant," and with respect to the problem of cause and effect.

Consider two events E_1 and E_2 which have space-time coordinates

$$E_1 \equiv (x_1, y_1, z_1, t_1) \quad \text{and} \quad E_2 \equiv (x_2, y_2, z_2, t_2)$$

according to A. Then according to B the events take place at the times

$$t_1' = \gamma\left[t_1 - \left(\frac{V x_1}{c^2}\right) \right] \quad \text{and} \quad t_2' = \gamma\left[t_2 - \left(\frac{V x_2}{c^2}\right) \right]$$

so that

$$t_2' - t_1' = \gamma\left[(t_2 - t_1) - \left(\frac{V}{c^2}\right)(x_2 - x_1) \right] \tag{4.13}$$

Consider first the case when $t_2 = t_1$, i.e. the events are simultaneous according to A. Then $t_2' - t_1'$ is positive or negative depending on whether $V(x_2 - x_1) \lessgtr 0$. In particular, by simply reversing the *direction* of B's motion w.r.t. A, B can change the apparent time sequence of the two events. Thus, for example, if $x_2 > x_1$, then for positive V (i.e., B moving to the "right" in the $+x$ direction) event E_1 occurs after E_2 according to B, but for negative V event E_2 occurs after event E_1; while according to A they are simultaneous!

Does this mean that the theory of relativity overthrows the concepts of "past," "present," and "future"? Certainly not. Rather it clarifies the true meaning of these concepts. For consider an event which took place on the star Proxima Centauri two years ago. This star is the nearest star to us (other than the sun) and is about four light-years† away from the earth; that is, it takes light four years to travel from the star to the earth. Hence no one on earth will find out about the

---

*This section may be omitted, at some cost.

†A light-year is the distance light travels in one year, and is roughly equal to 6×10^{12} miles.

event for another two years. (For our present purpose, we suppose the event to be quite dramatic and observable on earth—for example, a sudden tenfold increase in brightness.) We, the author and the reader, being omniscient, know that the event has occurred. But in what useful sense can someone on earth (other than ourselves) say that the event has happened, that he knows about it, that it was in his past? Until the first brighter light from the star reaches the earth in two years' time, the event will not have occurred as far as people on earth are concerned. There can be *no* possible consequences of the event on earth until that moment. After that moment in two years' time, the event will be in the "past" of everyone on earth forever, recorded in books and memories, and very possibly causing real consequences on earth. These consequences commencing in two years' time can reasonably be termed part of the "future" of the event, in that the event can *cause* consequences to occur in its "future."

We show these new definitions of past and future in Fig. 4.4. All events which occurred anywhere in the shaded region labeled "past" could have influenced the event E; and in particular, an observer at the event E could in principle know of all events which occurred anywhere in this "past." Similarly all events in the shaded region labeled "future" can be influenced by the event E; in particular an observer at any such event could in principle know of the event E. The remainder of the figure should probably be labeled "limbo." An event in limbo (call the event L) can neither be influenced by the event E, nor influence the

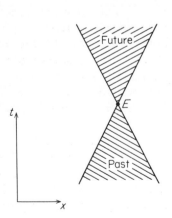

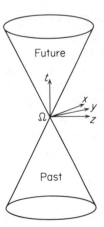

Fig. 4.4 The "past" and "future" of an event E. The heavy lines correspond to the speed of light, that is: $(x - x_E) = \pm c(t - t_E)$.

Fig. 4.5 The light cone, past, present and future. The surface of the cone is given by $x^2 + y^2 + z^2 = c^2 t^2$. This figure is a two-dimensional representation of a four-dimensional space.

event E; in particular, an observer at L cannot know of the event E, nor can an observer at E know of the event L. There is no meaningful causative relationship between E and L. It is customary to call "limbo" the "present."

In Fig. 4.4 we have only shown x and t. In reality there are three space coordinates x, y, z, and it is customary to represent the past and future of an event as the interior of cones as shown in Fig. 4.5, where we have placed the event at the origin. The actual "surface" of the cone is known as the light cone, and has the equation $x^2 + y^2 + z^2 = c^2 t^2$. Formally any event (x, y, z, t) can be located with respect to $\Omega \equiv (0, 0, 0, 0)$ in one of the four regions:

$$
\begin{aligned}
\text{past:} \quad & x^2 + y^2 + z^2 < c^2 t^2, \quad t < 0 \\
\text{future:} \quad & x^2 + y^2 + z^2 < c^2 t^2, \quad t > 0 \\
\text{light cone:} \quad & x^2 + y^2 + z^2 = c^2 t^2 \\
\text{"present":} \quad & x^2 + y^2 + z^2 > c^2 t^2.
\end{aligned}
\tag{4.14}
$$

With these definitions the event $\Omega \equiv (0, 0, 0, 0)$ can influence all events in its "future"; that is, it can cause a particular effect at any event in its future. Similarly any event in the past of Ω can cause a particular effect at Ω. The light cone forms a boundary between such events and the limbo of the present.

The alert reader may well object that we have assumed that no signal can travel faster than the speed of light. In our example of the star Proxima Centauri, it is conceivable that while light from the event cannot arrive on earth for another two years, some as yet undiscovered form of signal has already arrived with the information that the event has occurred. For instance, suppose that we were to discover "hyper-radio" waves with a speed of $4c$, and that these were emitted at the moment the star brightened. Then if we had already invented hyper-radio receivers, we would have known of the star event one year ago, and this knowledge might well have had consequences on earth. Clearly such a possibility completely overthrows our new definitions of past and future. The special theory of relativity simply postulates that no signal can travel with a speed greater than the speed of light. It is conceivable that "hyper-radio" waves will be discovered, but if they are, the *whole* theory of relativity will be overthrown. All present understanding of the basic forces of nature incorporates the theory of relativity; nowhere is there any indication of a "need" for a signal mechanism that propagates faster than the speed of light. Until such time as "hyper-radio" waves are discovered, we assume that the maximum attainable speed for *any* signal is indeed the speed of light.

Example 4.5. Show explicitly in a space-time diagram that if hyper-radio waves did exist, having a speed $v > c$, then it would be possible for an observer A to send information about himself into his own past, simply by communicating with various near and distant colleagues in relative motion.*

Answer 4.5. A possible method is shown in Fig. 4.6, which is drawn in A's frame of reference. Observer A uses the assistance of three other observers B, C, and D whose world lines are shown in the figure. Observers A and D

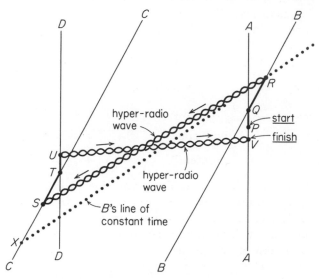

Fig. 4.6 How to signal into one's own past, using hyper-radio waves.

are far apart, and relatively at rest; and observers B and C are also far apart and relatively at rest, and both have a constant velocity $+V$ w.r.t. A and D. We consider an initial event P which occurs to A. At event Q, B meets A and is told by A about the event P. Shortly afterwards at event R, B transmits this information to C, using a hyper-radio signal which travels along the world line RS. This signal is such that it travels backward in time according to A (see below)! Shortly afterwards C meets D at event T, and gives the information to D. Finally at event U, D retransmits the information to A again using a hyper-radio signal, which A receives at event V (and which travels backward in time according to B). But V will be *before* the original event P (provided that the distance AD is sufficiently great).

The crucial feature of this "experiment" is the fact that according to A the hyper-radio wave RS travels backward in time. However, according to B, who transmitted the signal, it does travel forward in time, since it reaches C at the event S which is later than the event X. Here X is C's event which is simultaneous with B's event R, according to both B and C. The reason for this contradiction can be seen by using the velocity addition formula Eq.

*This example is due to Dr. Brian Easlea, and is given in a set of University of Sussex lecture notes (unpublished).

(4.8). For according to B the hyper-radio wave RS has a velocity $-v$, with $v > c$. But B has a velocity $+V$ w.r.t. A. Hence according to A the hyper-radio wave RS has a velocity*

$$w = \frac{-v + V}{1 - (vV/c^2)} = \frac{v - V}{(vV/c^2) - 1} > +c$$

provided $vV > c^2$. Naturally A insists that V satisfies this condition. (Note that V can remain less than c.) Thus the line RS has a *positive* slope. A similar condition must hold for the hyper-radio wave UV.

Comment. This experiment enables A to learn about the event P at the earlier event V. Suppose P is the unfortunate outcome of a choice A made at the event V. Then at the event V, if A has free will, he can now make another choice, and so avoid the unfortunate outcome, which however has already occurred! This self-contradiction shows that the special theory of relativity is incompatible with the existence of hyper-radio waves (or else with free will). It of course can*not* prove that hyper-radio waves do not exist.

After this lengthy digression on "past" and "future" let us return to the specific analysis at the beginning of this section, in particular Eq. (4.13) relating the time coordinates of two events E_1 and E_2 as seen by A and B. (As always, B's coordinates have primes.) Suppose the event E_2 is in the "future" of event E_1 according to A—that is, $t_2 > t_1$ and

$$c^2(t_2 - t_1)^2 > (x_2 - x_1)^2 + (y_2 - y_1)^2 + (z_2 - z_1)^2.$$

Then for all V such that $|V| \leq c$, we find that $t_2' - t_1' > 0$. Further, by a straightforward generalization of Eq. (3.17) it follows that

$$c^2(t_2' - t_1')^2 > (x_2' - x_1')^2 + (y_2' - y_1')^2 + (z_2' - z_1')^2.$$

Hence we see that: **If an event E_2 lies in the future of an event E_1 according to one observer, event E_2 also lies in the future of event E_1 according to all other observers who are moving w.r.t. the first observer at a relative velocity less than or equal to that of light. Similar results hold if according to the first observer, E_2 is in the past of E_1 (for then E_1 is in the future of E_2); or if E_2 and E_1 are in the present (or limbo) w.r.t. each other.**

These results show that our division into past, present, and future is meaningful and independent of the particular observer making the judgment, provided only that all such observers have relative velocities less than or equal to the velocity of light.†

---

*In fact, RS covers a negative distance in a negative time according to A, so that $w > 0$. Similarly UV has a *negative* velocity according to B.

†E. C. Zeeman [*J. Math. Phys.*, **5**, 490 (1964)] has proved that the requirement that the separation into past, present, and future be invariant under Lorentz transformations determines the latter function completely, up to a scale of V.

The concept of "now" or the "present" has become considerably weakened in the special theory of relativity compared with classical physics. While the concept still has significance, yet each observer has a *different* definition of "now," i. e., the set of all events synchronous with his event. (Of course, the concept "here and now" is invariant to all the observers, but simply denotes a *single* event.)

4.6 ABERRATION OF STARLIGHT*

After the somewhat discursive nature of the previous section, we turn to a much more concrete application of the Lorentz transformation, namely the aberration of starlight. The effect was first observed by Bradley in 1725, who explained it classically as arising from the motion of the earth. It played an important role in the development of special relativity, since it "demonstrated" that the ether drag did not occur,† and that indeed the earth had a speed of $\approx 30\,\mathrm{km/sec}$ relative to the fixed stars.

Consider a "fixed" star S, and an observer O with a telescope who is moving at a velocity $\mathbf{V}$ w. r. t. the star. In order to see the star in the center of the telescope field, should the observer point his telescope exactly at the star, or slightly ahead of it, or slightly behind it? [See Fig 4.7(a).]

This is a problem in the addition of velocities, and the classical solution is straightforward.‡ Relative to the frame of axes (Ox, Oy) fixed w. r. t. the star, the starlight must have a velocity

$$\mathbf{c} = (-c \sin \theta, \ -c \cos \theta)_{\text{star frame}} \,.$$

(Here we give the x and y components of velocity.) This star-frame-of-reference has a velocity $\mathbf{V} = (-V, 0)$ w. r. t. a frame of axes fixed w. r. t. the telescope. Then [cf. Eq. (2.4)] the velocity of the starlight relative to the telescope must be

$$\mathbf{c}' = \mathbf{c} + \mathbf{V} = (-c \sin \theta - V, \ -c \cos \theta) = -c'\sin \theta', \ -c' \cos \theta'$$

where [cf. Fig. 4.7(b)]

$$c' = (c^2 + V^2 + 2cV \sin \theta)^{1/2}$$

and

$$\frac{c}{\cos \theta'} = \frac{V}{\sin (\theta' - \theta)}, \quad \text{i. e.,} \quad \theta' \approx \theta + \frac{V}{c} \cos \theta. \tag{4.15}$$

*This section may be omitted.

†Cf. D. Bohm, *loc. cit.*, p. 19. The crucial remark is that light is a wave phenomenon.

‡We ignore extra smaller effects due to the rotation of the earth.

Here in the expression for θ' we have neglected terms of order V^2/c^2. We emphasize that in this classical result the speed of the starlight relative to the observer is not c, but c'. The angular effect is straightforward to understand if one realizes that during the time that the light is passing along the length of the telescope, the bottom of the

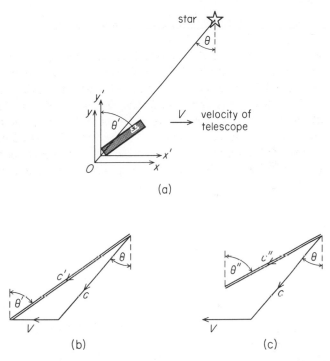

Fig. 4.7 Stellar aberration: (a) the geometry in the star frame of reference; (b) the classical solution shown in the telescope frame of reference; (c) the relativistic solution shown in the telescope frame of reference. The "triangle" does *not* close.

telescope moves slightly with respect to its location at the instant the light enters the top of the telescope. We illustrate this with a well-known analogy. If rain is falling vertically, then an umbrella held directly overhead keeps all of you dry, if you are stationary; but if you want to get home dry, that is, *move*, you should tilt the umbrella forward, and even then your lower legs will probably get wet.

The relativistic explanation is similar to the classical one in principle [cf. Fig. 4.7(c)], but now we must use the relativistic formula

(4.6).* Further, we expect that $c'' = c$. We find directly

$$v_x = -c'' \sin \theta'' = \frac{v_x' + V}{1 + (v_x' V/c^2)} = \frac{-c \sin \theta - V}{1 + (V \sin \theta /c)}$$

$$v_y = -c'' \cos \theta'' = \frac{v_y'}{\gamma[1 + (v_x' V/c^2)]} = \frac{-c \cos \theta \sqrt{1 - (V^2/c^2)}}{1 + (V \sin \theta /c)}$$

(4.16)

Hence

$$\tan \theta'' = \frac{\sin \theta + (V/c)}{\cos \theta \sqrt{1 - (V^2/c^2)}} \approx \tan \theta + V \sec \frac{\theta}{c},$$

(4.17)

which agrees with the classical expression for θ' only in the approximation of neglecting V^2/c^2. However, now we do find that $c'' = c$ (cf. problem 4.9); but note that the "velocity triangle" does *not* close.

It follows that for $V \approx 30$ km/sec, both the classical and relativistic discussions predict the same magnitude for the angular effect, within the limits of observational technique. In 1725 Bradley had studied the "apparent" motion of stars located in a direction perpendicular to the plane of the earth's orbit (cf. Fig. 4.8). He found that they "appar-

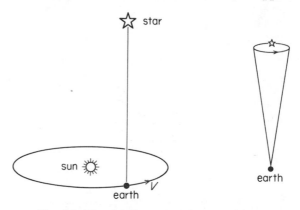

Fig. 4.8 The details of Bradley's explanation of stellar aberration (recall that the star is very much farther than the radius of the earth's orbit). Such a star, whose direction is perpendicular to the plane of the earth's orbit (or ecliptic), is said to be located at the pole of the ecliptic.

ently" moved in nearly circular orbits with a period of one year, the angular size of each such orbit being the same and equal to about

---

*One must be careful to distinguish between the time and location of the observer when the light is emitted by the star, and the time and location of the observer when he receives the light. (See problem 4.15.) In the present application all angles refer to the *single* ray connecting the single events of emission and reception of the light.

41.5 seconds of arc. (Stars in other locations were found to move in elliptic orbits. Why?) If we use Bradley's explanation of this effect we see that $2(\theta' - \theta) = 41.5''$, with $\theta = 0$. Hence

$$V = c \times \frac{40.5''}{2} \times \frac{1'}{60''} \times \frac{1°}{60'} \times \frac{3.14 \text{ radians}}{180°} = 29.5 \text{ km/sec}$$

which compares very closely with the known speed of the earth round the sun of 30 km/sec, already known to Bradley, of course.*

We remark that quite frequently, but not always, classical and relativity physics predict the same result to order V/c. In the present example, this was the case as regards the angular effect $\theta' = \theta''$, but note that $c' \neq c''$, even to this order.

4.7 THE DOPPLER EFFECT

We next turn to the Doppler effect.† Here again, the predictions of classical theory agree with the relativity predictions to order V/c. We will discuss the effect further in Section 7.4.

The classical effect is well known for the case of sound waves. A police-car siren has a higher pitch as heard by a stationary observer who is being approached rapidly by the car, than the siren has to the officers in the car. If the criminal is actually getting away from the police car, he hears a lower pitch.

Let us consider the above example in detail. Call the speed of the police car relative to the air V, and the speed of sound in air c, and assume that the police car is moving directly towards the observer. This is the easiest case to analyze, and is known as the longitudinal Doppler effect. In Fig. 4.9 we show this diagrammatically. (As usual t is plotted along the *vertical* direction.) For conceptual ease, let us replace the siren by a bell that is struck once every T_S seconds. What is the interval T_o between strikes as heard by the observer?

In Fig. 4.9 let P represent one moment (or event) at which the bell is struck in the police car, and Q the next such event. Then the time interval between events P and Q is T_S sec, i. e., $QL = T_S$, and $PL = VT_S$. The first "clang" then propagates at speed c along the "line" PMD, and is heard by the observer at the event D. Similarly the second "clang" is heard by the observer at the event E. Hence $DE = T_o$,

---

*In actual fact, Bradley's most accurate measurements were made on stars located nearly directly overhead, i.e., at the zenith. These stars would apparently move in ellipses. From such data Bradley obtained 41.5'' as the equivalent cone angle. We remark that these motions must be determined relative to astronomical coordinates fixed w.r.t. the earth, and not, of course, w.r.t. the star field!

†This is sometimes called the Doppler shift, since it leads to a shift in frequency.

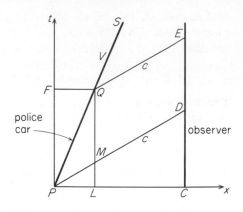

Fig. 4.9 The classical longitudinal Doppler-shift effect, for a moving source and fixed observer. *PS* represents the world line of the police car, and *CDE* that of the observer.

the unknown. But $DE = MQ = LQ - LM$. Further, $LM = (PL)/c$, since the line *PMD* corresponds to the velocity c. (But recall t is the vertical axis!) Also $PL = VT_S$ and $LQ = T_S$. Hence

$$T_o = T_S - \left(\frac{V}{c}\right)T_S = \frac{c - V}{c}\,T_S. \tag{4.18}$$

Since the period between strikes corresponds to the reciprocal of the frequency, we find that

$$\frac{f_o}{f_S} = \frac{c}{c - V}, \tag{4.19}$$

where f_o is the frequency of the sound as heard by the observer, and f_S is the frequency of the source of the sound. We see that the frequency heard by the observer is higher than that of the source. The reason for this is clear, namely: **the second clang has less far to travel from source to observer than the first clang, since the source has become closer to the observer in the meanwhile.**

It is left as problem 4.10 to prove that if the source has speed v_S relative to the air, and the observer speed v_o again relative to the air, and both of these are in the same direction, the observer being ahead of the source, then the frequency heard by the observer is given by

CLASSICAL LONGITUDINAL DOPPLER EFFECT:

$$\frac{f_o}{f_S} = \frac{c - v_o}{c - v_S} \tag{4.20}$$

where c is the velocity of sound in air, and f_S the frequency of the source.

Example 4.6. Consider two cases with the same relative velocity of approach of $\frac{1}{2}c$. Determine the magnitude of the classical Doppler effect for the two cases

   (a) the observer at rest,
   (b) the source at rest.

Answer 4.6. (a) For the observer at rest, we have $v_O = 0$, and $v_S = \frac{1}{2}c$. Hence from Eq. (4.20)

$$\frac{f_O}{f_S} = \frac{c}{c - \frac{1}{2}c} = 2.$$

   (b) For the source at rest, $v_S = 0$, and $v_O = -\frac{1}{2}c$ (note the minus sign). Hence

$$\frac{f_O}{f_S} = \frac{c + \frac{1}{2}c}{c} = 1.5.$$

This example, and Eq. (4.20), show that the classical longitudinal Doppler effect depends on the absolute speeds both of the source relative to the air, and of the observer relative to the air. Since air does exist, these absolute speeds are meaningful, and hence Eq. (4.20) is perfectly satisfactory for sound waves, and even agrees with experiment.*

However, if we turn to the case of light signals, then corresponding to a certain frequency of the source f_S, the frequency f_O "seen" by the observer cannot depend on the absolute speed of either the source *or* the observer relative to the ether, since the latter does not exist. The only quantity that can be relevant is the *relative* velocity between the observer and the source, which we call V. Further, the classical derivation ignored time dilation, which we know should be included. Hence we must calculate the Doppler effect using the Lorentz transformation.

For simplicity we again first consider the longitudinal effect. Since we want to prove that the effect depends only on the relative velocity V (taken as positive if the observer is moving towards the source), we should properly analyze the effect in an arbitrary frame of reference, in which both the source and the observer are moving, in such a way that their relative velocity is V. (Of course we must use the relativistic relationships for velocity addition, as given in Section 4.3.) We leave this most general case as a problem for the reader (problem 4.12), and here content ourselves with two special cases.† In the first we look at

---

*If $v_O > c$, the observer never hears the sound, while if $v_S > c$, the sound runs "backward" in time. With sufficiently high-velocity artillery fire, if you hear a shell coming towards you, it has already passed overhead!

†As partial justification, we will give another totally independent and *general* treatment of the Doppler effect in Section 7.7.

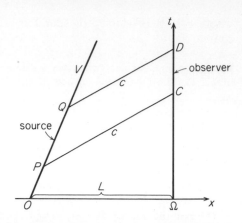

Fig. 4.10 The relativistic longitudinal Doppler shift, from the point of view of the observer (who is located at his spatial origin).

the experiment from the point of view of the observer, situated for definiteness at his own spatial origin, who sees the source moving with speed V along the observer's negative x axis in the positive x direction towards him (cf. Fig. 4.10). Suppose at $t = 0$ the source is at O, with $O\Omega = L$. The source emits one pulse of light (the equivalent of the "clang") at the event P, and the next at the event Q. These are received by the observer at the events C and D. According to the *observer*, events P and Q have x and t coordinates given by

$$P \equiv (x_P = -L + Vt_P, t_P) \quad \text{and} \quad Q \equiv (x_Q = -L + Vt_Q, t_Q).$$

Then, since the lines PC and QD correspond to the speed of light, and both C and D have $x = 0$,

$$t_C = t_P + \frac{|x_P|}{c} = t_P + \frac{L - Vt_P}{c} = \frac{L}{c} + t_P\left(1 - \frac{V}{c}\right),$$

and

$$t_D = \frac{L}{c} + t_Q\left(1 - \frac{V}{c}\right);$$

that is

$$t_D - t_C = (t_Q - t_P)\left(1 - \frac{V}{c}\right). \tag{4.21}$$

Equation (4.21) is very similar to that found for the classical result Eq. (4.18). But there is one crucial difference. In the classical case $t_Q - t_P = T_S$—that is, the time interval between the emission of the two pulses of light (or sound) *according to the observer* is equal to the time interval according to the emitter.* However, in the relativistic case we must also include the time-dilation effect, discussed in Section 3.6. We recall that an observer at rest w.r.t. two events finds that the (proper) time interval τ between the events is shorter by the factor γ^{-1} than does an observer moving at a velocity V w.r.t. the two events (who finds the interval has duration t); that is,

$$\tau = \gamma^{-1}t = \sqrt{1 - (V^2/c^2)}\,t\,.$$

Thus in our case the *proper* time interval τ_S between events P and Q is given by $\tau_S = \gamma^{-1}(t_Q - t_P)$, while $t_D - t_C$ is the proper time interval τ_O between events C and D as seen by the observer. Hence, substituting $t_D - t_C = \tau_O$ and $t_Q - t_P = \gamma\tau_S$ into Eq. (4.21) we obtain

$$\tau_O = \gamma\tau_S \left(1 - \frac{V}{c}\right) = \frac{1 - (V/c)}{\sqrt{1 - (V^2/c^2)}}\,\tau_S = \sqrt{\frac{1 - (V/c)}{1 + (V/c)}}\,\tau_S \quad (4.22)$$

or

$$\frac{f_O}{f_S} = \sqrt{\frac{1 + (V/c)}{1 - (V/c)}}\,. \quad (4.23)$$

Let us now consider the *same* experiment from the point of view of the source. We use the same names as before for the individual events, and show the full specification in Fig. 4.11, labeled with axes x' and t'. Notice that O' is *not* the same event as O, and hence that

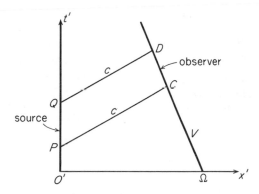

Fig. 4.11 The same relativistic longitudinal Doppler-shift experiment as in Fig. 4.10, but from the point of view of the source.

*The time interval between events P and Q "according to the observer" is of course to be measured by observers *at* the events P and Q who are at rest w.r.t. the observer, and whose clocks are synchronized with the observer's clock.

$O'\Omega = L'$. Otherwise all events are as before. By proceeding precisely as before (cf. problem 4.11) one *now* readily finds that

$$t'_Q - t'_P = (t'_D - t'_C)\left(1 + \frac{V}{c}\right), \tag{4.24}$$

which apparently *differs* from (4.21), if we ignore the difference between the primed and unprimed time coordinates.* However, we have yet to include time-dilation effects. In the present case we see that $t'_Q - t'_P = \tau_S$, the *proper* time interval between the source events P and Q according to the source; but

$$t'_D - t'_C = t'_0 = \gamma\tau_0 = \left(1 - \frac{V^2}{c^2}\right)^{-1/2}\tau_0,$$

where τ_0 is the *proper* time interval between the observer events C and D. Hence from (4.24) we are *again* led to the *same* results as before, namely Eqs. (4.22) and (4.23). We state without proof (but see problem 4.12) that these results hold for the most general frame of reference for the longitudinal Doppler effect where V is the relative velocity of *approach* of the source and receiver.

It is in fact crucial to the assumed equivalence of all frames of reference in constant relative velocity w.r.t. one another, that there be a *single* relativistic longitudinal Doppler-shift effect, and associated formula. It is meaningless to distinguish between the cases "stationary source and moving receiver" and "stationary receiver and moving source." In the case of sound, an *absolute* frame of reference is provided by the air or other medium through which the sound propagates, so that the lack of symmetry in Eq. (4.20) is understandable. For light, such a medium (the ether) does *not* exist. In fact it can be argued that if we had not already discovered the need for time dilation, the above derivation would demonstrate its existence, since otherwise absolute motion could be detected!

In summary we have found

$$\boxed{\begin{array}{c} \text{LONGITUDINAL DOPPLER EFFECT:} \\[4pt] \dfrac{f_0}{f_S} = \sqrt{\dfrac{1 + (V/c)}{1 - (V/c)}} \end{array}} \tag{4.25}$$

where V is the relative velocity of approach.

*The classical theory assumes $t' = t$. Equation (4.24) then corresponds to an observer moving with $v_0 = -V$ and a stationary source, so that for this case $f_0 = [1 - (v_0/c)]f_S$. By combining this result with the previous classical result (4.19) rewritten as $f_0 = [1 - (v_S/c)]f_S$ for the case of moving source and stationary observer, one obtains the classical general result (4.20). What is the proper (classical) justification for this "combining" operation? Think of a suitable two-stage experiment.

Example 4.7. Consider the same problem as in Example 4.6, but determine the magnitude of the relativistic Doppler shift, appropriate to light or radio waves.

Answer 4.7. In this case we *must* obtain the same answer for both case (a) and case (b). This is given by Eq. (4.25) as

$$\frac{f_o}{f_s} = \sqrt{\frac{1 + \frac{1}{2}}{1 - \frac{1}{2}}} = \sqrt{3} = 1.732.$$

This result is the geometrical mean of the two results of Example 4.5.

We remark that if $V/c \ll 1$, then we can expand Eq. (4.25) and find

$$\frac{f_o}{f_s} \approx 1 + \frac{V}{c} : \qquad \text{Relativistic, } V \ll c. \qquad (4.26)$$

However, from (4.20) we find for $v_o \ll c$, $v_s \ll c$, that

$$\frac{f_o}{f_s} \approx 1 - \frac{v_o}{c} + \frac{v_s}{c} = 1 + \frac{V}{c} : \qquad \text{Classical, } V \ll c,$$

which agrees exactly with the relativistic result for small velocities. However, to second order in V/c the relativistic prediction differs from the classical theory.

Another difference, again only to order V^2/c^2, is the relativistic prediction of a transverse Doppler effect. This applies to observations made at right angles to the direction of motion of the source. Classically there should be *no* effect, but relativistically there is an effect due simply to the time-dilation effect, so that

$$\boxed{\begin{array}{l} \text{TRANSVERSE DOPPLER EFFECT:} \\[4pt] \dfrac{f_o}{f_s} = \sqrt{1 - \dfrac{V^2}{c^2}} \, . \end{array}} \qquad (4.27)$$

We see that the true experimental test of the relativity predictions lies in the second-order terms in V/c in the expansion of (4.25), i.e., in

$$\frac{f_o}{f_s} = \sqrt{\frac{1 + (V/c)}{1 - (V/c)}} = 1 + \frac{V}{c} + \frac{1}{2}\frac{V^2}{c^2} + \cdots$$

for the longitudinal effect; and in the existence of the transverse effect. Both these effects were investigated experimentally in the classic work of H. E. Ives and G. R. Stilwell [*J. Opt. Soc. Am.*, **28**, 215 (1938)], who used beams of fast-moving atoms as their source of light. The Doppler effect leads to a frequency shift in the observed light, which can be detected spectroscopically. Ives and Stilwell investigated the effect for *all* angles of observation w.r.t. the direction of motion of the source, and found excellent agreement with the predictions of the special theory of relativity.

4.8 THE TWIN PARADOX REVISITED*

Now that we have discussed the Doppler effect, we return to the twin paradox (cf. Section 4.2). We start with a numerical example.

Example 4.8. Consider the twins A and B described in Section 4.2. Suppose that during the course of the experiment each twin sends signals to the other twin, the signals in each case being transmitted at the *same* constant rate of f pulses per unit time. Naturally, however, each twin determines his own transmission rate according to his *own* clock (i.e., according to his own proper time). The signals in each case are received by the other twin, who then compares their rate as *received* with his own transmission rate. Discuss the observations of each twin, for the case in which the relative velocity of the twins is $0.8c$. Assume the accelerations happen "instantaneously," and that each half of the trip takes 6 years according to the traveler B. Furthermore assume that the signaling rate is one pulse per year. (Note that the data correspond to those in Section 4.2.)

Answer 4.8. We first consider the signals sent by B and received by A, and show these in a space-time diagram drawn from A's point of view [Fig. 4.12(a)]. PR represents the world line of A, and PQR the world line of B.

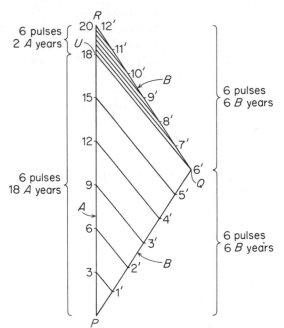

Fig. 4.12(a) The signals emitted by the traveling twin B, and received by the stay-at-home twin A.

*This section may be omitted, but at some loss.

Throughout this part of the experiment the source B is transmitting at a frequency $f_S = 1$ pulse/year. For those signals emitted during the first 6 years (as determined by B), the receiver A is approaching the source with a speed $V = -0.8c$ (note the minus sign, which arises since A and B are in fact separating). Hence a Doppler effect is introduced, and by using Eq. (4.25) we see that A receives at a frequency f_0 given by

$$\frac{f_0}{f_S} = \sqrt{\frac{1-0.8}{1+0.8}} = \sqrt{\frac{0.2}{1.8}} = \frac{1}{3}.$$

Hence A receives the pulses emitted along PQ at a rate of one pulse every *three* years. Let us call U the event at which A receives the sixth pulse emitted by B. We then see that A finds U to occur 6×3 years $= 18$ years after event P.

We next consider the signals emitted by B along QR. Now $V = +0.8c$ and $f_0/f_S = 3$, so that A receives these six pulses at the rate of 3 per year. Thus A finds that a further two years passes between U and R, so that in total 20 years elapses between P and R. *In summary, A receives 6 pulses each separated by 3 years, and then a further 6 pulses each separated by 1/3 year.* Thus A receives, and B emits, 12 pulses in all, even though A says that a total of 20 years elapses.

We next consider the signals emitted by the stay-at-home A, and received by B [cf. Fig. 4.12(b)]. A says that the whole trip takes 20 years, so that he

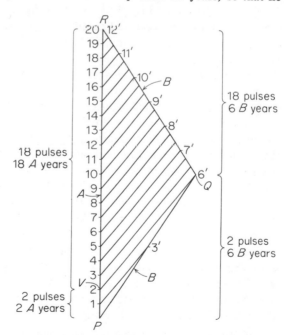

Fig. 4.12(b) Similarly showing the signals emitted by A and received by B.

transmits 20 pulses (*not* 12!). We consider first the signals received by B during the initial period of separation, i.e., along the world line PQ. Since A and B are separating, we find that $f_o/f_S = 1/3$. But $f_S = 1$ pulse/year, so that f_o, the frequency heard by B, is given by 1 pulse every 3 years. Hence in the 6-year period PQ, B receives only two pulses. Therefore the second pulse which B received at event Q was emitted by A at event V, 2 years after the event P. Thus during the period VR, A emits a further 18 pulses which B receives during the period QR which lasts 6 B-years. *In summary B receives 2 pulses each separated by 3 years, and then a further 18 pulses each separated by 1/3 year.* Thus B receives, and A emits, 20 pulses in all, even though B says that a total of 12 years elapses. This agrees exactly with our previous conclusions based on the time-contraction factor $\gamma^{-1} = 3/5$.

The two sentences in italics show that the two twins receive very different sets of pulses. Furthermore, each statement is made in terms of the receiving twin's clock, so that they are well-defined statements about events, and are independent of any choice of reference frame. Thus the two twins are indeed not equivalent.

However, even in the above discussion, we have drawn our space-time figures from A's point of view. We hence should also consider B's point of view. Before doing so, we superpose Figs. 4.12(a) and 4.12(b), as shown in Fig. 4.13. In this figure events on A's world line are denoted by the year indicated on A's clock, e.g., 6 means the event that happened to A a time $6\,(A)$ years after the start P; while B's events and years are indicated by a prime; e.g., $4'$ means the event that happened to B a time $4\ (B)$ years after the start P.

We see from Fig. 4.13 that both A and B have a set of to-and-fro light signals, which enable either observer to work out where the other observer is, at a given moment.* Thus, for instance, the light signals $13'$ and $3'9$ enable A to compute that the event $3'$ occurred at the time midway between events 1 and 9; that is, A says that event $3'$ occurred at a time of $\frac{1}{2}(1 + 9) = 5\ (A)$ years. Further, A can deduce the distance of B at event $3'$, since the to-and-fro light signal took $9 - 1 = 8$ years. Hence A says that the event $3'$ occurred a distance of 4 light-years away from A. We call this method of determining distance the *radar method*. Thus A finds that the B event $3'$ occurred at a time of 5 years and at a distance of 4 light-years. This agrees with the statement made by A, that B is separating from A at a speed of $0.8c$. Proceeding in this way, A can analyze the whole of B's motion by the radar method, and will indeed find that B separated from A at $0.8c$ for 10 years, traveling 8 light-years, and then turned around

---

*Of course, we must assume that each light signal carries with it the information of when it was emitted, and what signal was then being received. This is a minor technical problem.

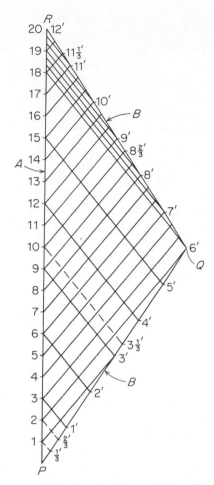

Fig. 4.13 The superposition of Figs. 4.12(a) and 4.12(b), showing how each of *A* and *B* can "survey" the motion of the other. The dashed lines represent extra signals.

and approached *A* at $0.8c$, reaching *A* in a further 10 years. This corresponds precisely to *A*'s point of view shown in Fig. 4.13.

We now consider *B*'s point of view. He also can attempt to interpret the data from his point of view. But he finds that *A*'s motion consists of *three* parts, not (as one might expect) simply two parts. The first part consists of the period between event *P* and event 2. All such events can be "surveyed" by *B* while he is still on world line *PQ*. That is, he both sends out a signal and receives its "reflected" signal while he, *B*, is on *PQ*. Thus, for instance (cf. Fig. 4.13), if we consider a signal emitted by B at the event $\frac{1}{3}'$, reflected at the event 1, and received again by B at the event $3'$, B finds that A's event 1 took place at the B time of $\frac{1}{2}[\frac{1}{3} + 3] = 1\frac{2}{3}$ B-years, and at a distance of $\frac{1}{2}[3 - \frac{1}{3}] = 1\frac{1}{3}$ light-years. Similarly he finds the A event 2 to be at a time $3\frac{1}{3}$ B-years after P, and at a distance of $2\frac{2}{3}$ light-years from B at this time. Thus B says that during the period $P2$, A is traveling at a speed of $0.8c$ away from B, and that this period lasts for $3\frac{1}{3}$ (B) years.

In precisely the same way, B can analyze the A period 18 to 20, during which all the surveying signals can be sent while B is on QR. For this A region, B finds that A's event 18 occurs at a B time of $\frac{1}{2}(6 + 11\frac{1}{3}) = 8\frac{2}{3}$ B-years, and at a distance of $\frac{1}{2}(11\frac{1}{3} - 6) = 2\frac{2}{3}$ light-years. During the next $3\frac{1}{3}$ B-years, B says that A approaches him at a speed of $0.8c$, reaching him in $(2\frac{2}{3}$ light-years$)/(0.8c) = 3\frac{1}{3}$ years, in other words at B's time of 12 B-years.

These A motions as determined by B are understandable, and at least have the "correct" relative velocities. But when B considers A's intermediate period between events 2 and 18, a most remarkable thing happens. **B finds that throughout the period 2 to 18, A is a constant distance of $2\frac{2}{3}$ light-years away from B.** (We leave the proof of this to problem 4.14; however, for example, one readily sees that A's event 10 does occur at a distance of $\frac{1}{2}(8\frac{2}{3} - 3\frac{1}{3}) = 2\frac{2}{3}$ light-years.)

We show these most remarkable conclusions in Fig. 4.14. **There is no symmetry at all between Figs. 4.14(a) and 4.14(b).** Notice that from B's point of view, B does understand why it is that A's event 2 happens at a true (B) time of $3\frac{1}{3}$ years, yet A says it happens at an (A) time of 2 years. These are related by the time-contraction factor of $\gamma^{-1} = \frac{3}{5}$, and from B's point of view, since A is moving, A's clock should do the slowing down. But when B considers A's middle period 2 to 18, he is totally *unable* to explain why A's clock shows this to last 16 years, yet B knows that it only lasts $5\frac{1}{3}$ years. **During this period, even though B and A are relatively at rest (according to B), B says that A's clock is going three times as fast as it should be going.**

This last result is extremely disturbing from B's point of view, since each of A and B has an identical clock. B can now look back at the Doppler-effect data [Example 4.8, and Fig. 4.12(b)]. The signal emitted by A at event 2 only reaches B at B's event $6'$, this result being understandable both from Fig. 4.12(b) and from Fig. 4.14(b), so that here A and B agree. Thus, B "understands" why A says event 2 is only 2 years after P, since A is a "moving" clock, and hence is time-dilated. Hence B also understands why he only receives two (equally spaced) pulses during the period P $6'$. He next observes that the signal from A's event 18 reaches him at his event $11\frac{1}{3}'$. During the B

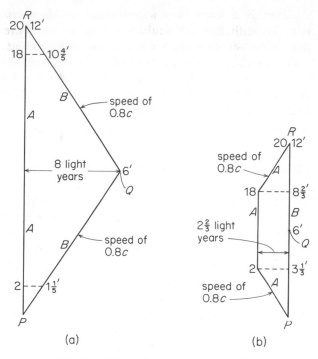

Fig. 4.14 The twin paradox example shown (a) from A's point of view (the stay-at-home), and (b) from B's point of view. Both figures are drawn to the *same* scale.

interval $6'$ to $11\frac{1}{3}'$, B receives signals at the rate of 3 per (B) year, owing to the "fact" that during the A period 2 to 18, A's clock goes at a (somewhat perplexing) tripled rate (even though A and B are relatively at rest). Finally, B receives A's final two signals sent during the A interval 18 to 20 again at this tripled rate of 3 per (B) year; but this he interprets as due to the fact that A is approaching B. Mysteriously A's clock is now back to "normal," and only suffers the expected time dilation due to A's motion.

If B is intelligent, he now realizes that throughout the period $6'$ to $12'$ he has been receiving signals at a constant rate, emitted by A during the period 2 to 20. In one sense *nothing changes* at A's event 18. B sees that he can explain the peculiar behavior of A's clock during the "relatively at rest" period between A's events 2 and 18, if he once admits that possibly it is he, B, who is doing the traveling. Then indeed A's event 18 is not singled out, and all B's observations now fit into place. (For they can all be immediately interpreted as in Fig 4.13.)

Even if B were not to capitulate at this point, we are not finished with his difficulties. For there are other methods that B can use to determine A's distance from B at a given moment, other than the radar method. One such method is to use the angle subtended at B by a meter stick which A holds transverse to their line of motion. Because of the phenomenon of aberration (cf. Section 4.6), one readily finds (cf. problem 4.15) that*

$$\phi'' \approx \phi \sqrt{\frac{1 - (V/c)}{1 + (V/c)}} \qquad (4.28)$$

Here V is the relative velocity of approach of the observer to a (small) body, ϕ being the *small* angle subtended by the body at the position of the observer measured in the frame in which the *body* is at rest; and ϕ'' is the angular size of the body as measured by the observer in his frame of reference. We note that the square-root factor in Eq. (4.28) is the reciprocal of that in the Doppler-effect formula (4.25). In fact, the two phenomena are very closely related, as discussed further in Section 7.4 and problem 7.5.

Consider first A's observations of B's distance by this method. To be specific, consider the light emitted by B at his event $2'$, and received by A at his event 6. We first consider this in A's frame of reference (cf. Fig. 4.13) in which A has already determined by the radar method that B's event $2'$ occurred at a time of $3\frac{1}{3}$ A-years after P, and at a distance of $2\frac{2}{3}$ light-years. Then, in this frame, A of course finds that corresponding to the event $2'$ the angular size ϕ'' of B is given by (1 meter)/($2\frac{2}{3}$ light-years). The effect of aberration is that B will say that the light that was emitted by the two ends of his meter stick at event $2'$ in fact defined an angle ϕ given by

$$\phi = \phi'' \sqrt{\frac{1 + (V/c)}{1 - (V/c)}} = \frac{1}{3} \phi'' = (1 \text{ meter})/(8 \text{ light-years})$$

(recall that V is negative).† Yet according to B, at A's event 6, A and B are relatively at rest and separated by only $2\frac{2}{3}$ light-years, *not* 8 light-years. It is not hard to find the reason for this peculiar result. For if B had *continued* his outward motion, and *not* turned around at the event Q, he would say that A's event 6 occurred at a time of 10 B-years after P, and at a distance of 8 light-years [cf. problem 4.16(e)]. The light signal from $2'$ to 6 cannot care about the future behavior of either A or B; and its angular spread does indeed correspond to A's distance from B at the reception event 6, that distance being as

---

*The reader who has skipped Section 4.6 should accept Eq. (4.28), and read on.

†We assume B uses two lasers to define *narrow* pulsed *beams* of light, which strike A together at the A-event 6.

computed by B on the basis of the relative velocity of A and B at the moment of emission of the signal from B.

Here we see the crux of the problem, and why it is absolutely impossible for B to consistently interpret all possible data on the assumption that he is the one who is at rest. For when B considers an event which takes place away from him, e.g., A's event 6, B can only locate it in space and time relative to an *inertial* frame of reference. But B changes his frame of reference at the event Q. Hence A's event 6 has one set of coordinates relative to the inertial frame that B was in before the turn around Q; and event 6 has *another* set of coordinates relative to B's later inertial frame. Those B experiments which investigate the coordinates of the A-event 6 in such a way that all information is effectively determined by happenings along the first part PQ of B's world line will be consistent with the B-coordinates (-8 light-years, $0, 0, 10$ light-years) for the event 6.* Similarly when B investigates the A-event 6 in such a way as only to use B-events along QR, he will get another consistent set of information, but this time determined by the coordinates of 6 in B's *second* frame.†

However, if B performs any experiments in which he uses events happening to him along *both* parts PQ and QR of his motion, he will get completely misleading results. The results will not be *consistently* interpretable in any inertial frame, since they do not belong in any *single* such frame. This is why the radar method of determining A's time and distance led B to such a peculiar result for A's events between 2 and 18; namely, A and B relatively at rest, and yet A's clock going three times as fast as it should!

Let us summarize. **B can determine the motion of A in many different ways. If he insists on interpreting his data on the basis that he, B, is at rest, then different experiments will lead him to inconsistent results. The only hypothesis which will make *all* the results consistent is the one where B assumes that actually it is he, B, who is doing all the moving, and that A is in fact at rest. Similarly A can investigate B's motion in many different ways. All these ways will lead to a consistent set of results as long as A assumes that he is at rest. If A were to try**

*This, for instance, includes our previous example of the determination by B of the angular spread ϕ of the two laser beams emitted at the two ends of the B meter stick at the event $2'$, this angular spread being such that the two beams hit A together at A's event 6. Of course B only learns at his event $7\frac{1}{3}'$ that he was successful in his choice of ϕ; but this does not alter the fact that the essential experiment was performed by B at the point $2'$, i.e., on PQ.

†An example would be the experiment in which B observes at his event $7\frac{1}{3}'$ the angular size of A's transverse meter stick at the A-event 6. We leave this as problem 4.17.

to interpret the results on the basis that he, A, was the traveler, and that B was the stay-at-home, then A would also find inconsistencies.*

In summary, B did change from one inertial frame to another at the event Q, and this change of inertial frames is detectable to both observers. It has many physical consequences, including in particular the fact that B only ages by 12 years while A ages by 20 years. Such a description is consistent to both observers, and is the only possible consistent description.

In fact B has many other ways of knowing that he changed inertial frames, not least the fact that he was accelerated at the event Q. He feels this in the small of his back, precisely as you feel the acceleration of a car. A never feels any acceleration, so that necessarily he is always in the same inertial frame.

The crucial significance of inertial frames of reference will be discussed further in later chapters. In particular in Chapter 8 we show how inertial frames are only defined relative to the positions of all the masses in the universe. If our twins were in an otherwise empty universe, it would be impossible for only one of them to accelerate. They would each have to accelerate by exerting forces on the other, so that their accelerations would be symmetric, as would their aging. The importance of the rest of the universe to the "twin paradox" cannot be overemphasized, even though the Special Theory of Relativity is completely adequate to discuss the paradox.†

As a final remark, it has been emphasized by H. Bondi that we do not find it surprising that the twins cover different distances in their respective trips between P and R. The distance covered in a trip between two points depends on the route taken. In the theory of relativity, so does the time. The time taken for a trip between two events depends on the route taken. **Elapsed time is a route-dependent quantity.** This certainly goes against our preconceptions, but once it is understood, no difficulty remains with the twin paradox. In fact, it is not a paradox, since we now understand the *unique* result from the point of view of *either* twin.

*In fact, neither A nor B could exclude the possibility that A had a constant velocity throughout the whole of the period, since a constant velocity is undetectable by the principle of relativity. What is detectable is the *change* from one state of constant velocity to another *different* constant velocity.

†At one time there was great controversy concerning the twin paradox. Some of this is easily accessible to the reader in the reprint volume referred to in the footnote on p. 69. A very thorough paper on the subject of the twin paradox is by J. Terrell, *Nuovo Cimento*, **16**, 457 (1960), reprinted in that volume. Our treatment is based partly on that of Terrell, who also discusses various other experiments that A and B can perform. He also remarks that B can detect his acceleration, or change of inertial frame, by seeing a shift in the positions of the fixed stars, due to stellar aberration effects.

4.9 TRANSFORMATION OF ACCELERATION*

As our final present example of the application of the Lorentz transformation, we consider the acceleration of a particle as measured by two observers A and B, B moving at a constant velocity V w.r.t. A. Do A and B see the same acceleration when the particle is at a particular space-time event? If not, what is the relationship between **a** and **a′**, these being respectively the acceleration as measured by A, and as measured by B?

We recall that for the Galilean transformation $\mathbf{a'} = \mathbf{a}$ [Eq. (2.5)], so that according to classical physics the acceleration of a particle is *invariant* for all observers in constant relative motion w.r.t. each other. This has very important consequences for the development of Newtonian mechanics. In the relativistic case, it will turn out that $\mathbf{a'} \neq \mathbf{a}$, and the transformation law is rather involved and untransparent—so much so, that it is often not discussed! We present it here to demonstrate that $\mathbf{a'} \neq \mathbf{a}$. The details of the derivation and the result are not particularly illuminating insofar as the physics underlying the special theory of relativity is concerned, and the reader can safely skim this section lightly.

The derivation proceeds similarly to the classical derivation of Section 2.4, but now we must use the relativistic velocity transformation Eq. (4.6), and the Lorentz transformation. We consider the position of the particle at two instants of time t_1 and t_2 according to observer A, and t'_1 and t'_2 according to B. At these two instants, let the velocities be denoted by subscripts 1 and 2. Then

$$v_{x2} = \frac{v'_{x2} + V}{1 + (v'_{x2}V/c^2)}, \qquad v_{x1} = \frac{v'_{x1} + V}{1 + (v'_{x1}V/c^2)}$$

$$v_{y2} = \frac{v'_{y2}}{\gamma[1 + (v'_{x2}V/c^2)]}, \qquad v_{y1} = \frac{v'_{y1}}{\gamma[1 + (v'_{x1}V/c^2)]}$$

and similarly for v_{z2} and v_{z1}. Here γ is a constant, of course. Further [cf. Eq. (4.4)] we have that

$$(t_2 - t_1) = \gamma\left[1 + \frac{V}{c^2}\frac{(x'_2 - x'_1)}{(t'_2 - t'_1)}\right](t'_2 - t'_1).$$

From these equations, it is already clear that $a_x \neq a'_x$, and $a_y \neq a'_y$, since the various denominators enter in an involved way. To make the problem algebraically easier we here resort to calculus.†

*This section may be omitted.

†The reader whose calculus is unable to follow the remainder of this section need not despair. We have already communicated the main message of this section. He may safely move on to the next section.

We have

$$v_x = \frac{v'_x + V}{1 + (v'_x V/c^2)}, \qquad v_y = \frac{v'_y}{\gamma[1 + (v'_x V/c^2)]}.$$

Let us take differential increments in v'_x and v'_y, corresponding to the change over the time interval $dt' = t'_2 - t'_1$ in the limit as t'_2 approaches t'_1. These lead to corresponding differentials in v_x and v_y, and in t. Thus

$$dv_x = d\left(\frac{v'_x + V}{1 + v'_x V/c^2}\right) = \frac{dv'_x}{1 + v'_x V/c^2} - \frac{(v'_x + V)}{(1 + v'_x V/c^2)^2}\frac{V}{c^2} dv'_x$$

$$= \frac{(1 - V^2/c^2)}{(1 + v'_x V/c^2)^2} dv'_x = \frac{\gamma^{-2}}{(1 + v'_x V/c^2)^2} dv'_x$$

and

$$dv_y = \frac{dv'_y}{\gamma(1 + v'_x V/c^2)} - \frac{v'_y}{\gamma(1 + v'_x V/c^2)^2}\frac{V}{c^2} dv'_x,$$

similarly for dv_z, and finally of course

$$dt = \gamma(1 + v'_x V/c^2) dt'.$$

Hence

$$a_x = \frac{dv_x}{dt} = \frac{\left\{\dfrac{\gamma^{-2} dv'_x}{[1 + (v'_x V/c^2)]^2}\right\}}{\gamma[1 + (v'_x V/c^2)] dt'} = \frac{\gamma^{-3}}{[1 + (v'_x V/c^2)]^3} a'_x,$$

and similarly

$$a_y = \frac{dv_y}{dt} = \frac{a'_y}{\gamma^2[1 + (v'_x V/c^2)]^2} - \frac{(v'_y V/c^2)a'_x}{\gamma^2[1 + (v'_x V/c^2)]^3}.$$

(Similarly for a_z.)

These results, while correct, are not very useful, since they are so involved. Certainly acceleration is anything but Lorentz-invariant. However, one particular case is of some interest, namely that in which B is moving *with* the particle at the instant at which the acceleration is being determined. That is, we let the primed variables refer to the *instantaneous rest frame* of the particle. (Of course the particle may still have an acceleration in this frame, in which case the instantaneous rest frame changes with time.) Then we have $v'_x = v'_y = v'_z = 0$, so that the results collapse to

$$a_x = \gamma^{-3}a'_x, \quad a_y = \gamma^{-2}a'_y, \quad a_z = \gamma^{-2}a'_z.$$

In this special case, the observer whose coordinates are unprimed has a velocity along his x axis of $-V$, w.r.t. the particle which is instantaneously at rest. The results in our last equations do *not* depend on the *sign* of V, and the x component is singled out only because it is *parallel* to the relative velocity. We use the subscript $||$ to denote the "parallel" component of a vector, and the subscript $\perp$ to denote the "perpendicular" component. We can then generalize our result to:

> Acceleration components $a_\parallel$ and $a_\perp$ as seen by observer moving at V w.r.t. rest-frame accelerations $a'_\parallel$ and $a'_\perp$:
> $$a_\parallel = \gamma^{-3} a'_\parallel, \qquad a_\perp = \gamma^{-2} a'_\perp.$$

(4.29)

This result is reasonably straightforward and useful. The general case is too messy to be worthwhile. (In Appendix A of this chapter, on four-vectors, we briefly discuss much more useful *redefinitions* of velocity and acceleration. These are "more useful" by definition, since they are carefully constructed to transform *easily* under the Lorentz transformation. They do, however, contain precisely as much information as is contained in the usual definitions.)

4.10   REVIEW EXAMPLE

Example 4.9. The following example contains a review of most of relativistic kinematics. For your own sake, attempt to work it through before looking at the solution, which is given on p. 110.

A man B standing at the rear end of a railroad car fires a bullet towards the front end of the car. The velocity of the bullet as measured by the gunman is $0.6c$. The length of the car as measured by the gunman is 375 m. An observer A on the ground observes all this as the train passes him with velocity $0.8c$. What values does this observer measure for the following quantities:

(a) Length of the railroad car?
(b) Velocity of the bullet?
(c) Length of time the bullet is in the air?
(d) Distance the bullet travels?

PROBLEMS

(Essential problems are indicated by !, difficult problems by *.)

4.1 A radioactive nucleus is moving with velocity $0.3c$ along the x axis, when it emits an electron with a speed of $0.5c$ relative to the nucleus. What is the velocity of the electron in the laboratory for the two cases:

(a) the electron is emitted along the x axis,
(b) the electron is emitted parallel to the y axis w.r.t. the nucleus?

4.2 In the experiment of problem 4.1, suppose that the electron is seen to go off parallel to the y axis in the laboratory. Then what was the direction of emission of the electron relative to the nucleus; and what is its laboratory speed?

4.3 Consider the "addition of parallel velocities" formula

$$V = \frac{u+v}{1+(uv/c^2)}.$$

Prove that

$$1 - (V^2/c^2) \equiv \frac{[1 - (u^2/c^2)] [1 - (v^2/c^2)]}{[1 - (uv/c^2)]^2}.$$

(This result is often very useful in problems.)

*4.4 Prove the velocity addition formula (4.6) using calculus directly in the proof, and considering instantaneous velocities throughout. [Note that there is only one independent variable, so that x, y, z, t and also x', y', z' may each be considered a function of t'. Thus, for example, $dx/dt = (dx/dt')/(dt/dt')$.]

*4.5 Consider three frames S, S' and S'' with parallel axes and common origins at $t = t' = t'' = 0$. Let S' have velocity v_1 w. r. t. S along the x axis, and S'' have velocity v_2 w. r. t. S' along the x' axis. By substituting one Lorentz transformation into the other, obtain the effective transformation between S and S'', and show that this corresponds to a velocity $(v_1 + v_2)/[1 + (v_1 v_2/c_2)]$ of S'' w. r. t. S along the x axis. [*Hint*: Use the result of problem 4.3.]

4.6 Obtain the "inverse" relativistic velocity addition formula Eq. (4.7).

4.7 One event A occurs at the spatial origin of S at $t = 0$. A second event B occurs at the spatial location $(10c, 0, 0)$ at $t = 8$ sec according to S. Find the *velocities* w. r. t. S of the frame S' in which
   (a) events A and B are simultaneous,
   (b) event B occurs 4 sec before event A,
   (c) event A occurs 4 sec before event B.
In case (a), what is then the distance between A and B?

4.8 One event A occurs at the spatial origin of S, at $t = 0$. Another event B occurs at the spatial location $(8c, 0, 0)$ at $t = 10$ sec according to S. Find the velocities w. r. t. S of the frames S' for which
   (a) events A and B occur at the same point,
   (b) events A and B are simultaneous (careful!).
In case (a), what is then the time interval between A and B?

4.9 In Section 4.6, stellar aberration was discussed. Prove that $c'' = c$. Also prove that $\theta'' = \theta'$, for the case that V^2/c^2 is negligible compared with unity.

4.10 Consider the *classical* Doppler effect, for instance for sound waves in air, and obtain the result of Eq. (4.20), where v_S and v_O are the velocities of the source and of the observer w. r. t. the air.

4.11 By considering the Doppler experiment of Fig. 4.11, prove Eq. (4.24).

*4.12 Consider the longitudinal Doppler-shift effect in an arbitrary frame. Suppose that both the source and the observer are moving along the same line, with velocities v_S and v_O, such that

$$V = \frac{v_S - v_O}{1 - (v_S v_O / c^2)}$$

is the relative velocity of approach of the source and the observer. Prove explicitly in this frame that the Doppler effect is still given by Eq. (4.25). (You may find the result of problem 4.3 useful.)

*4.13 Consider light reflected at normal incidence off a mirror which is moving with constant velocity v "into" the light beam. If the incident light has frequency ν in the laboratory, find the frequency of the reflected light in the laboratory. Relate your result to the viewpoint in which the light is emitted by the *image* of the source, which is moving with a speed $(v + v)/[1 + (v^2/c^2)]$ w. r. t. the laboratory. [*Hint*: Work in the frame of reference of the mirror.]

4.14 In the twin paradox example discussed in Section 4.8, prove that when B uses the radar method to determine the motion of A, he does find that throughout the A interval 2 to 18, A is at rest and a distance of $2\frac{2}{3}$ light-years away from B. ("Naturally" B assumes that he himself is at rest.)

4.15 (a) Prove the angle transformation Eq. (4.28) directly from Eq. (4.17).

(b) Prove the same equation explicitly by considering a source of finite transverse size, and an observer, who are approaching each other at a relative velocity V. Consider a single light ray which leaves the edge of the source at one space-time event and reaches the observer at a *later* space-time event. For each of the two frames (i) the observer at rest, (ii) the source at rest, construct a complete space-time diagram of the experiment, and determine the space-time coordinates of the emission event and of the reception event. From these data, obtain Eq. (4.28) (cf. footnote on p. 84).

4.16 Consider the twin paradox example discussed in Section 4.8. Show the whole experiment in the (proper) inertial frame in which B is at rest for the period PQ, and has a velocity of

$$\frac{-0.8 - 0.8}{1 + (0.8)^2} c = \frac{40}{41} c$$

for the period QR. In *this* frame:

(a) What is the time of the event R? of the event Q?

(b) How much time does A *say* has elapsed between P and R?

(c) How much time does B *say* has elapsed between Q and R? between P and Q? between P and R along the world line PQR?

(d) Which A event is synchronous with the event Q in this frame?

(e) Prove that in this frame A's event 6 is a distance of 8 light-years from the origin, and occurs 10 years after P (cf. the discussion on p. 98).

*4.17 Consider the twin paradox example of Section 4.8. Determine the angular size of A's transverse meter stick as seen by B at B's event $7\frac{1}{3}'$. Show how this is related to B's determination of A's coordinates at event 6, in a (proper) inertial frame in which B is at rest throughout QR.

4.18 Consider the experiment of Example 4.8, but with the following algebraic data. According to A, B moves away at a constant velocity V to a distance L, and then instantaneously turns around and returns again at a constant velocity V. A and B transmit signals to each other at a *constant* frequency of f, according to their own clocks. Use the Doppler-effect equation, Eq. (4.25), and fill in all the entries in the table below:

Quantity	Measured by A (the stay-at-home)	Measured by B (the traveler)
1. Time of total trip	$T = 2L/V$	$T' = 2L/(\gamma V)$ *
2. Total number of signals sent	$fT =$	$fT' =$
3. Time of B's turn around (*A deduces this quantity*)		
4. Time of detecting B's turn around		
5. Effective frequency f' of received signals during "first" stage of trip		
6. Number of signals received at f'		
7. Effective frequency f'' of received signals during "second" stage of trip		
8. Number of signals received at f''		
9. Total number of signals received		
10. Conclusion as to the other observer's measure of time taken		

*This entry assumes the validity of the Einstein result that the traveler comes home the younger of the twins.

Here $\gamma = [1 - (V^2/c^2)]^{-1/2}$. Naturally, you should analyze this from the *consistent* viewpoint that B is indeed the traveler. You should find that each observer will deduce that the other observer did indeed *measure* his trip to be as long as originally stated [i.e., entry 10 agrees with entry 1]. Thus each twin will *agree* to disagree about their respective measures of the total time taken. Note that the reason for the asymmetry is that A goes on receiving signals at the rate f' for *more* than half the trip, because of the difference between entry 3 and entry 4 in A's column. However, B detects the changeover in frequency from f' to f'' at the midpoint of the trip.

This question is based upon the discussion given in *Physics—A New Introductory Course: Part III—Relativity*, by A. P. French (Science Teaching Center, Massachusetts Institute of Technology, 1966.)

4.19 Spectral lines from the quasi-stellar object 3C 245 are observed to be "red-shifted" in wavelength by a factor of 2.028 ± 0.005; that is, $\lambda_{obs} = (2.028 \pm 0.005)\lambda_{source}$. Calculate the velocity of recession of 3C 245, assuming that *all* the red-shift is due to the Doppler effect.

4.20 The k Calculus. Consider three observers A, B, and C, whose world lines are shown in Fig 4.15a. This also shows the world lines of light signals emitted at regular intervals by A at events $A_1, A_2, A_3, \ldots$, received by B at regular intervals at events $B_1, B_2, B_3, \ldots$, and received by C at regular intervals at events $C_1, C_2, C_3, \ldots$. Each observer has his own clock (all identical), and each measures the time interval between his sequence of events, finding

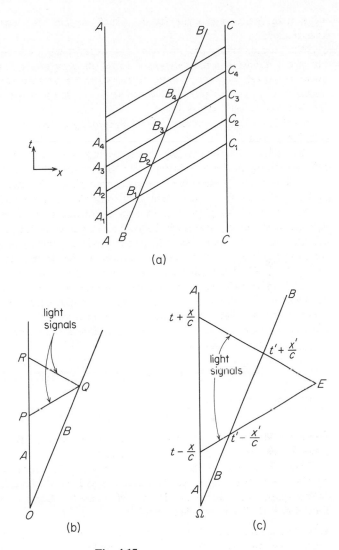

Fig. 4.15

periods T_A, T_B, and T_C. Clearly $T_A = T_C$. Also clearly $T_B > T_A$, since B is receding from A at a velocity V. Hence we define a function k by $T_B = kT_A$, $k > 1$, where k depends on V (and can only depend on the *relative* velocity). [Clearly k is simply the Doppler-effect factor.] Now we can think of the events $B_1, B_2, B_3, \ldots$ as a sequence of emissions of light by B, which are received by C at $C_1, C_2, C_3, \ldots$. But now C and B are approaching each other at a velocity V, and we know that $T_C = k^{-1}T_B$. It follows that k for an observer approaching a source at a relative velocity V is the reciprocal of k for an observer receding from a source at a relative velocity V. By k

we will in future mean the factor which applies for separation of source and receiver.

With these definitions, consider the experiment shown in Fig. 4.15(b). Two observers A and B with relative velocity of separation V pass each other at event O. At P, A emits a light signal which B receives at Q. B immediately retransmits it to A, who receives it again at R. Suppose the time interval OP has duration T according to A.

(a) What is the duration of OQ according to B? (Express this in terms only of T and k.)

(b) Call this time T'. Then, considering only the time intervals OQ and OR, how long is OR according to A? Re-express this in terms of T and k.

(c) From this information, deduce the time of event Q according to A, and its distance from A, in terms of k and T. Hence express k in terms of V.

All of relativity physics is in fact contained in this calculation, since it has assumed the equivalence of the observers A and B; and also the constancy of the speed of light according to A, and hence also according to B. It follows that the Lorentz transformation is also implicitly contained in this calculation. We prove this explicitly in parts (d) and (e).

(d) Consider the slightly more involved experiment shown in Fig. 4.15(c), in which each of A and B determines the coordinates of the event E. The other events are labeled by the *time* of each event as determined by the observer *at* that event. What is the meaning of (x, t); of (x', t')?

(e) One clearly has

$$t' - \frac{x'}{c} = k\left(t - \frac{x}{c}\right) \quad \text{and} \quad t + \frac{x}{c} = k\left(t' + \frac{x'}{c}\right).$$

From these deduce that

$$x^2 - c^2 t^2 = x'^2 - c^2 t'^2.$$

Solve for x' and t' in terms of x, t, and k; and finally re-express these in terms of x, t, and V. Interpret your result.

[This "k Calculus" is simply another algebraic formulation of the usual special theory of relativity. It was developed by H. Bondi, and is described in his (paperback) book *Relativity and Common Sense* (Garden City, N.Y.: Doubleday & Company, Inc., 1964).]

4.21 *Alternative derivation of the length-contraction effect and the Lorentz transformation.* (a) In Section 4.1 we treated the time-dilation effect by discussing the light clock. In that section, the "arm" of the light clock was transverse to the relative motion, so that its length l was the same according to *each* of the two observers A and B. To be specific, let the clock be at rest w.r.t. B, and let B be moving with velocity V w.r.t. A along the $+x$ direction. As usual, we denote B's coordinates with primes, A's coordinates being unprimed. We found that $t' = \gamma^{-1} t = [1 - (V^2/c^2)]^{1/2} t$, where t' is the *proper* time duration of an interval which is stationary w.r.t. B, and t is the duration of the *same* interval as measured by A, A having to use two clocks to measure this interval. This time-dilation effect must hold for *all* clocks, and hence in particular also for a light clock whose arm is directed *parallel* to V. (This can also be proved directly by considering the null result of the Michelson-Morley experiment.)

Consider such a light clock at rest w.r.t. B, in which the arm has a length l' according to B, with $t' = 2l'/c$. Assume that A determines the length of the light clock to be l, $l \neq l'$, and evaluate directly the time t for a to-and-fro light-pulse trip as *calculated* by A, who knows the arm of length l has a velocity V directed along its length. Since one must also have $t = \gamma t'$, prove that $l = \gamma^{-1} l'$. This is the length-contraction effect for a rod of *proper* length l' moving w.r.t. A who observes a contracted length l.

(b) Consider a rod at rest w.r.t. B, which lies along B's x axis, having one end at B's spatial origin, and the other end at B's spatial point $(x', 0, 0)$. According to A, one end of the rod has x coordinate Vt, and the other end has x coordinate $Vt + \gamma^{-1} x'$. [Here we have used the result of part (a).] Hence it follows that

$$x = Vt + [1 - (V^2/c^2)]^{1/2} x' \quad \text{or} \quad x' = \frac{x - Vt}{\sqrt{1 - (V^2/c^2)}}.$$

This is half of the Lorentz transformation. Now use "symmetry" between A and B to write down an equation which expresses x in terms of x', t', and V. (Be careful.) Solve these two equations to obtain the complete Lorentz transformation. [This question is based upon the treatment given by H. D. Young in *Fundamentals of Mechanics and Heat* (New York: McGraw-Hill Book Company, 1964).]

*4.22 Consider a telescope filled with water which is used to observe the "apparent" position of a star. The telescope is on the earth, and has a velocity of $V = 30$ km/sec relative to the star. Prove, by means of the principle of relativity, that the star's apparent position will be the same as that measured with an ordinary (empty) telescope (cf. Sections 4.4 and 4.6). (Note. This is *not* a problem in computation, but requires thought on the physics involved.) Also determine the prediction of classical physics, and compare the two. This experiment was actually performed, and played an important role in the development of the theory.

4.23 Consider three clocks in a satellite which is circling the earth "slightly" above ground level, taking 83 minutes per revolution. The three clocks are (a) a "light-clock," (b) a hairspring and balance-wheel clock, and (c) a pendulum clock. How many seconds will each clock have gained or lost in an earth-measured period of one year? Ignore the rotation of the earth. (Be careful, there is a catch in this question.)

4.24 Prove the *vectorial* formula for velocity addition Eq. (4.11).

*4.25 A "rigid" army tank 6 meters long moves along a horizontal road in which there is a deep hole 6 meters long. Suppose the speed of the tank is such that the Lorentz contraction factor is 6. Then to the driver of the tank the hole seems only 1 meter long so that the tank should pass over it. But to an outside observer the tank seems only 1 meter long, and so the tank should fall into the hole. Discuss. [This is discussed in detail by

W. Rindler, *Am. J. Phys.*, **29**, 365 (1961), and also by R. Shaw, *Am. J. Phys.*, **30**, 72 (1962).]

We now present the answer to the Review Example 4.9 (see p. 103).

Answer 4.9. It is a grievous error to think that this problem can be worked without at least one diagram. We give two (Fig. 4.16)—one from A's and one from B's point of view. For convenience, we assume that the bullet is fired at the common space-time origin $\Omega = (0, 0, 0, 0)$. We note that A and B have a relative velocity $V = 0.8c$ with $\gamma = (1 - 0.8^2)^{-1/2} = (0.36)^{-1/2} = (0.6)^{-1} = 5/3$.

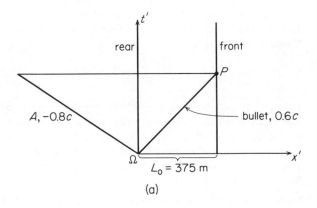

(a)

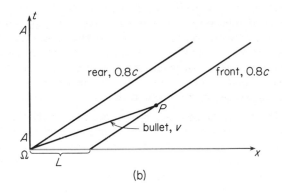

(b)

Fig. 4.16

(a) The length as measured by B is truly a proper length so that we can set $L_0 = 375$ m. Then as seen by A, for whom L_0 is moving at a velocity of $V = 0.8c$, the length L of the train suffers the "standard" length *contraction*, i. e., $L = \gamma^{-1} L_0 < L_0$ or $L = \frac{3}{5} \times 375$ m $= 225$ m.

(b) Again this is straightforward. We have $v' = 0.6c$, $V = 0.8c$, so

$$v = \frac{v' + V}{1 + (v'V/c^2)} = \frac{0.6 + 0.8}{1 + (0.6)(0.8)} c = \frac{35}{37} c = 0.946c.$$

(c) Now comes the punch line. If you computed (correctly) that the bullet was in the air a time

$$t' = \frac{375}{0.6c} = \frac{375}{0.6 \times 3 \times 10^8} = 2.08 \times 10^6 \text{ sec}$$

according to B, and if you then simply said that $t = \gamma t'$, **REREAD ALL** of Chapter 3. For t' is not a proper time!

Thus you must be more clever. There are many equivalent procedures.

(i) (Most straightforward.) According to B, the event P has $x'_P = 375$ m, $t'_P = 375/0.6c$ sec. Hence, according to A, it has

$$t_P = \gamma (t'_P + Vx'_P/c^2)$$

$$= \frac{5}{3} \left[\frac{375}{0.6c} + \frac{(0.8c)(375)}{c^2} \right]$$

$$= \frac{5 \times 375}{3c} (1.66 + 0.800) = 5.14 \times 10^{-6} \text{ sec.}$$

(ii) (Most physical?) According to A, in a time t the bullet, traveling at $v = 0.946c$, covers a distance d which is greater by $L = 225$ m than the distance the train covers at a velocity of $V = 0.8c$. Thus

$$d = vt = 225 \text{ m} + (0.8)ct$$

or

$$t = \frac{d}{v - V} = \frac{225 \text{ m}}{(0.946 - 0.800)c} = 5.14 \times 10^{-6} \text{ sec.}$$

[Question: Can you prove the equivalence of (i) and (ii) algebraically?]

(d) This part is now easy since $d = vt = 0.946c \times 5.14 \times 10^{-6}$ sec $= 1460$ meters.

Final check—alternative calculation of d. From (c) method (i), you know x'_P and t'_P. Hence calculate d directly. **Do it!** Then prove algebraically that this method is equivalent to the previous method.

SPACE-TIME

A.1 INTRODUCTION

In 1908, H. Minkowski presented a new view of space and time, based on the theory of relativity. His opening words were: "The views of space and time which I wish to lay before you have sprung from the soil of experimental physics, and therein lies their strength. They are radical. Henceforth space by itself, and time by itself, are doomed to fade away into mere shadows, and only a union of the two will preserve an independent reality."[*]

What does this mean? Consider our two observers A and B looking at the *same* event E. If A says it has coordinates (x, y, z, t) and B says its coordinates are (x', y', z', t'), then not only does x' depend on both x *and* t, but also t' depends on both t *and* x. Thus space and *time* are united. In this union, however, something is left invariant, namely

$$x^2 + y^2 + z^2 - c^2 t^2 \equiv x'^2 + y'^2 + z'^2 - c^2 t'^2. \tag{A.1}$$

Let us recall vector geometry. Consider two observers A and B, with two three-dimensional rectangular coordinate systems S and S'. Let both S and S' have the same origin O, but suppose their axes are rotated with respect to each other. In particular, consider the case shown in Fig. A.1, in which S' is rotated w.r.t. S by an angle θ about the z axis. If the point P has coordinates (x, y, z) in S according to A, then according to B in S' it has coordinates (x', y', z'). Here

$$x' = (\cos \theta)x + (\sin \theta)y$$
$$y' = (-\sin \theta)x + (\cos \theta)y \tag{A.2}$$
$$z' = z.$$

Nonetheless (x', y', z') and (x, y, z) refer to the same point, and the

[*]Reprinted with the kind permission of Methuen & Company, Ltd., from *The Principle of Relativity*, trans. W. Perrett and G. B. Jeffery (London: Methuen & Co., Ltd., 1923; reprinted in paperback by Dover Publications, Inc., New York).

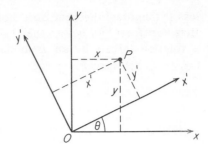

Fig. A.1 Two sets of axes rotated by an angle θ w.r.t. each other.

distance OP is a *constant*; that is,

$$x^2 + y^2 + z^2 = x'^2 + y'^2 + z'^2. \tag{A.3}$$

Similarly if Q is another point, then the distance PQ is the same according to both observers, as is the angle POQ; further, all other geometrical relationships are the same, insofar as they do not refer to the particular coordinate axes.* These invariance properties are emphasized in vector algebra, in which *no* reference is made to an explicit set of coordinate axes. The physics lies wholly in the interrelationship of different vectors, or of the different points.

Returning now to the relativistic case, we see that Eq. (A.1) is very similar to Eq. (A.3). In fact, Eqs. (A.2) are also very similar in form to those of the Lorentz transformation. If we define new variables by

$$x_1 = x, \quad x_2 = y, \quad x_3 = z, \quad x_4 = ict \tag{A.4}$$

(where $i = \sqrt{-1}$), then Eq. (A.1) can be rewritten as

$$x_1^2 + x_2^2 + x_3^2 + x_4^2 = x_1'^2 + x_2'^2 + x_3'^2 + x_4'^2. \tag{A.5}$$

In these variables the Lorentz transformation, Eqs. (3.13), can be formally written as

$$x_1' = \gamma x_1 + \left(\frac{i\gamma V}{c}\right)x_4 = (\cos \chi)x_1 + (\sin \chi)x_4$$

$$x_4' = -\left(\frac{i\gamma V}{c}\right)x_1 + \gamma x_4 = -(\sin \chi)x_1 + (\cos \chi)x_4 \tag{A.6}$$

with

$$\cos \chi = \gamma = \frac{1}{\sqrt{1 - (V^2/c^2)}} > 1, \quad \sin \chi = \frac{i\gamma V}{c} = i\,\frac{V/c}{\sqrt{1 - (V^2/c^2)}} \tag{A.7}$$

and

$$\cos^2\chi + \sin^2\chi = 1.$$

[Of course, we also have $x_2' = x_2$, and $x_3' = x_3$.] Equations (A.6) and (A.7) are only formal, since χ is actually an imaginary angle. Nonethe-

*Thus, for example, the angle POx is certainly *different* from POx'.

less Pythagoras' theorem does hold, as shown in Fig. A.2. We thus see that, *at least formally*, the Lorentz transformation corresponds to a rotation (albeit by an imaginary angle) in the (x_1, x_4) plane in the (x_1, x_2, x_3, x_4) space.

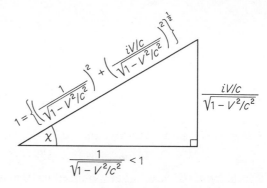

Fig. A.2 The imaginary angle χ.

In this sense, Einstein's relativity postulate states that all physical laws must be expressible in terms of relationships between events in the (x_1, x_2, x_3, x_4) space, formulated in such a way that they do not refer to any particular coordinate axes.

It is, of course, more convenient to continue to use the *real* variables (x, y, z, t). In these variables, **the relativity postulate states that *all* physical laws must be expressible in terms of relationships between events in the (x, y, z, t) space, so formulated that all physical relationships must be invariant under the Lorentz transformation.**

A.2   THREE-VECTORS

To see the meaning of this requirement, let us return to the three-dimensional example. To say simply that an event occurred at the point P with coordinates (x, y, z) is in itself properly meaningless. It does have meaning, however, because we understand the continuation "relative to the point O, with coordinates $(0, 0, 0)$, and taken w.r.t. coordinate axes which join O to the points $X \equiv (1, 0, 0)$, $Y \equiv (0, 1, 0)$, and $Z \equiv (0, 0, 1)$." Thus the point P is properly specified relative to the four points O, X, Y, and Z (cf. Fig. A.3). The length OP is an invariant, as is the angle POX. Since these quantities are invariants, it follows that each is expressible in a form independent of the choice of axes. Thus

$$OP^2 = (x_P - x_0)^2 + (y_P - y_0)^2 + (z_P - z_0)^2 \tag{A.8}$$

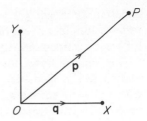

Fig. A.3 The complete specification of the point P. For simplicity the z axis is not shown.

and similarly for OX^2, OY^2, and OZ^2. Further,

$$\cos POX = \frac{PX^2 - PO^2 - OX^2}{2(PO)(OX)} \tag{A.9}$$

where $PO = \sqrt{PO^2}$. Equations (A.8) and (A.9) involve only invariant lengths. Even though Eq. (A.8) involves the components of the vector $\overrightarrow{OP}$, yet the length OP is an invariant, and does *not* depend on the choice of coordinates.*

In fact the operational definition of the length of a *straight* line OP consists in laying a meter stick as many times as necessary along the line OP and simply counting. According to this definition, length is clearly invariant, and is the basis of vector algebra. From this viewpoint, there is one vector $\mathbf{p} \equiv \overrightarrow{OP}$, and another vector $\mathbf{q} \equiv \overrightarrow{OX}$, each with an invariant length, p and q respectively. The angle between them is given by $\cos POX = \mathbf{p} \cdot \mathbf{q} / (pq)$, which is itself an invariant since

$$\mathbf{p} \cdot \mathbf{q} = \tfrac{1}{2}(\mathbf{p} + \mathbf{q})^2 - \tfrac{1}{2}p^2 - \tfrac{1}{4}q^2. \tag{A.10}$$

Thus the inner (or dot) product of two vectors is an invariant, since it can be rewritten in terms of invariant lengths.

The conclusion of this discussion is that any relationship involving vectors which does not depend on the choice of axes must have one of the forms:

$$\text{(invariant)} + \text{(invariant)} + \ldots = 0 \quad \text{or} \tag{A.11a}$$

$$\text{(invariant coefficient)} \times \textbf{(vector)} + \text{(inv. coef.)} \times \textbf{(vector)} + \ldots = 0 \tag{A.11b}$$

Thus $\mathbf{p}^2 + \mathbf{q}^2 = \mathbf{r}^2$ is a satisfactory equation, as is $\mathbf{p} \cdot \mathbf{q} = \mathbf{r}^2$; furthermore, both $\mathbf{p} + \mathbf{q} = \mathbf{r}$ and $(\mathbf{p}^2)\mathbf{q} = \mathbf{r}$ are proper equations.† However, an

*It does depend on the standard of length, of course.

†Note that these can be rewritten typically as $\mathbf{p}^2 + \mathbf{q}^2 - \mathbf{r}^2 = 0$; and $\mathbf{p} + \mathbf{q} - \mathbf{r} = 0$. The null length and the null vector are both invariant.

equation such as $(\mathbf{p}^2) = \mathbf{q}$ is improper,* since the left-hand side has the same value in all coordinate systems, while the right-hand side has different components in different systems.

Let us see how this works from the point of view of the transformation (A.2). Consider two vectors $\mathbf{a} \equiv (a_x, a_y, a_z)_S$ and $\mathbf{b} \equiv (b_x, b_y, b_z)_S$, where the coordinates are those appropriate to the S frame. According to B in the S' frame the vectors become

$$\mathbf{a}' \equiv (a'_x = a_x \cos \theta + a_y \sin \theta, \quad a'_y = -a_x \sin \theta + a_y \cos \theta, \quad a'_z = a_z)_{S'}$$

and similarly for $\mathbf{b}' \equiv (b'_x, b'_y, b'_z)_{S'}$. It is then easy to verify explicitly that

$$\mathbf{a}^2 = a_x^2 + a_y^2 + a_z^2 \equiv a_x'^2 + a_y'^2 + a_z'^2 = \mathbf{a}'^2$$

and

$$\mathbf{a} \cdot \mathbf{b} = a_x b_x + a_y b_y + a_z b_z \equiv a'_x b'_x + a'_y b'_y + a'_z b'_z = \mathbf{a}' \cdot \mathbf{b}'.$$

As already stated, the invariance of $\mathbf{a} \cdot \mathbf{b}$ is a consequence of the invariance of $\mathbf{a}^2$, and can be obtained by considering the invariance of $(\mathbf{a} + \mathbf{b})^2$. **In summary, the transformation (A.2) which takes a vector a into an apparently different vector a' (and b into b') is such that in fact $\mathbf{a}'^2 = \mathbf{a}^2$ and $\mathbf{a}' \cdot \mathbf{b}' = \mathbf{a} \cdot \mathbf{b}$.** From the "passive"† point of view $\mathbf{a}$ and $\mathbf{a}'$ represent the same vector, as viewed by two different observers.

A.3   FOUR-VECTORS

With this three-dimensional example to guide us, let us return to the four-dimensional world of relativity. We consider the event $E \equiv (x, y, z, t) \equiv (\mathbf{r}, t)$ as represented by a 4-vector $\underline{s}$, which points from the 4-origin $\Omega \equiv (0, 0, 0, 0)$ to the 4-point (x, y, z, t) [cf. Fig. A.4]. We arbitrarily define the square of the 4-length of this 4-vector by

$$s^2 = -x^2 - y^2 - z^2 + c^2 t^2. \tag{A.12}$$

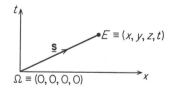

Fig. A.4 The 4-vector $\underline{s} \equiv (x, y, z, t)$. As usual we are unable to show the y and z axes.

---

*Except for the special case $\mathbf{p}^2 = \mathbf{q} = 0$, since this really means $\mathbf{p}^2 = 0$, $\mathbf{q} = 0$.
†Cf. the later discussion in Section 5.1.

Note the factor of c^2 in our definition.* Note also that s^2 can be *either* positive *or* negative.

Under a Lorentz transformation the four components of $\underline{s}$ are transformed to new components, and $\underline{s}$ apparently goes to a new 4-vector $\underline{s}' = (x', y', z', t')$. However, we can think of this as the *same* 4-vector, but viewed by the different observer B who is using his system of coordinates S' (cf. Fig. A.5). Both observers A and B calculate the

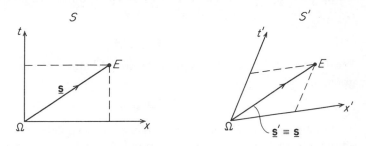

Fig. A.5 The *same* 4-vector $\underline{s} \equiv \underline{s}'$ seen in two different 4-coordinate systems S and S'. (Compare with Fig. 3.6.)

same 4-length for $\underline{s}$ and $\underline{s}'$, as can be seen from the definition (A.12) and Eq. (A.1). We remark that in order to determine either the x' or the t' component of $\underline{s}'$, we need to know *both* the space and time components of $\underline{s}$.

Consider two such 4-vectors $\underline{p}$ and $\underline{q}$, which according to A have components

$$\underline{p} \equiv (p_x, p_y, p_z, p_t)_A \quad \text{and} \quad \underline{q} \equiv (q_x, q_y, q_z, q_t)_A \qquad (A.13)$$

and which transform to

$$\underline{p}' \equiv (p'_x, p'_y, p'_z, p'_t)_B \quad \text{and} \quad \underline{q}' \equiv (q'_x, q'_y, q'_z, q'_t)_B. \qquad (A.14)$$

Then of course we have $p^2 = p'^2$ and $q^2 = q'^2$. (Here p denotes the 4-length of $\underline{p}$, etc.) But we can also consider the 4-vector

$$\underline{p} + \underline{q} \equiv (p_x + q_x,\ p_y + q_y,\ p_z + q_z,\ p_t + q_t)_A. \qquad (A.15)$$

The square of its 4-length is then given by

$$(\underline{p} + \underline{q})^2 \equiv -(p_x + q_x)^2 - (p_y + q_y)^2 - (p_z + q_z)^2 + c^2(p_t + q_t)^2$$
$$= (-p_x^2 - p_y^2 - p_z^2 + c^2 p_t^2) + (-q_x^2 - q_y^2 - q_z^2 + c^2 q_t^2)$$
$$+ 2(-p_x q_x - p_y q_y - p_z q_z + c^2 p_t q_t). \qquad (A.16)$$

*There are several different ways of defining a 4-vector, and also its length, some of which incorporate the c into the "time" component. All definitions lead to the same physics. Our notation for $\underline{s}$ is not the usual one, but is convenient.

This suggests that we should define the 4-dot (or 4-scalar) product of two 4-vectors $\underline{p}$ and $\underline{q}$ by

$$\underline{p} \cdot \underline{q} \equiv -p_x q_x - p_y q_y - p_z q_z + c^2 p_t q_t. \tag{A.17}$$

Equation (A.16) can then be rewritten as

$$(\underline{p} + \underline{q})^2 = \underline{p}^2 + 2\underline{p} \cdot \underline{q} + \underline{q}^2. \tag{A.16'}$$

Using $\underline{p}^2 = \underline{p}'^2$, $\underline{q}^2 = \underline{q}'^2$, and $(\underline{p} + \underline{q})^2 = (\underline{p}' + \underline{q}')^2$, we immediately deduce from (A.16') and (A.17) that

$$\underline{p} \cdot \underline{q} = \underline{p}' \cdot \underline{q}'. \tag{A.18}$$

We further note that the square of the 4-length of the 4-vector $\underline{p}$ is given by

$$p^2 \equiv \underline{p} \cdot \underline{p}. \tag{A.19}$$

Equations (A.12) to (A.19) define a complete 4-vector calculus, analogous to the usual 3-vector calculus. Such 4-vectors have different components when referred to two different sets of coordinates; that is, as seen by two different observers A and B having a constant relative velocity V w.r.t. each other. But they always represent the *same* events.

A.4   THE 4-VECTOR FORMULATION OF THE SPECIAL THEORY OF RELATIVITY

Since two such different observers A and B are fully equivalent to each other by the First Relativity Postulate, it then follows that all *physical* statements must refer *only* to 4-vector quantities. One *cannot* single out particular components of such quantities (not even the "partial" 3-vector!). Furthermore, any physical law must have the form

$$\text{(invariant)} + \text{(invariant)} + \ldots = 0 \tag{A.20a}$$

or

$$\text{(invariant coefficient)} \times \textbf{(4-vector)} + \text{(inv. coef.)} \times \textbf{(4-vector)} + \ldots = 0$$
$$\tag{A.20b}$$

[cf Eq. (A.11)]. Here by "invariant" we mean expressions such as $\underline{p}^2$ or $\underline{p} \cdot \underline{q}$, or any such quantity which is invariant under a Lorentz transformation.

The statement implied by Eq. (A.20) is very restrictive, and hence very powerful. But before we can make use of it, we need to have a method of "generating" 4-vectors. At the moment the only 4-vector we know is the basic 4-vector $\underline{s} \equiv (x, y, z, t)$. Clearly we can multiply (or divide) this by an invariant to get other 4-vectors, but this is not very useful. Instead we proceed to define the differential 4-vector

$$\underline{\mathbf{ds}} \equiv (dx, dy, dz, dt). \tag{A.21}$$

If we can find a suitable differential invariant by which to divide $\underline{\mathbf{ds}}$, we will have generated a new 4-vector. But the square of the 4-length of $\underline{\mathbf{ds}}$ is an invariant, so that one such differential invariant, namely $d\tau$, is immediately given by

$$c^2\, d\tau^2 = c^2\, dt^2 - dx^2 - dy^2 - dz^2 = c^2 \gamma^{-2}\, dt^2. \tag{A.22}$$

Here

$$\gamma = \left[1 - \frac{1}{c^2}\left(\frac{dx}{dt}\right)^2 - \frac{1}{c^2}\left(\frac{dy}{dt}\right)^2 - \frac{1}{c^2}\left(\frac{dz}{dt}\right)^2 \right]^{-1/2} = \left[1 - \left(\frac{v^2}{c^2}\right) \right]^{-1/2}, \tag{A.23}$$

so that this is the *same* γ as previously defined.

We hence can define the 4-vector $\underline{\boldsymbol{\omega}}$ by

$$\underline{\boldsymbol{\omega}} \equiv \left(\frac{dx}{d\tau}, \frac{dy}{d\tau}, \frac{dz}{d\tau}, \frac{dt}{d\tau} \right)$$

$$\equiv \left(\gamma\frac{dx}{dt}, \gamma\frac{dy}{dt}, \gamma\frac{dz}{dt}, \gamma \right) \equiv (\gamma v_x, \gamma v_y, \gamma v_z, \gamma). \tag{A.24}$$

We note that the fourth component of $\underline{\boldsymbol{\omega}}$ has a direct physical interpretation as the time dilation factor, since $d\tau$ is a proper time interval, while dt is the associated laboratory time interval. Since $\underline{\boldsymbol{\omega}}$ is a 4-vector, its length must be invariant, and one readily finds that $\boldsymbol{\omega}^2 = c^2$. Note that when $v \ll c$, $\gamma \to 1$, and $\underline{\boldsymbol{\omega}}$ reduces to $\underline{\boldsymbol{\omega}} \equiv (\mathbf{v}, 1)$. Thus $\underline{\boldsymbol{\omega}}$ is the generalization of the ordinary 3-velocity, and is called the 4-velocity.

We are now able to show the power of the 4-vector formulation of relativity. Since $\underline{\boldsymbol{\omega}}$ is a 4-vector, we *immediately* know how it transforms under a Lorentz transformation. From our standard transformation, but now applied to $(\omega_x, \omega_y, \omega_z, \omega_t)$ instead of to (x, y, z, t), we **immediately** obtain

$$\omega_x' = \frac{1}{\sqrt{1 - (V^2/c^2)}} (\omega_x - V\omega_t)$$

$$\omega_y' = \omega_y$$

$$\omega_z' = \omega_z \tag{A.25}$$

$$\omega_t' = \frac{1}{\sqrt{1 - (V^2/c^2)}} \left(\omega_t - \frac{V\omega_x}{c^2} \right).$$

Using the explicit definition of Eq. (A.24), we see that this is equivalent to

$$\frac{1}{\sqrt{1 - (v'^2/c^2)}}\, v'_x = \frac{v_x - V}{\sqrt{1 - (V^2/c^2)}\,\sqrt{1 - (v^2/c^2)}}$$

$$\frac{1}{\sqrt{1 - (v'^2/c^2)}}\, v'_y = \frac{1}{\sqrt{1 - (v^2/c^2)}}\, v_y \tag{A.26}$$

$$\frac{1}{\sqrt{1 - (v'^2/c^2)}}\, v'_z = \frac{1}{\sqrt{1 - (v^2/c^2)}}\, v_z$$

and

$$\omega'_t = \frac{1}{\sqrt{1 - (v'^2/c^2)}} = \frac{1 - (Vv_x/c^2)}{\sqrt{1 - (V^2/c^2)}\,\sqrt{1 - (v^2/c^2)}}. \tag{A.27}$$

Notice that we obtain Eq. (A.27) only because we bothered to evaluate the fourth component ω'_t! Using Eq. (A.27), we can rewrite (A.26) as

$$v'_x = \frac{v_x - V}{1 - (Vv/c^2)}$$

$$v'_y = \frac{\sqrt{1 - (V^2/c^2)}\, v_y}{1 - (Vv_x/c^2)} \tag{A.28}$$

$$v'_z = \frac{\sqrt{1 - (V^2/c^2)}\, v_z}{1 - (Vv_x/c^2)}.$$

Equation (A.28) should be compared with Eq. (4.7). Our present derivation is operationally much more direct, if possibly more mysterious (at least at first sight). Actually, about the same amount of algebra really goes into each derivation [though Eq. (A.27) is a very useful bonus of this method, cf. problem 4.3]. The key step in each case is the recognition and subsequent use of

$$d\tau^2 = \left(1 - \frac{v^2}{c^2}\right) dt^2 = \left(1 - \frac{v'^2}{c^2}\right) dt'^2.$$

We can easily go on to define the four-acceleration $\underline{\alpha}$ by

$$\underline{\alpha} \equiv \left(\frac{d^2x}{d\tau^2}, \frac{d^2y}{d\tau^2}, \frac{d^2z}{d\tau^2}, \frac{d^2t}{d\tau^2}\right) \tag{A.29}$$

which in fact depends on both **v** and **a**. By relating $\underline{\alpha}$ to $\underline{\alpha}'$ one could obtain the transformation equations for the 3-acceleration **a**. In this case the 4-vector method would really win, since once the principle is understood, all operations become very straightforward.

A.5   THE 4-VECTOR FORMULATION OF MOMENTUM, ENERGY, AND MASS

We now turn to an example which shows the full power of the 4-vector formulation. Our discussion will be formal, and hence should be taken only as a guide for a full treatment of relativistic dynamics. Thus, although we will obtain the correct relativistic definitions of momentum and energy, yet in order to set up a connection with the real world it is necessary to give a much further *physical* discussion of these concepts. This is given in Chapters 5 and 6.

With this proviso, we proceed to consider the concept of momentum. In Newtonian mechanics, the principle of conservation of momentum for an *isolated* two-body system (for example, in a collision) may be written as

$$\mathbf{P}_{\text{before}} = \mathbf{P}_{\text{after}} \tag{A.30}$$

with

$$\mathbf{P} = \mathbf{p}_1 + \mathbf{p}_2, \qquad \mathbf{p}_1 = m_1 \mathbf{v}_1, \qquad \text{etc.} \tag{A.31}$$

Here $\mathbf{p}_1$ refers to particle 1, having mass m_1 and velocity $\mathbf{v}_1$; and $\mathbf{p}_2$ refers to particle 2. The importance and usefulness of Eq. (A.30) lies in the assertion that it holds in *all* (inertial) frames of reference. That is, if we consider our two standard observers A and B, then if A observes a collision in which Eq. (A.30) holds, it follows that B *also* asserts that momentum is conserved; that is, B finds that

$$\mathbf{P}'_{\text{before}} = \mathbf{P}'_{\text{after}} \tag{A.30'}$$

with

$$\mathbf{P}' = \mathbf{p}'_1 + \mathbf{p}'_2, \qquad \mathbf{p}'_1 = m_1 \mathbf{v}'_1, \qquad \text{etc.} \tag{A.31'}$$

Here $\mathbf{v}'_1$ is the velocity of particle 1 as measured by B, etc.

In pre-relativity mechanics, in which one assumes an absolute time, one is led to the Galilean transformation, and in particular to $\mathbf{v}' = \mathbf{v} - \mathbf{V}$ [cf. Chapter 2, in particular Eqs. (2.3) and (2.4)]. Using this equation, it is easy to deduce Eq. (A.30') from Eq. (A.30), *if* one also asserts that each of $m_{1,\text{before}}$, $m_{2,\text{before}}$, $m_{1,\text{after}}$, and $m_{2,\text{after}}$ are invariants, *and* that

$$(m_1 + m_2)_{\text{before}} = (m_1 + m_2)_{\text{after}}. \tag{A.32}*$$

That is, it is necessary to *postulate* the conservation of mass in order to prove the invariance of the principle of conservation of momentum.

*We are allowing for the possibility of mass transfer. **Problem:** Prove the stated theorem.

In relativity physics, we know that the Galilean transformation must be replaced by the Lorentz transformation. Yet we still desire to preserve the principle of conservation of momentum. This means that we must ensure that if momentum is conserved according to observer *A*, it must *automatically* be conserved according to observer *B*. In other words, Eq. (A.30) is to be an invariant equation, leading *automatically* to Eq. (A.30′). But by our previous discussion [cf. Eq. (A.20)], this means that in fact **there must be a four-vector generalization of the principle of conservation of momentum.**

In particular, therefore, we must define a four-vector $\underline{\Pi} = \underline{\pi}_1 + \underline{\pi}_2$, where $\underline{\pi}$ is the four-vector generalization of **p**. The definition must be such that in *some* frame it does lead to conservation of Π, the three-momentum part of $\underline{\Pi}$, and *also* to conservation of Π_t. Once this is arranged, it will follow *automatically* that Π is conserved in all frames, and further that Π_t is conserved in all frames.

The easiest way to find the proper definition of $\underline{\pi}$ is to look for a 4-vector generalization of $m\mathbf{v}$, since after all we know that for $v \ll c$, the Newtonian definition does work. The obvious generalization is then to guess that

$$\underline{\pi} = m_0 \underline{\boldsymbol{\omega}} = (m_0 \gamma \mathbf{v}, m_0 \gamma) \qquad (A.33)$$

where we have written m_0 instead of m. Here m_0 is necessarily a true constant (i.e., an invariant), and is customarily called the rest mass. This guess has the feature that for $v \ll c$ one has $\underline{\pi} = m_0 \mathbf{v} = \mathbf{p}_{\text{Newton}}$, and $\pi_t = m_0$. Hence, at least for frames in which all velocities are nonrelativistic, it is true that

$$(\boldsymbol{\pi}_1 + \boldsymbol{\pi}_2)_{\text{before}} = (\boldsymbol{\pi}_1 + \boldsymbol{\pi}_2)_{\text{after}} \qquad (A.34)$$

and *also* that

$$(\pi_{1,t} + \pi_{2,t})_{\text{before}} = (\pi_{1,t} + \pi_{2,t})_{\text{after}}. \qquad (A.35)$$

These are correct because Eq. (A.34) is then the same as Eq. (A.30), and Eq. (A.35) is the same as Eq. (A.32).

We now assert that the proper relativistic definition of momentum is given by Eq. (A.33) for *all* velocities. The three-vector part of $\underline{\pi}$ is then given by

$$\boldsymbol{\pi} = m_0 \gamma \mathbf{v} = \frac{m_0 \mathbf{v}}{\sqrt{1 - (v^2/c^2)}} = m\mathbf{v} \qquad (A.36)$$

where *m now* denotes the "relativistic mass" $m = m_0 \gamma$, and is *not* an invariant. Of course, this assertion must still be compared with experiment for the case in which the velocities are comparable with the speed of light. Only then can we justify our assertion (see Chapters 5 and 7). For the moment we simply state that our assertion is indeed found to be correct.

What, however, is the significance of the time component of $\underline{\pi}$, which also has a conservation law associated with it! We have directly

$$\pi_t = m_0 \gamma = m_0 \left(1 - \frac{v^2}{c^2}\right)^{-1/2} \approx m_0 + \frac{1}{2} \frac{m_0 v^2}{c^2} + \cdots$$

$$= \frac{1}{c^2} \left(m_0 c^2 + \frac{1}{2} m_0 v^2 + \cdots\right)$$

$$= \frac{1}{c^2} \left(m_0 c^2 + T + \cdots\right). \tag{A.37}$$

Here T is the Newtonian definition of kinetic energy. Thus for non-relativistic velocities the conservation of π_t is exactly equivalent to the conservation of (Newtonian) kinetic energy. Here, of course, we assume that Eq. (A.32), i.e., mass conservation, also holds. We therefore see that $c^2(\pi_t - m_0)$ is the relativistic generalization of kinetic energy T.

It is more convenient to define a "total" energy E by

$$E = c^2 \pi_t = m_0 c^2 + T = m_0 \gamma c^2$$

$$= \frac{m_0 c^2}{\sqrt{1 - (v^2/c^2)}} = mc^2 \tag{A.38}$$

where again $m = m_0 \gamma$ and is *not* an invariant. The conservation of π_t for an isolated system then leads directly to the conservation of total energy E. As we will discuss in Chapter 6, it is possible to have a process in which the rest masses are *not* conserved. In this case it does turn out that the true conservation law is the conservation of total energy E, and *not* the conservation of kinetic energy T. We do not discuss this further here, but leave this question until Chapter 6.

We close with the remark that the square of the length of the 4-vector $\underline{\pi}$ must, of course, be an invariant, equal to $m_0^2 \underline{\omega}^2 = m_0^2 c^2$. Making use of our definitions of $\underline{\pi}$ and $E = \pi_t/c^2$ we readily see that this leads to the statement that

$$E^2 - c^2 \underline{\pi}^2 = m_0^2 c^4. \tag{A.39}$$

As we warned at the beginning of this section, our discussion has only been formal. In order to connect with physics it is essential to test our conclusions against the results of *experiment*. Furthermore, conservation laws do not form the whole of dynamics, though they are very important and very useful. In Chapter 5 we therefore discuss these concepts from a related but more physical point of view. Naturally the two viewpoints do go together, and in Section 6.5 we will revert to the 4-vector viewpoint. But by that time much more physics will have gone into the discussion.

A.6 RELATIVISTIC EQUATIONS OF MOTION. THE "ORDINARY" AND "MINKOWSKI" FORCES. TRANSFORMATION OF FORCE

Now that we have determined a suitable relativistic generalization of momentum, we can go on to look for a generalization of Newton's Laws of Motion, i.e., of $\mathbf{F} = m\mathbf{a}$. In the 4–dimensional framework, we should look first for a 4–acceleration and then attempt to set it proportional to a 4–force. In Eq. (A.29) we defined a 4–acceleration by

$$\underline{\alpha} = \left(\frac{d^2x}{d\tau^2}, \frac{d^2y}{d\tau^2}, \frac{d^2z}{d\tau^2}, \frac{d^2t}{d\tau^2} \right) \tag{A.29}$$

which, however, does depend on both $\mathbf{v}$ and $\mathbf{a}$. Nonetheless, it is then tempting to define a 4–force $\underline{\mathbf{K}} = (\mathbf{K}, K_0)$ and equate it to $m_0\underline{\alpha}$. Here m_0 is necessarily an invariant and is taken to be the same "rest-mass" as previously introduced in Eq. (A.33). Thus we write

$$\underline{\mathbf{K}} = m_0\underline{\alpha} = \frac{d}{d\tau}(m_0\underline{\omega}) = \frac{d}{d\tau}(\underline{\pi}). \tag{A.40}$$

Of necessity, this 4–force $\underline{\mathbf{K}}$ transforms as a 4–vector, i.e., very straightforwardly [cf. Eq. (A.45)]. It was first introduced by Minkowski and is customarily called the **Minkowski 4–force**.

Historically, however, another force was introduced first, which has rather nice properties for the case of electric and magnetic forces on charged relativistic particles. This is a 3–force $\mathbf{F}$ and is defined by the most simple three-generalization of Newton's law $\mathbf{F} = m\mathbf{a}$. That is, we define $\mathbf{F}$ as

$$\mathbf{F} = \frac{d}{dt}(\pi) = \frac{d}{dt}(m_0\gamma\mathbf{v}) = \frac{d}{dt}\left(\frac{m_0}{\sqrt{1 - (v^2/c^2)}}v \right). \tag{A.41}$$

Since $dt = \gamma d\tau$ [cf. Eq. (A.22)], we therefore immediately obtain

$$\mathbf{F} = \gamma^{-1}\mathbf{K}, \qquad \mathbf{K} = \gamma\mathbf{F}. \tag{A.42}$$

Thus $\mathbf{K}$ has a clear significance as another generalization of the (Newtonian) $\mathbf{F}$. But what is the significance of K_0? We have

$$K_0 = \frac{d}{d\tau}(\pi_0) = \frac{d}{d\tau}\left(\frac{E}{c^2} \right) = \gamma\frac{d}{dt}\left(\frac{E}{c^2} \right). \tag{A.43}$$

But dE/dt is simply the rate at which work is done by the net applied force $\mathbf{F}$; that is, $dE/dt = \mathbf{F}\cdot\mathbf{v}$ (at least in Newtonian physics). Thus

$$K_0 = \gamma c^{-2}\mathbf{F}\cdot\mathbf{v} = \frac{d\pi_0}{d\tau}, \tag{A.44}$$

and this equation is in fact valid relativistically (cf. Chapter 6).

Equation (A.40) gives the Minkowski formulation of mechanics. Of course, we must still determine $\mathbf{K}$ by experiment. An absolutely equivalent formulation of mechanics is then given by Eq. (A.41), in which $\mathbf{F}$ must be determined by experiment, with of course $\mathbf{K}$ and $\mathbf{F}$ related by Eq. (A.42). Both formulations are therefore really identical, but in fact the Einstein formulation in terms of $\mathbf{F}$ is the one more often used.

We hence close by determining the transformation properties of $\mathbf{F}$ as seen by our two standard observers. Of course, we could obtain these by "brute force," since $\mathbf{F}$ is given in terms of kinematical quantities by Eq. (A.41), and we know how all the kinematical quantities involved transform. However, we can be much cleverer and save ourselves work by using $\underline{\mathbf{K}}$. For we *immediately* know that

$$K_x' = g\left(K_x - \frac{VK_0}{c^2}\right)$$

$$K_y' = K_y$$
$$K_z' = K_z \qquad\qquad \text{with } g = \left(1 - \frac{V^2}{c^2}\right)^{-1/2}. \qquad (A.45)$$

$$K_0' = g\left(K_0 - \frac{VK_x}{c^2}\right)$$

Now $\underline{\mathbf{K}}'$ involves $\gamma' = [1 - (v'^2/c^2)]^{-1/2}$, so that our labors are not yet over. But Eq. (A.27) tells us that

$$\gamma' = \gamma g\left(1 - \frac{Vv_x}{c^2}\right) \qquad (A.27')$$

where $\gamma = [1 - (v^2/c^2)]^{-1/2}$. Hence we obtain immediately

$$F_x' = \frac{1}{1 - (Vv_x/c^2)}\left(F_x - \frac{V\mathbf{F}\cdot\mathbf{v}}{c^2}\right)$$

$$F_y' = \frac{F_y\sqrt{1 - (V^2/c^2)}}{1 - (Vv_x/c^2)} \qquad (A.46)$$

$$F_z' = \frac{F_z\sqrt{1 - (V^2/c^2)}}{1 - (Vv_x/c^2)}$$

and

$$\mathbf{F}'\cdot\mathbf{v}' = \frac{1}{1 - (Vv_x/c^2)}(\mathbf{F}\cdot\mathbf{v} - VF_x). \qquad (A.47)$$

Equation (A.46) can be rewritten three–vectorially as

$$\mathbf{F}' = \frac{\sqrt{1 - \frac{V^2}{c^2}}\,\mathbf{F} + \mathbf{V}\left\{\frac{\mathbf{V}\cdot\mathbf{F}}{V^2}\left[1 - \sqrt{1 - \frac{V^2}{c^2}}\right] - \frac{\mathbf{v}\cdot\mathbf{F}}{c^2}\right\}}{1 - (\mathbf{V}\cdot\mathbf{v}/c^2)}. \qquad (A.48)$$

These equations are very messy, and yet must apply to any real force. Note that Eq. (A.47) can be derived from Eq. (A.46). Nonetheless, the velocity $\mathbf{v}$ of the particle on which the force $\mathbf{F}$ acts appears explicitly in

Eq. (A.46). This is very remarkable, and actually implies a severe restriction on the possible allowed forms for the force $\mathbf{F}$; in particular such forces must often have a velocity dependence. A well-known example is the electromagnetic force $\mathbf{F} = q(\mathbf{E} + \mathbf{v} \times \mathbf{B})$. We discuss this further in Appendix C of Chapter 7, in which we show that the very existence of the second term $q\,\mathbf{v} \times \mathbf{B}$ can be deduced from the static Coulomb force $\mathbf{F} = q\mathbf{E}$.

ON THE ELECTRODYNAMICS
OF MOVING BODIES

By A. EINSTEIN*

It is known that Maxwell's electrodynamics—as usually understood at the present time—when applied to moving bodies, leads to asymmetries which do not appear to be inherent in the phenomena. Take, for example, the reciprocal electrodynamic action of a magnet and a conductor. The observable phenomenon here depends only on the relative motion of the conductor and the magnet, whereas the customary view draws a sharp distinction between the two cases in which either the one or the other of these bodies is in motion. For if the magnet is in motion and the conductor at rest, there arises in the neighbourhood of the magnet an electric field with a certain definite energy, producing a current at the places where parts of the conductor are situated. But if the magnet is stationary and the conductor in motion, no electric field arises in the neighbourhood of the magnet. In the conductor, however, we find an electromotive force, to which in itself there is no corresponding energy, but which gives rise—assuming equality of relative motion in the two cases discussed—to electric currents of the same path and intensity as those produced by the electric forces in the former case.

Examples of this sort, together with the unsuccessful attempts to discover any motion of the earth relatively to the "light medium," suggest that the phenomena of electrodynamics as well as of mechanics possess no properties corresponding to the idea of absolute rest. They suggest rather that, as has already been shown to the first order of small quantities, the same laws of electrodynamics and optics will be valid for all frames of reference for which the equations of mechanics

*First published in *Ann. Physik*. **17**, 891 (1905); trans. W. Perrett and G. B. Jeffery in *The Principle of Relativity* (London: Methuen & Co., Ltd., 1923; reprinted in paperback by Dover Publications, Inc., New York). I am grateful to Methuen & Co., Ltd., for their gracious permission to reproduce this translation. We here only present the first part of this paper.

hold good. We will raise this conjecture (the purport of which will hereafter be called the "Principle of Relativity") to the status of a postulate, and also introduce another postulate, which is only apparently irreconcilable with the former, namely, that light is always propagated in empty space with a definite velocity c which is independent of the state of motion of the emitting body. These two postulates suffice for the attainment of a simple and consistent theory of the electrodynamics of moving bodies based on Maxwell's theory for stationary bodies. The introduction of a "luminiferous ether" will prove to be superfluous inasmuch as the view here to be developed will not require an "absolutely stationary space" provided with special properties, nor assign a velocity-vector to a point of the empty space in which electromagnetic processes take place.

The theory to be developed is based—like all electrodynamics—on the kinematics of the rigid body, since the assertions of any such theory have to do with the relationships between rigid bodies (systems of co-ordinates), clocks, and electromagnetic processes. Insufficient consideration of this circumstance lies at the root of the difficulties which the electrodynamics of moving bodies at present encounters.

I. KINEMATICAL PART

§ 1. DEFINITION OF SIMULTANEITY

Let us take a system of co-ordinates in which the equations of Newtonian mechanics hold good.* In order to render our presentation more precise and to distinguish this system of co-ordinates verbally from others which will be introduced hereafter, we call it the "stationary system."

If a material point is at rest relatively to this system of co-ordinates, its position can be defined relatively thereto by the employment of rigid standards of measurement and the methods of Euclidean geometry, and can be expressed in Cartesian co-ordinates.

If we wish to describe the *motion* of a material point, we give the values of its co-ordinates as functions of the time. Now we must bear carefully in mind that a mathematical description of this kind has no physical meaning unless we are quite clear as to what we understand by "time." We have to take into account that all our judgments in which time plays a part are always judgments of *simultaneous events*.

*i.e. to the first approximation.

If, for instance, I say, "That train arrives here at 7 o'clock," I mean something like this: "The pointing of the small hand of my watch to 7 and the arrival of the train are simultaneous events."*

It might appear possible to overcome all the difficulties attending the definition of "time" by substituting "the position of the small hand of my watch" for "time." And in fact such a definition is satisfactory when we are concerned with defining a time exclusively for the place where the watch is located; but it is no longer satisfactory when we have to connect in time series of events occurring at different places, or—what comes to the same thing—to evaluate the times of events occurring at places remote from the watch.

We might, of course, content ourselves with time values determined by an observer stationed together with the watch at the origin of the co-ordinates, and co-ordinating the corresponding positions of the hands with light signals, given out by every event to be timed, and reaching him through empty space. But this co-ordination has the disadvantage that it is not independent of the standpoint of the observer with the watch or clock, as we know from experience. We arrive at a much more practical determination along the following line of thought.

If at the point A of space there is a clock, an observer at A can determine the time values of events in the immediate proximity of A by finding the positions of the hands which are simultaneous with these events. If there is at the point B of space another clock in all respects resembling the one at A, it is possible for an observer at B to determine the time values of events in the immediate neighbourhood of B. But it is not possible without further assumption to compare, in respect of time, an event at A with an event at B. We have so far defined only an "A time" and a "B time." We have not defined a common "time" for A and B, for the latter cannot be defined at all unless we establish *by definition* that the "time" required by light to travel from A to B equals the "time" it requires to travel from B to A. Let a ray of light start at the "A time" t_A from A towards B, let it at the "B time" t_B be reflected at B in the direction of A, and arrive again at A at the "A time" t'_A.

In accordance with definition the two clocks synchronize if

$$t_B - t_A = t'_A - t_B.$$

We assume that this definition of synchronism is free from contradictions, and possible for any number of points; and that the following relations are universally valid:—

*We shall not here discuss the inexactitude which lurks in the concept of simultaneity of two events at approximately the same place, which can only be removed by an abstraction.

1. If the clock at B synchronizes with the clock at A, the clock at A synchronizes with the clock at B.

2. If the clock at A synchronizes with the clock at B and also with the clock at C, the clocks at B and C also synchronize with each other.

Thus with the help of certain imaginary physical experiments we have settled what is to be understood by synchronous stationary clocks located at different places, and have evidently obtained a definition of "simultaneous," or "synchronous," and of "time." The "time" of an event is that which is given simultaneously with the event by a stationary clock located at the place of the event, this clock being synchronous, and indeed synchronous for all time determinations, with a specified stationary clock.

In agreement with experience we further assume the quantity

$$\frac{2AB}{t'_A - t_A} = c,$$

to be a universal constant—the velocity of light in empty space.

It is essential to have time defined by means of stationary clocks in the stationary system, and the time now defined being appropriate to the stationary system we call it "the time of the stationary system."

§ 2.   ON THE RELATIVITY OF LENGTHS AND TIMES

The following reflections are based on the principle of relativity and on the principle of the constancy of the velocity of light. These two principles we define as follows:—

1. The laws by which the states of physical systems undergo change are not affected, whether these changes of state be referred to the one or the other of two systems of coordinates in uniform translatory motion.

2. Any ray of light moves in the "stationary" system of co-ordinates with the determined velocity c, whether the ray be emitted by a stationary or by a moving body. Hence

$$\text{velocity} = \frac{\text{light path}}{\text{time interval}}$$

where time interval is to be taken in the sense of the definition in §1.

Let there be given a stationary rigid rod; and let its length be l as measured by a measuring-rod which is also stationary. We now imagine the axis of the rod lying along the axis of x of the stationary system of co-ordinates, and that a uniform motion of parallel translation with velocity v along the axis of x in the direction of increasing x is then imparted to the rod. We now inquire as to the length of the moving rod, and imagine its length to be ascertained by the following two operations:—

(*a*) The observer moves together with the given measuring-rod and the rod to be measured, and measures the length of the rod directly by superposing the measuring-rod, in just the same way as if all three were at rest.

(*b*) By means of stationary clocks set up in the stationary system and synchronizing in accordance with § 1, the observer ascertains at what points of the stationary system the two ends of the rod to be measured are located at a definite time. The distance between these two points, measured by the measuring-rod already employed, which in this case is at rest, is also a length which may be designated "the length of the rod."

In accordance with the principle of relativity the length to be discovered by the operation (*a*)—we will call it "the length of the rod in the moving system"—must be equal to the length l of the stationary rod.

The length to be discovered by the operation (*b*) we will call "the length of the (moving) rod in the stationary system." This we shall determine on the basis of our two principles, and we shall find that it differs from l.

Current kinematics tacitly assumes that the lengths determined by these two operations are precisely equal, or in other words, that a moving rigid body at the epoch t may in geometrical respects be perfectly represented by *the same* body *at rest* in a definite position.

We imagine further that at the two ends A and B of the rod, clocks are placed which synchronize with the clocks of the stationary system, that is to say that their indications correspond at any instant to the "time of the stationary system" at the places where they happen to be. These clocks are therefore "synchronous in the stationary system."

We imagine further that with each clock there is a moving observer, and that these observers apply to both clocks the criterion established in § 1 for the synchronization of two clocks. Let a ray of light depart from A at the time* t_A, let it be reflected at B at the time t_B, and reach A again at the time t'_A. Taking into consideration the principle of the constancy of the velocity of light we find that

*"Time" here denotes "time of the stationary system" and also "position of hands of the moving clock situated at the place under discussion."

$$t_B - t_A = \frac{r_{AB}}{c - v} \quad \text{and} \quad t'_A - t_B = \frac{r_{AB}}{c + v}$$

where r_{AB} denotes the length of the moving rod—measured in the stationary system. Observers moving with the moving rod would thus find that the two clocks were not synchronous, while observers in the stationary system would declare the clocks to be synchronous.

So we see that we cannot attach any *absolute* signification to the concept of simultaneity, but that two events which, viewed from a system of co-ordinates, are simultaneous, can no longer be looked upon as simultaneous events when envisaged from a system which is in motion relatively to that system.

§ 3. THEORY OF THE TRANSFORMATION OF COORDINATES AND TIMES FROM A STATIONARY SYSTEM TO ANOTHER SYSTEM IN UNIFORM MOTION OF TRANSLATION RELATIVELY TO THE FORMER

Let us in "stationary" space take two systems of coordinates, i.e. two systems, each of three rigid material lines, perpendicular to one another, and issuing from a point. Let the axes of X of the two systems coincide, and their axes of Y and Z respectively be parallel. Let each system be provided with a rigid measuring-rod and a number of clocks, and let the two measuring-rods, and likewise all the clocks of the two systems, be in all respects alike.

Now to the origin of one of the two systems (k) let a constant velocity v be imparted in the direction of the increasing x of the other stationary system (K), and let this velocity be communicated to the axes of the co-ordinates, the relevant measuring-rod, and the clocks. To any time of the stationary system K there then will correspond a definite position of the axes of the moving system, and from reasons of symmetry we are entitled to assume that the motion of k may be such that the axes of the moving system are at the time t (this "t" always denotes a time of the stationary system) parallel to the axes of the stationary system.

We now imagine space to be measured from the stationary system K by means of the stationary measuring-rod, and also from the moving system k by means of the measuring-rod moving with it; and that we thus obtain the co-ordinates x, y, z, and ξ, η, ζ respectively. Further, let the time t of the stationary system be determined for all points thereof at which there are clocks by means of light signals in the manner indicated in § 1; similarly let the time τ of the moving system be determined for all points of the moving system at which there are clocks at rest relatively to that system by applying the method, given in § 1, of light signals between the points at which the latter clocks are located.

To any system of values x, y, z, t, which completely defines the place and time of an event in the stationary system, there belongs a system of values ξ, η, ζ, τ, determining that event relatively to the system k, and our task is now to find the system of equations connecting these quantities.

In the first place it is clear that the equations must be *linear* on account of the properties of homogeneity which we attribute to space and time.

If we place $x' = x - vt$, it is clear that a point at rest in the system k must have a system of values x', y, z, independent of time. We first define τ as a function of x', y, z, and t. To do this we have to express in equations that τ is nothing else than the summary of the data of clocks at rest in system k, which have been synchronized according to the rule given in § 1.

From the origin of system k let a ray be emitted at the time τ_0 along the X-axis to x',* and at the time τ_1 be reflected thence to the origin of the co-ordinates, arriving there at the time τ_2; we then must have $\frac{1}{2}(\tau_0 + \tau_2) = \tau_1$, or, by inserting the arguments of the function τ† and applying the principle of the constancy of the velocity of light in the stationary system:—

$$\frac{1}{2}\left[\tau(0, 0, 0, t) + \tau\left(0, 0, 0, t + \frac{x'}{c-v} + \frac{x'}{c+v}\right)\right] = \tau\left(x', 0, 0, t + \frac{x'}{c-v}\right).$$

Hence, if x' be chosen infinitesimally small,

$$\frac{1}{2}\left(\frac{1}{c-v} + \frac{1}{c+v}\right)\frac{\partial \tau}{\partial t} = \frac{\partial \tau}{\partial x'} + \frac{1}{c-v}\frac{\partial \tau}{\partial t},$$

or

$$\frac{\partial \tau}{\partial x'} + \frac{v}{c^2 - v^2}\frac{\partial \tau}{\partial t} = 0.$$

It is to be noted that instead of the origin of the co-ordinates we might have chosen any other point for the point of origin of the ray, and the equation just obtained is therefore valid for all values of x', y, z.

An analogous consideration—applied to the axes of Y and Z—it being borne in mind that light is always propagated along these axes,

*That is, to a point at rest in k, which therefore has a constant x'—*footnote added by author.*

†That is, writing τ explicitly as $\tau(x', y, z, t)$—*footnote added by author.*

when viewed from the stationary system, with the velocity $\sqrt{c^2 - v^2}$, gives us

$$\frac{\partial \tau}{\partial y} = 0, \qquad \frac{\partial \tau}{\partial z} = 0.$$

Since τ is a *linear* function, it follows from these equations that

$$\tau = a \left(t - \frac{v}{c^2 - v^2} x' \right)$$

where a is a function $\phi(v)$ at present unknown, and where for brevity it is assumed that at the origin of k, $\tau = 0$, when $t = 0$.

With the help of this result we easily determine the quantities ξ, η, ζ by expressing in equations that light (as required by the principle of the constancy of the velocity of light, in combination with the principle of relativity) is also propagated with velocity c when measured in the moving system. For a ray of light emitted at the time $\tau = 0$ in the direction of the increasing ξ

$$\xi = c\tau \quad \text{or} \quad \xi = ac \left(t - \frac{v}{c^2 - v^2} x' \right).$$

But the ray moves *relatively to the initial point** of k, when measured in the stationary sytem, with the velocity $c - v$, so that

$$\frac{x'}{c - v} = t.$$

If we insert this value of t in the equation for ξ, we obtain

$$\xi = a \frac{c^2}{c^2 - v^2} x'.$$

In an analogous manner we find, by considering rays moving along the two other axes, that

$$\eta = c\tau = ac \left(t - \frac{v}{c^2 - v^2} x' \right)$$

when

$$\frac{y}{\sqrt{c^2 - v^2}} = t, \qquad x' = 0.$$

Thus

$$\eta = a \frac{c}{\sqrt{c^2 - v^2}} y \quad \text{and} \quad \zeta = a \frac{c}{\sqrt{c^2 - v^2}} z.$$

Substituting for x' its value, we obtain

$$\tau = \phi(v)\beta(t - vx/c^2),$$

Italics added by author.

$$\xi = \phi(v)\beta(x - vt),$$
$$\eta = \phi(v)y,$$
$$\zeta = \phi(v)z,$$

where

$$\beta = \frac{1}{\sqrt{1-(v^2/c^2)}},$$

and ϕ is an as yet unknown function of v. If no assumption whatever be made as to the initial position of the moving system and as to the zero point of τ, an additive constant is to be placed on the right side of each of these equations.

We now have to prove that any ray of light, measured in the moving system, is propagated with the velocity c, if, as we have assumed, this is the case in the stationary system; for we have not as yet furnished the proof that the principle of the constancy of the velocity of light is compatible with the principle of relativity.

At the time $t = \tau = 0$, when the origin of the co-ordinates is common to the two systems, let a spherical wave be emitted therefrom, and be propagated with the velocity c in system K. If (x, y, z) be a point just attained by this wave, then

$$x^2 + y^2 + z^2 = c^2t^2.$$

Transforming this equation with the aid of our equations of transformation we obtain after a simple calculation

$$\xi^2 + \eta^2 + \zeta^2 = c^2\tau^2.$$

The wave under consideration is therefore no less a spherical wave with velocity of propagation c when viewed in the moving system. This shows that our two fundamental principles are compatible.*

In the equations of transformation which have been developed there enters an unknown function ϕ of v, which we will now determine.

For this purpose we introduce a third system of co-ordinates K', which relatively to the system k is in a state of parallel translatory motion parallel to the axis of X, such that the origin of co-ordinates of system k moves with velocity $-v$ on the axis of X. At the time $t = 0$ let all three origins coincide, and when $t = x = y = z = 0$ let the time t' of the system K' be zero. We call the co-ordinates, measured in the system K', x', y', z', and by a twofold application of our equations of transformation we obtain

*The equations of the Lorentz transformation may be more simply deduced directly from the condition that in virtue of those equations the relation $x^2 + y^2 + z^2 = c^2t^2$ shall have as its consequence the second relation $\xi^2 + \eta^2 + \zeta^2 = c^2\tau^2$. *Footnote added by original translators.*

$$t' = \phi(-v)\beta(-v)(\tau + v\xi/c^2) = \phi(v)\phi(-v)t,$$
$$x' = \phi(-v)\beta(-v)(\xi + v\tau) \quad = \phi(v)\phi(-v)x,$$
$$y' = \phi(-v)\eta \qquad\qquad\quad = \phi(v)\phi(-v)y,$$
$$z' = \phi(-v)\zeta \qquad\qquad\quad = \phi(v)\phi(-v)z.$$

Since the relations between x', y', z' and x, y, z do not contain the time t, the systems K and K' are at rest with respect to one another, and it is clear that the transformation from K to K' must be the identical transformation. Thus

$$\phi(v)\phi(-v) = 1.$$

We now inquire into the signification of $\phi(v)$. We give our attention to that part of the axis of Y of system k which lies between $\xi = 0$, $\eta = 0$, $\zeta = 0$ and $\xi = 0$, $\eta = l$, $\zeta = 0$. This part of the axis of Y is a rod moving perpendicularly to its axis with velocity v relatively to system K. Its ends possess in K the co-ordinates

$$x_1 = vt, \qquad y_1 = \frac{l}{\phi(v)}, \qquad z_1 = 0$$

and

$$x_2 = vt, \qquad y_2 = 0, \qquad z_2 = 0.$$

The length of the rod measured in K is therefore $l/\phi(v)$; and this gives us the meaning of the function $\phi(v)$. From reasons of symmetry it is now evident that the length of a given rod moving perpendicularly to its axis, measured in the stationary system, must depend only on the velocity and not on the direction and the sense of the motion. The length of the moving rod measured in the stationary system does not change, therefore, if v and $-v$ are interchanged. Hence follows that $l/\phi(v) = l/\phi(-v)$, or

$$\phi(v) = \phi(-v).$$

It follows from this relation and the one previously found that $\phi(v) = 1$, so that the transformation equations which have been found become

$$\tau = \beta(t - vx/c^2),$$
$$\xi = \beta(x - vt),$$
$$\eta = y,$$
$$\zeta = z,$$

where

$$\beta = 1/\sqrt{1 - (v^2/c^2)}.$$

§4. PHYSICAL MEANING OF THE EQUATIONS OBTAINED IN RESPECT TO MOVING RIGID BODIES AND MOVING CLOCKS

We envisage a rigid sphere* of radius R, at rest relatively to the moving system k, and with its centre at the origin of co-ordinates of k. The equation of the surface of this sphere moving relatively to the system K with velocity v is

$$\xi^2 + \eta^2 + \zeta^2 = R^2.$$

The equation of this surface expressed in x, y, z at the time $t = 0$ is

$$\frac{x^2}{(\sqrt{1 - (v^2/c^2)})^2} + y^2 + z^2 = R^2.$$

A rigid body which, measured in a state of rest, has the form of a sphere, therefore has in a state of motion—viewed from the stationary system—the form of an ellipsoid of revolution with the axes

$$R\sqrt{1 - (v^2/c^2)}, R, R.†$$

Thus, whereas the Y and Z dimensions of the sphere (and therefore of every rigid body of no matter what form) do not appear modified by the motion, the X dimension appears shortened in the ratio $1 : \sqrt{1 - (v^2/c^2)}$, i.e. the greater the value of v, the greater the shortening. For $v = c$ all moving objects—viewed from the "stationary" system—shrivel up into plane figures. For velocities greater than that of light our deliberations become meaningless; we shall, however, find in what follows, that the velocity of light in our theory plays the part, physically, of an infinitely great velocity.

It is clear that the same results hold good of bodies at rest in the "stationary" system, viewed from a system in uniform motion.

Further, we imagine one of the clocks which are qualified to mark the time t when at rest relatively to the stationary system, and the time τ when at rest relatively to the moving system, to be located at the origin of the co-ordinates of k, and so adjusted that it marks the time τ. What is the rate of this clock, when viewed from the stationary system?

Between the quantities x, t, and τ, which refer to the position of the clock, we have, evidently, $x = vt$ and

---

*That is, a body possessing spherical form when examined at rest.

†Einstein's comments in this paragraph and the next are misleading. They are to be understood in the sense explained on p. 48. Contrast with the discussion in Section 3.5, particularly p. 53. *Footnote added by author.*

$$\tau = \frac{1}{\sqrt{1 - (v^2/c^2)}}\,(t - vx/c^2).$$

Therefore,

$$\tau = t\sqrt{1 - (v^2/c^2)} = t - [1 - \sqrt{1 - (v^2/c^2)}]t$$

whence if follows that the time marked by the clock (viewed in the stationary system) is slow by $1 - \sqrt{1 - (v^2/c^2)}$ seconds per second, or —neglecting magnitudes of fourth and higher order—by $\frac{1}{2}v^2/c^2$.

From this there ensues the following peculiar consequence. If at the points A and B of K there are stationary clocks which, viewed in the stationary system, are synchronous; and if the clock at A is moved with the velocity v along the line AB to B, then on its arrival at B the two clocks no longer synchronize, but the clock moved from A to B lags behind the other which has remained at B by $\frac{1}{2}tv^2/c^2$ (up to magnitudes of fourth and higher order), t being the time occupied in the journey from A to B.

It is at once apparent that this result still holds good if the clock moves from A to B in any polygonal line, and also when the points A and B coincide.

If we assume that the result proved for a polygonal line is also valid for a continuously curved line, we arrive at this result: If one of two synchronous clocks at A is moved in a closed curve with constant velocity until it returns to A, the journey lasting t seconds, then by the clock which has remained at rest the travelled clock on its arrival at A will be $\frac{1}{2}tv^2/c^2$ second slow. Thence we conclude that a balance-clock* at the equator must go more slowly, by a very small amount, than a precisely similar clock situated at one of the poles under otherwise identical conditions.

§ 5.   THE COMPOSITION OF VELOCITIES

In the system k moving along the axis of X of the system K with velocity v, let a point move in accordance with the equations

$$\xi = w_\xi\tau, \qquad \eta = w_\eta\tau, \qquad \zeta = 0,$$

where w_ξ and w_η denote constants.

Required: the motion of the point relatively to the system K. If with the help of the equations of transformation developed in §3 we introduce the quantities x, y, z, t into the equations of motion of the point, we obtain

---

*Not a pendulum-clock, which is physically a system to which the Earth belongs. This case had to be excluded. *Footnote added by original translators.*

$$x = \frac{w_\xi + v}{1 + vw_\xi/c^2}\, t,$$

$$y = \frac{\sqrt{(1 - v^2/c^2)}}{1 + vw_\xi/c^2}\, w_\eta t,$$

$$z = 0.$$

Thus the law of the parallelogram of velocities is valid according to our theory only to a first approximation. We set

$$V^2 = \left(\frac{dx}{dt}\right)^2 + \left(\frac{dy}{dt}\right)^2,$$

$$w^2 = w_\xi^2 + w_\eta^2,$$

$$\alpha = \tan^{-1} w_y/w_x,$$

α is then to be looked upon as the angle between the velocities v and w. After a simple calculation we obtain

$$V = \frac{\sqrt{[(v^2 + w^2 + 2vw \cos \alpha) - (vw \sin \alpha/c^2)^2]}}{1 + vw \cos \alpha/c^2}.$$

It is worthy of remark that v and w enter into the expression for the resultant velocity in a symmetrical manner. If w also has the direction of the axis of X, we get

$$V = \frac{v + w}{1 + vw/c^2}.$$

It follows from this equation that from a composition of two velocities which are less than c, there always results a velocity less than c. For if we set $v = c - \kappa, w = c - \lambda$, κ and λ being positive and less than c, then

$$V = c\frac{2c - \kappa - \lambda}{2c - \kappa - \lambda + \kappa\lambda/c} < c.$$

It follows, further, that the velocity of light c cannot be altered by composition with a velocity less than that of light. For this case we obtain

$$V = \frac{c + w}{1 + w/c} = c.$$

We might also have obtained the formula for V, for the case when v and w have the same direction, by compounding two transformations in accordance with §3. If in addition to the systems K and k figuring in §3 we introduce still another system of co-ordinates k' moving parallel to k, its initial point moving on the axis of X with the velocity w, we obtain equations between the quantities x, y, z, t and the corresponding quantities of k', which differ from the equations found in §3 only in that the place of "v" is taken by the quantity

$$\frac{v + w}{1 + vw/c^2};$$

from which we see that such parallel transformations—necessarily—form a group.

We have now deduced the requisite laws of the theory of kinematics corresponding to our two principles, and we proceed to show their application to electrodynamics.

5

INVARIANCE IN PHYSICS. RELATIVISTIC MASS

In the previous chapters we studied the concepts of space and time as viewed by Newton, and as modified by Einstein. These concepts enable us to study motion by using the derived concepts of velocity and acceleration. This study is usually given the name of kinematics. Only after one has quantified motion is it possible to study dynamics, that is, the detailed laws of motion. In classical physics these laws are summarized in Newton's laws of motion. While Newton stated that both space and time are absolute, in fact his laws of motion do **not** determine an absolute space (as Newton was well aware). In terms of our familiar observers *A* and *B*, both *A* and *B* have the *same* set of Newtonian laws of motion, if we use classical kinematics. Stated more formally, Newton's laws of motion are invariant under the Galilean transformation.

The concept of the invariance of physical laws under certain types of transformation is of great importance in physics, and has often led to new developments in the forefront of physics. We often postulate invariance principles as primary, even though they are obtained originally from observations of the real world; and then we go on to use these principles to restrict the possible laws of physics.*

In the present chapter, we first state the Relativity Principle in a form applicable both to classical and relativistic physics, and briefly discuss how Newton's classical laws of motion satisfy this principle. We then restate the First Relativity Postulate of Einstein. With this as our basis, we study the principle of conservation of (linear) momentum in relativity physics. We will discover that to preserve the principle we are forced to redefine mass. By considering a special experiment as seen by two different observers, we obtain the relativistic definitions of momentum and mass.

5.1   THE RELATIVITY PRINCIPLE

While Newton states that both space and time are absolute, classical mechanics as developed by Newton does not contain any real reference to absolute space. An assumption that has to be made before one can develop a scientific view of the world is that space is homogeneous and isotropic. In other words, an experiment performed in New York must lead to the same results as the identical experiment in California, *once* one has allowed for various external effects, such as the difference in the acceleration due to gravity *g* at the two places. We are able to explain this difference in itself not as an effect of the nonuniformity of empty space, but as due to *physical* causes well understood on the basis of homogeneous *empty* space.

Even more important, science cannot proceed *at all* until we believe in the uniformity of time; that is, we *must* assume that the same experiment repeated on two occasions will lead to the same results, *once* one has allowed for all other *changed* influences.†

Hence the most basic invariance principle of physics is:

The laws of physics are independent of absolute position or absolute time, but can only depend on relative positions or relative times.   (I)

---

*Of course, subsequent experiments can then prove that the assumed invariance principle is not obeyed by nature. An example is the overthrow of parity in the weak interactions. Cf. P. Morrison, "The Overthrow of Parity," *Scientific American*, April 1957, Scientific American Reprint No. 231 (San Francisco: W. H. Freeman and Co.).

†The early Greeks did not understand this principle of removing "extraneous" variation. They believed the variations were in the nature of things, and "explained" them by the arbitrariness of the Gods. Hence they never pursued physics as an *experimental* but logical science (with the possible exception of the Pythagorean school).

Stated more formally, the laws of physics are invariant under a change of the spatial origin, or under a change of the temporal origin. Here, of course, the origin is associated with the frame of reference set up by the observer, so that what is really being said is that different observers in different locations and at different times see the same laws of physics.*

Another invariance principle with very powerful consequences is the invariance of physical laws under a change of the direction of the axes of the observer. With this example we can demonstrate two complementary points of view, the "passive" and the "active," which apply to all invariance principles. In the passive view, we imagine one experiment viewed by two different observers (who in our example have made two different choices of axes). Each of them apparently sees a different experiment, and each finds that the experiment he observes proceeds in a way that agrees with all the laws of physics, In the active view, we consider *one* observer with two *actually* different experiments, so arranged that to this *one* observer they look exactly like the two views in the passive case seen by the two observers of the *one* experiment. We then postulate that both these experiments proceed in identical ways, according to the same laws of physics. Whenever one discusses an invariance principle one implies the validity of both the passive and the active views.

We stress that such invariance principles must in general be postulated, and then tested by comparison with experiment, the test being primarily a search to root out all the inessential, extraneous, apparently invariance-violating effects.

After this preamble, we now simply state the Relativity Principle:

> **First Relativity Postulate: The basic laws of physics are identical to two observers who have a constant relative velocity w.r.t. each other.** (R1)

In this general form, the relativity principle applies both to classical and relativity physics. Only when (in the passive viewpoint) we ask how the observations of the two observers are related, must we distinguish the two cases. Calling the two observers A and B, do we relate their two space-time descriptions of the same experiment by means of the Galilean or the Lorentz transformation? Of course, we now know that the latter is the correct transformation to use. However, for pedagogical reasons, we consider the relationship between "Galilean invariance" and Newton's laws of motion in the next section.

*Of course, this principle does not necessarily apply over cosmological distances or times. These are questions for cosmology, and hopefully ultimately for experiment.

5.2 NEWTON'S LAWS AND GALILEAN INVARIANCE

Newton's laws of dynamics are:

I: A body which has no net external forces acting upon it remains in a state of rest or uniform motion forever. Symbolically,

$$\mathbf{F} = 0 \Rightarrow \mathbf{a} = 0: \quad N_I$$

II: The effect of a net external force $\mathbf{F}$ acting on a·body of mass m is to produce an acceleration given by

$$\mathbf{F} = m\mathbf{a}: \quad N_{II}$$

III: Whenever two bodies interact, the force $\mathbf{F}_{1 \to 2}$ on the second body exerted by the first body is equal and opposite to the force $\mathbf{F}_{2 \to 1}$ on the first body due to the second; that is,

$\mathbf{F}_{1 \to 2} = -\mathbf{F}_{2 \to 1}$; action and reaction are equal and opposite: N_{III}.

These "laws" are very powerful, and contain a great deal of physics; and yet logically they are very ill-defined. We do not intend to go into this problem here, nor into the various attempts at reformulation. Here we simply point out that Newton's laws apply only in inertial frames of reference. A (somewhat circular) definition of an inertial frame is a frame in which Newton's laws do hold, with no necessity to introduce fictitious forces; that is, all the forces introduced into $\mathbf{F} = m\mathbf{a}$ correspond to *real* interactions, e.g., electrical and gravitational.* (As an example of "fictitious" forces, we mention the Coriolis force introduced to compensate for the rotation of the earth, which "explains" the anticlockwise sense of rotation of cyclones and bath water in the Northern hemisphere.)†

A most important property of inertial frames is that any frame of reference moving with constant velocity w.r.t. an inertial frame is also an inertial frame. We have already seen [Eq. (2.5)] that under a Galilean transformation the acceleration $\mathbf{a}$ is an invariant; that is, it remains unchanged under the transformation. Thus if observer A writes $\mathbf{F} = m\mathbf{a}$, observer B writes $\mathbf{F}' = m\mathbf{a}'$; but $\mathbf{a}' = \mathbf{a}$, therefore $\mathbf{F}' = \mathbf{F}$. (Notice also that we have assumed that mass is invariant.) We hence have shown that *if* the classical relativity postulate is true, the force exerted on one body by another must be independent of the motion of the two

*But see Chapter 8.
†On this subject, see the film already recommended in the footnote on p. 11.

bodies relative to the observer, but can depend only on their relative position and motion.*

Newtonian mechanics does obey the requirement that forces are invariant under a Galilean transformation. On the other hand, electromagnetic forces are governed by Maxwell's equations, and these are *not* invariant under the Galilean transformation. (Rather they are invariant under the Lorentz transformation, provided one transforms the electric and magnetic fields suitably.) In fact it is this lack of invariance under the Galilean transformation which apparently implies the existence of an absolute electromagnetic frame defined by the ether.†

5.3   CONSERVATION OF MOMENTUM AND THE LORENTZ TRANSFORMATION

One of the more basic deductions from Newton's laws of motion is the principle of the conservation of (linear) momentum. In fact, it is so basic that many people prefer to use this principle as the starting point, and define mass and then force operationally as deductions from it. Whatever one's predilection here, this law is one of the cornerstones of classical physics. Stated briefly, it is:

> LAW OF CONSERVATION OF MOMENTUM: The total momentum of any system remains constant throughout time, provided only that no net external force acts on the system.

All we now have to do to give this principle some substance is to define momentum. In Newtonian physics, the momentum $\mathbf{p}$ of a mass m having a velocity $\mathbf{v}$ is given by $\mathbf{p} = m\mathbf{v}$; and the momentum of a system of bodies is the vector sum of the momenta of its parts. We now ask: is the law of conservation of momentum compatible with the First Relativity Postulate (that is, the *Newtonian* definition $\mathbf{p} = m\mathbf{v}$ and the classical Galilean invariance)? The answer, of course, is "yes," but let us prove this.

*That is, if the force between the earth and the apple in the tree is mg, it has this value to all observers. This does not in any way imply that the force between an apple and the earth is still mg when the apple is moving at $0.9c$ w.r.t. the earth. Only a specific theory such as Einstein's General Theory of Relativity can answer this question (cf. Chapter 8).

†This absolute electromagnetic frame of reference was looked for, and *not* found, in a very famous experiment performed by F. T. Trouton and H. R. Noble [*Phil. Trans.*, **A202**, 165 (1903)]. This is described in Appendix C, p. 216.

Consider a set of N particles with initial masses m_i and initial velocities $\mathbf{u}_i$ $(i = 1, 2, \ldots, N)$. Suppose after some time the particles have recombined into $\tilde{N}$ particles with masses $\tilde{m}_j$ and velocities $\tilde{\mathbf{u}}_j$ $(j = 1, 2, \ldots, \tilde{N})$. And suppose no external forces have acted. Then the principle of conservation of momentum says

$$\sum_{i=1}^{N} m_i \mathbf{u}_i = \sum_{j=1}^{\tilde{N}} \tilde{m}_j \tilde{\mathbf{u}}_j. \tag{5.1}$$

To an observer moving with velocity $\mathbf{V}$, the initial velocities are given by $\mathbf{u}_i' = \mathbf{u}_i - \mathbf{V}$, and the final velocities are given by $\tilde{\mathbf{u}}_j' = \tilde{\mathbf{u}}_j - \mathbf{V}$. We ask

$$\sum_{i=1}^{N} m_i \mathbf{u}_i' \stackrel{?}{=} \sum_{j=1}^{\tilde{N}} \tilde{m}_j \tilde{\mathbf{u}}_j'. \tag{5.2}$$

But from (5.1) we have that

$$\sum_{i}^{N} m_i (\mathbf{u}_i' + \mathbf{V}) = \sum_{j}^{\tilde{N}} \tilde{m}_j (\tilde{\mathbf{u}}_j' + \mathbf{V}). \tag{5.3}$$

Further, in Newtonian mechanics, mass is absolutely conserved in all systems; that is,

$$\sum_{i}^{N} m_i = \sum_{j}^{\tilde{N}} \tilde{m}_j. \tag{5.4}$$

By using (5.4) in (5.3) we immediately prove (5.2). That is, **the law of conservation of (Newtonian) momentum is invariant under the Galilean transformation,** *if* **we also assume the absolute conservation of mass.**

It is nearly self-evident that the same law of conservation of (Newtonian) momentum cannot then be invariant under the Lorentz transformation, since velocities now do not add in a direct manner. We demonstrate this by a simple example, shown in Fig. 5.1. Observer C sees two identical balls each of mass m coming together with equal and opposite velocities $\mathbf{u}$ and $-\mathbf{u}$. They collide and stick together, remaining at rest. Momentum is clearly conserved. Observer D "flies over" the same experiment with a velocity $-\mathbf{u}$, so that any velocity as seen by D is the "sum" of the velocity of the object as seen by C, "added" to $+\mathbf{u}$. Using Eq. (4.8), we readily obtain the various velocities as seen by D. These are shown in the figure. According to D, the total momentum before $= 2m\mathbf{u}[1 + (u^2/c^2)]^{-1}$, while the total momentum after $= 2m\mathbf{u}$. Momentum has been created!

What can we do to save the situation? (For if we believe that absolute motion is undetectable, save it we must, as otherwise that

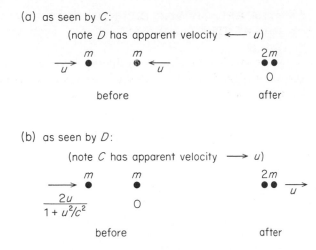

Fig. 5.1 A simple collision experiment which shows that conservation of Newtonian momentum is not invariant under the Lorentz transformation.

frame in which momentum is conserved is *the* absolute frame.) Since we are pragmatic empirical physicists, we have a *choice* of overthrowing one of our two postulates, or of redefining certain concepts in such a way that all remains well. Naturally whatever we do must agree with experiment. As physicists, we consider conservation laws as much too valuable to give up lightly. Rather the history of physics has always been one in which we look for new forms of the quantities involved such that the conservation law remains valid. The most famous example is the "invention" of a new particle, the neutrino, by W. Pauli and E. Fermi, to save simultaneously the three conservation laws of energy, momentum, and angular momentum.* A lighthearted analogy is given by Feynman in Chapter 4 of *The Feynman Lectures on Physics*.†

In the present case we look for some modification of the definition of momentum which agrees with the previous definition at nonrelativistic velocities (for notice that the discrepancy was of order u^2/c^2), and which preserves the invariance of the law of conservation of momentum under the Lorentz transformation. Our derivation of the new form is given in the next section, and proceeds by studying the same (carefully chosen) experiment as seen by two different observers.

*See the article by P. Morrison "The Neutrino," *Scientific American,* January 1956; Scientific American Reprint No. 231 (San Francisco: W.H. Freeman and Co.). The neutrino has been found experimentally, two decades after its "invention."

†R.P. Feynman, R.B. Leighton, and M. Sands, *The Feynman Lectures on Physics* (Reading, Mass.: Addison-Wesley Publishing Co., 1963).

**5.4 THE RELATIVISTIC DEFINITION OF
MOMENTUM AND MASS**

We consider an elastic collision between two identical particles,
shown in Fig. 5.2. Two views of the *same* experiment are given, as seen
by two observers C and D. Let us first consider the experiment as seen

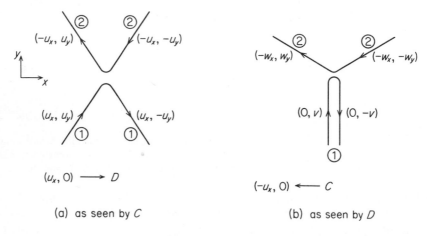

(a) as seen by C (b) as seen by D

Fig. 5.2 Two views of an elastic collision used in
obtaining the relativistic expression for momentum.

by C [Fig. 5.2(a)]. The identical particles come in with equal and
opposite velocities along some straight line, so that the total momentum
is zero. They collide, and then separate with equal and opposite new
velocities along some other straight line, with again zero total momentum. So far we have not had to use any specific definition of momentum other than that it is a *vector* directed along the line of
motion, whose magnitude for these *identical particles* is a monotonic
function only of their speed. If we assume that energy is also a monotonic function of speed for these identical particles, and if energy is
conserved, it follows that all four speeds in the problem are equal, as
seen by C. Let C choose his x and y axes so that the incoming and
outgoing directions of the particles are symmetrically arranged w.r.t.
these axes. We can then describe the complete experiment as seen by
C by the velocity components given in Fig. 5.2(a). We stress that in
this view we insisted that energy and momentum be conserved, but
made no other *specific* assumptions; so that the experiment as seen by
C is certainly a possible *real* experiment. We assume that it is also
general, so that all values of u_x and u_y are possible.

We now look at the *same* experiment from the point of view of an observer D who "flies" over C's experiment with a velocity $(u_x, 0)$, and sees the experiment as shown in Fig. 5.2(b), in which the various velocity components according to D are given. The symmetry of Fig. 5.2(b) arises since there is no real distinction between the $+y$ and $-y$ directions. But since we know the relative velocity of C and D, we can determine v, w_x, and w_y explicitly by use of the results of Section 4.3, in particular Eq. (4.7). For if we let the unprimed coordinates refer to C's view, and the primed coordinates to D's view, and take $V = u_x$, the identification is complete. Thus we have

$$(0, v)_D \sim (u_x, u_y)_C \sim \left\{ \frac{u_x - u_x}{1 - (u_x^2/c^2)}, \frac{u_y}{\gamma[1 - (u_x^2/c^2)]} \right\}_D$$

$$= (0, \gamma u_y)_D \qquad (5.5)$$

and

$$(-w_x, w_y)_D \sim (-u_x, u_y)_C \sim \left\{ \frac{-2u_x}{1 + (u_x^2/c^2)}, \frac{u_y}{\gamma[1 + (u_x^2/c^2)]} \right\}_D \qquad (5.6)$$

where $\sim$ denotes "corresponds to," and

$$\gamma = (1 - u_x^2/c^2)^{-1/2}. \qquad (5.7)$$

Notice that $v \neq w_y$!

Now let us look at D's experiment and impose the *requirement* that momentum is conserved. We assume that the momentum of a particle can be written as

$$\mathbf{p} = m(u)\mathbf{u} \qquad (5.8)$$

where $\mathbf{u}$ is the velocity of the particle, u the magnitude of $\mathbf{u}$, and $m(u)$ is some function of u. Let $w^2 = w_x^2 + w_y^2$, where w is the speed of particle 2. Then if momentum is to be conserved in the y direction according to D, we must require that

$$w_y m(w) = v m(v). \qquad (5.9)$$

(Clearly momentum is conserved in the x direction.) Now we make use of (5.5) and (5.6) to rewrite (5.9) as

$$\frac{u_y}{\gamma[1 + (u_x^2/c^2)]} m(w) = \gamma u_y m(\gamma u_y)$$

or

$$m(w) = \frac{1 + (u_x^2/c^2)}{1 - (u_x^2/c^2)} m(\gamma u_y). \qquad (5.10)$$

Notice that the u_y have canceled. We hence can *now* take the limit $u_y \to 0$, keeping u_x finite. In that case

$$\gamma u_y \to 0, \qquad w \to \frac{2u_x}{1 + (u_x^2/c^2)}.$$

Hence

$$u_x = \frac{c - \sqrt{c^2 - w^2}}{w/c}, \qquad u_x^2 = \frac{2c(c - \sqrt{c^2 - w^2}) - w^2}{w^2/c^2}$$

and

$$\frac{1 + (u_x^2/c^2)}{1 - (u_x^2/c^2)} = \frac{2c(c - \sqrt{c^2 - w^2})}{2w^2 - 2c(c - \sqrt{c^2 - w^2})} = \frac{1}{\sqrt{1 - (w^2/c^2)}}. \quad (5.11)$$

Substituting (5.11) into (5.10) in this limit of $u_y \to 0$, we find

$$m(w) = \frac{1}{\sqrt{1 - (w^2/c^2)}} \, m(0)$$

or

$$\boxed{m = \gamma m_o, \qquad \gamma = \left(1 - \frac{v^2}{c^2}\right)^{-1/2}} \qquad (5.12)$$

where we have set $m(0) = m_o$, the **rest mass** of the particle, and m is the (effective) mass of the particle when its speed is v. This effective mass is the correct mass to use in the definition of momentum; that is,

$$\boxed{\textbf{MOMENTUM} \equiv \mathbf{p} = m\mathbf{v} = \gamma m_o \mathbf{v}.} \qquad (5.13)$$

In Fig. 5.3 we show the variation of m with v. For $v > c$, m becomes imaginary! — still another indication that no particle can travel faster than the speed of light. (We discuss this further in the next chapter.) We observe that the variation of m with v is negligible for nonrelativistic v, is still less than $\frac{1}{2}$ per cent for $v = 0.1c$, and that $m/m_o = 2$ at $v \approx 0.87c$.

The derivation we have given above for $m(v)$ is admittedly a little cumbersome algebraically at the end.* However, the detailed *algebraic* steps in the derivation are not of great importance (and certainly should not be memorized). Much more important is the realization that we were *forced* to the unique definitions (5.12) and (5.13) in order to make the law of conservation of momentum invariant under the Lorentz transformation. Our derivation is not yet complete, since we should still consider the most general process or collision. For this we must wait till the next chapter.

*Some of the algebra can be avoided by introducing a third observer E who flies over C's experiment with velocity $(-u_x, 0)$; cf. Feynman, *op. cit.* A very clear treatment is given in *Space Time Physics* by E. F. Taylor and J.A. Wheeler (San Francisco: W. H. Freeman and Co., 1966). Einstein's proof made use of electromagnetic theory.

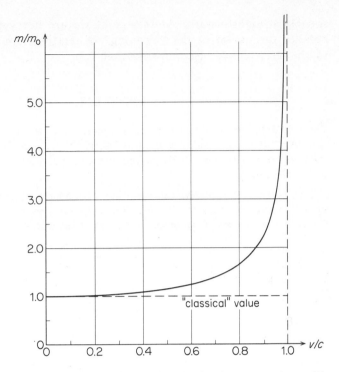

Fig. 5.3 The variation of relativistic mass with speed.

5.5 SUMMARY

In this chapter we first discussed the general concept of an invariance law, and then stated the First Relativity Postulate. This states that the laws of physics are identical to two observers in constant relative motion w.r.t. each other. The classical relationship between two such observers is given by the Galilean transformation, and we briefly considered the invariance of Newton's laws under the Galilean transformation.

A very important principle of classical physics is the law of conservation of momentum. This law is invariant under the Galilean transformation, but *not* under the relativistic Lorentz transformation, if we use the Newtonian definition of momentum. We looked for, and found, a relativistic generalization of the definition of momentum which agrees with the Newtonian definition for small velocities, but has the property of giving a law of conservation of momentum which is invariant under the Lorentz transformation. The "derivation" made use of a specially chosen collision experiment as viewed by two observers; but the conclusion is general, and the relativistic definition of momentum is reasonably straightforward. At this point we are not yet ready to give a detailed discussion of the "meaning" of relativistic mass, but leave this to the next chapter (see also Section 7.3).

PROBLEM

There is only one problem for this chapter, since we have only learned one new fact, although several new ideas. Actually, we must investigate the properties of rest mass more fully before we can consider even a general two body collision.

!5.1 Show that the relativistic definition of momentum given in Eq. (5.13) is such that the collision of Fig. 5.1 does conserve this momentum, both when the collision is viewed by observer C, and when viewed by observer D.

6

FORCE AND
KINETIC ENERGY

In the previous chapter we saw that to preserve the invariance of the law of conservation of momentum under the Lorentz transformation, we had to redefine momentum, so that $\mathbf{p} = m\mathbf{v} = m_0\gamma\mathbf{v}$. In Newtonian mechanics, force is defined by

$$\mathbf{F} = m_0\mathbf{a} = m_0\frac{d\mathbf{v}}{dt} = \frac{d}{dt}(m_0\mathbf{v}) = \frac{d\mathbf{p}}{dt} \qquad \text{(Newtonian).} \qquad (6.1)$$

In Eq. (6.1) we have written m_0 rather than m, but in fact in Newtonian mechanics there is only one mass, and $m\mathbf{a} \equiv d\mathbf{p}/dt$ (for any body which does not break up as the force acts*). Hence all the four forms in (6.1) are equivalent. Since for *relativistic* speeds we now know that $\mathbf{p}$ becomes $m_0\gamma\mathbf{v}$, the various expressions in (6.1) are no longer equivalent, even if we replace m_0 by $m = m_0\gamma$. So which one should we use?

In this chapter we first discuss whether there is a unique "correct" definition of force, and then make one particular choice (really guided by electromagnetic theory). We then go on to consider kinetic energy. We derive the result $E = mc^2$, and discuss both its significance and the validity of our proof!

*For a rocket ship, which ejects mass as it travels, the correct Newtonian equation is $\mathbf{F} = d\mathbf{p}/dt$.

6.1   THE DEFINITION OF FORCE

We have already presented Newton's laws of motion in Section 5.2. Newton's first law tells us when the net force on a body is zero, *without* requiring a full definition of force. This definition of force is apparently provided by Newton's second law, but this law in turn apparently defines force in terms of another new concept, that of mass. Newton's own definition of mass as the amount of matter in a body does not help in the logical problem of *really* defining force.* This certainly does not imply that Newton's laws have no content. In a sense they contain all of classical mechanics, which after all was able to predict the existence of Neptune (see Chapter 1).

For the moment, we restrict ourselves to classical physics. Then the real content of $\mathbf{F} = m\mathbf{a}$ lies in the constancy of the various factors which appear in it, in a given series of experiments. It is possible to state when two forces are equal *without* measuring them; for instance, if each force stretches the same spring by the same amount, they are equal. Furthermore, **if** we *define* mass as an additive quantity, so that two identical blocks have twice the mass of one such block *by definition*, it is then possible to test that, for a given fixed force **F** acting on different masses, the acceleration produced is along **F** and inversely proportional to m. (Notice, however, that our "force meter" has to move with the variously accelerated bodies!)

Once we have tested experimentally that a constant **F** produces a constant $m\mathbf{a}$, it is possible to use $m\mathbf{a}$ as a measure of **F**, so that by definition $\mathbf{F} = m\mathbf{a}$. However, an equally possible choice of definition would be that $\mathbf{F} = m^2 a\mathbf{a}$, where a is the magnitude of the acceleration **a**.† The reason that $\mathbf{F} = m\mathbf{a}$ is preferred over other possible definitions has to do primarily with our local environment, the surface of the earth. A remarkable property of this environment (at least if we remove the air from it!) is that all free bodies accelerate "downwards" with the *same, constant* acceleration g, *independent* of their velocity. *If* we blame this on "the force due to gravity," usually called the weight of a body, and if we *assume* that the weight of two identical blocks is twice the weight of one such block, then we are led to choose $\mathbf{F} = m\mathbf{a}$ rather than $\mathbf{F} = m^2 a\mathbf{a}$. But there is no possible experiment which can

---

*There is another formulation of mechanics, due to E. Mach, which starts by defining mass by using the law of conservation of momentum, the latter being taken as an *empirical* synthesis of experiment. This reformulation avoids the logical problems of Newton's laws, but contains only the same "useful" physics.

†We must be careful to preserve the "vector = vector" nature of the defining equation.

"prove" that weight is additive, until we know independently how to measure forces.*

The point we are trying to make is that as pragmatic physicists we are entitled to make any definitions we like, provided only that they are compatible with experiment.† Our choice is determined by questions of utility or convenience. It is convenient to have as many things as possible "constant," since this simplifies our view of the external world. The prime test of any set of definitions, concepts, and laws is only whether they agree with all experiments, help to codify knowledge, and enable us to make correct predictions. If two alternative sets are totally equivalent in all predictions, the physicist tends to prefer that with the fewer number of *ad hoc* "assumptions," or the one which is aesthetically more "pleasing."‡ Of course, if one theory has a wider domain of application than another, it is to be preferred.

On this criterion, when applied to classical physics, Newton's laws of motion are indeed the most satisfactory formulation. It has not been our purpose to cast doubt on these laws in the classical domain; only to make the point that the definition of force is partly a convention. The reason for this preamble is that there is *more than one* useful relativistic definition of force!

Let us therefore now simply give one possible definition of force appropriate to relativistic velocities, which is the *most* common definition adopted, but by no means the only definition that is used.§ (In reading the more advanced literature, great care must be taken to discover which definition is being used.) The definition is

$$\boxed{\mathbf{F} = \frac{d\mathbf{p}}{dt} = \frac{d}{dt}(m_0 \gamma \mathbf{v}).} \tag{6.2}$$

---

*Neither a "spring balance" nor a "chemical balance" can help us here. Why not? Similarly no possible experiment can tell us whether mass is additive.

†We might even have started with another definition of acceleration, if "g" had not been constant; for example, $v(dv/dt)$ or even $\mathbf{v}(dv/ds)$.

‡The Nobel laureate P. A. M. Dirac has even gone so far as to state "that it is more important to have beauty in one's equations than to have them agree with experiment." Part of Dirac's meaning is that later experiments may show the validity of one's equations, as was the case historically with Schrödinger's discovery and rejection of the Klein-Gordon equation, later resuscitated in *another* separate application. See "The Evolution of the Physicist's Picture of Nature," *Scientific American*, May 1963; Scientific American Reprint No. 292 (San Francisco: W. H. Freeman and Co.).

§To the initiated the other definition of which we are thinking is the Minkowski 4-force, discussed further in Appendix A.

It is sometimes useful to write this out in detail. Thus*

$$\mathbf{F} = \frac{d}{dt}\left[m_0 \frac{1}{\sqrt{1 - (v^2/c^2)}}\, \mathbf{v} \right]$$

$$= m_0 \frac{1}{\sqrt{1 - (v^2/c^2)}}\, \mathbf{a} + m_0 \mathbf{v} \frac{d}{dt}\left(1 - \frac{v^2}{c^2}\right)^{-1/2}$$

$$= m_0 \gamma \mathbf{a} + m_0 \mathbf{v} \frac{(\mathbf{a} \cdot \mathbf{v})/c^2}{[1 - (v^2/c^2)]^{3/2}}$$

$$= m\mathbf{a} + \frac{m\mathbf{v}\gamma^2(\mathbf{a} \cdot \mathbf{v})}{c^2}. \tag{6.3}$$

Notice that **a** need not even be directed along **F**, nor *vice versa*!

6.2   THE TRANSFORMATION PROPERTIES
OF FORCE

Before discussing the further implications of this definition, we consider the question of how the "same" force looks to different observers. In Eq. (6.2) the force **F** is the force as "seen," "defined," or "measured" by an observer. This force is acting on a body traveling with velocity **v**, and v can well be comparable with c. This force **F** must ultimately be due to another body, which can itself have a velocity which is either nonrelativistic or comparable with c. Since "absolute motion" is meaningless, the actual force exerted between the two bodies can depend only on their relative velocity and orientation.†

Let us first therefore consider the case when the relative velocity is nonrelativistic. An observer to whom each of the bodies has a nonrelativistic velocity can then observe their motions and deduce the law of force between them; or if he is given the law of force for this case, he can apply Newton's (prerelativity) laws and deduce the motion. Consider another observer "flying" over the experiment at a relativistic velocity. By using the Lorentz transformation and its *kinematic* consequences, we can determine the *motion* which would be seen by this

---

*This requires calculus, and in particular differentiation of the scalar product of two vectors. Quite generally $d(\mathbf{p} \cdot \mathbf{q}) = (d\mathbf{p}) \cdot \mathbf{q} + \mathbf{p} \cdot (d\mathbf{q})$, which can be proved by writing out the full form $p_x q_x + p_y q_y + p_z q_z$. For our case

$$\frac{d}{dt}(v^2) = \frac{d}{dt}(\mathbf{v} \cdot \mathbf{v}) = 2\mathbf{v} \cdot \frac{d\mathbf{v}}{dt} = 2\mathbf{v} \cdot \mathbf{a}.$$

†This is true even in the case of electromagnetic forces. However, since the electromagnetic interaction propagates with a finite speed, that of light, one usually formulates this as a field theory, rather than as a "retarded" action-at-a-distance theory. In Einstein's General Theory of Relativity, even gravitation is converted from an action-at-a-distance theory to a field theory.

observer. By putting this motion into the right-hand side of Eq. (6.2) we can then *deduce* the force which is acting between the two bodies as determined by the second observer. Hence, by using the active view of the First Relativity Postulate, we have determined the law of force between the two bodies when they are both moving with speeds comparable to c, but with a *nonrelativistic* relative velocity.

Example 6.1. "The force due to gravity." Consider the earth and an apple, at the instant that the apple breaks off from the tree. In a frame of reference fixed to the earth, with the z direction corresponding to "up," the apple has instantaneous velocity components $(0, 0, 0)$ and acceleration $(0, 0, -g)$. Consider an observer moving along the x direction (that is, along a line perpendicular to that joining the earth and the apple). Let the observer have a velocity $(V, 0, 0)$, with V comparable to c. What force does this observer see?

Answer 6.1. We apply our *kinematic* relations of Chapter 4 and obtain the instantaneous velocity $(-V, 0, 0)$ and the instantaneous acceleration $(0, 0, \gamma^{-2} g)$ [cf. Eq. (4.29)]. Making use of (6.3), we immediately obtain that **F** has components $(0, 0, m\gamma^{-2} g) = (0, 0, m_0 \gamma^{-1} g)$.

Comment. Thus to this observer the "weight" of the apple is not $m_0 g$, but $m_0 \gamma^{-1} g$, which is less than $m_0 g$. (We see that this result is closely related to time dilation.) We remark that an observer moving "up" or "down" with the *same* speed V would find *yet another* "weight" for the apple (cf. problem 6.1).

This example shows the power of (the active view of) the Principle of Relativity. Notice, however, that we used the principle to determine the new *kinematics* as seen by the second observer. The new force was then obtained by using the *definition* (6.2); another definition would have led to a "different" force, but the different equation of motion would then again lead to the *same* motion. The motion describes a physical experiment, and so must be unique; but the force is a derived concept, and provided the laws associated with the force lead to the true motion, we are free to define force as we like.

By using our definition of force, we were able to determine the transformation law of the force due to gravity as seen by different observers, for a *non*relativistic velocity between the source of the force (the earth) and the body on which it acts (the apple),* starting from the *"observed"* Newtonian force when *all* velocities are nonrelativistic. However, using only the relativity principle, it is impossible to obtain from this observation the "law of force" between the two bodies when their relative velocity is relativistic. This requires a separate *experiment*.

Such experiments have not been carried out for the gravitational force, except when one of the bodies is a beam of light. For two ma-

*In our example the relative velocity was zero, but this was not essential.

terial bodies, it is very hard to conceive such an experiment, since the gravitational force is so much smaller than all other forces. The case when one of the bodies is a beam of light is highly relevant to the general theory of relativity (see Chapter 8). The latter makes a definite *prediction* for that case.

The force which is best understood in this respect is the electro-magnetic force.* Experiments have been performed in which charged particles with relativistic speeds have been deflected by electric and magnetic fields. In these experiments, the fields can previously be *measured* by their effect on particles moving with *non*relativistic speeds. As a result of such experiments, one finds that with our definition of force, the electromagnetic force is *always* given by the nonrelativistic (or classical) expression

$$\mathbf{F} = q(\mathbf{E} + \mathbf{v} \times \mathbf{B}). \tag{6.4}$$

Here q is the charge of the particle, and $\mathbf{v}$ is its velocity, which may be comparable to c. $\mathbf{E}$ and $\mathbf{B}$ are the electric and magnetic fields, *as measured by a nonrelativistic* charged particle. That is, the motion of *all* charged particles is given by

$$q(\mathbf{E} + \mathbf{v} \times \mathbf{B}) = \frac{d}{dt}(m_0 \gamma \mathbf{v}). \tag{6.5}$$

It is the simplicity of this equation which makes our definition of force the most useful one in practical applications. (Such applications in most cases do deal with electromagnetic forces. Nuclear and ele-mentary-particle forces are not so well understood that they influence our choice, and are in any case usually treated by a formalism which uses energy as its basic concept.) For *formal* analysis there is another *different* definition—the Minkowski four-force—which has attractive properties. This is discussed in Section A.6 of Appendix A, p. 124.

In final summary, the definition of force is somewhat arbitrary. In any case one must always study the result of an experiment before one can determine the force, *whatever* definition one adopts. We adopt the definition given in Eq. (6.2), namely

$$\mathbf{F} = \frac{d}{dt}(m_0 \gamma \mathbf{v}) = \frac{d}{dt}(m\mathbf{v}). \tag{6.2}$$

*The reader who has not yet studied electricity and magnetism should neverthe-less read the rest of this section. The (very important) message can be understood without knowing in detail the meaning of $\mathbf{E}$ and $\mathbf{B}$.

This choice is really guided by the properties of the electromagnetic force.* We keep to this definition throughout the rest of the book. With this definition one can immediately obtain the transformation equations for force. However, the algebra is rather involved, and will only be given in Section 6.6 (see also problem 6.2).

6.3 ENERGY IN NEWTONIAN MECHANICS

Having treated force, we should properly next "solve some problems." However, in Newtonian mechanics, problem-solving is made much easier by using the general theorems of conservation of momentum, energy, and angular momentum whenever these are valid, even though they are all consequences of $\mathbf{F} = m\mathbf{a}$. Hence for the rest of this chapter we discuss energy, leaving applications to the next chapter. In the present section we recall the "Newtonian" development of energy (not in fact carried out by Newton).

Consider a force $\mathbf{F}$, which can be a function of position, acting on a particle of mass m. Then if s denotes the position of the particle at any instant (and hence also the point of application of the force), we *define* the work done by the force when it moves the particle along some path from a point P to a point Q (see Fig. 6.1) as the integral

$$W_{P \to Q} = \int_P^Q \mathbf{F} \cdot \mathbf{ds} = \int_P^Q F \, ds \, \cos \theta. \tag{6.6}$$

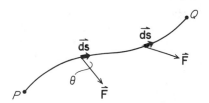

Fig. 6.1 Classical definition of work done by a force.

For certain types of force, which are called conservative forces, this work is independent of the path between P and Q, and depends only on the location of the end points P and Q themselves. In that case we can write

*We recall that the relationship of electromagnetism and mechanics was one of the basic problems at the time of the development of the theory of relativity. Many relationships were in fact first derived by Einstein for the electromagnetic field and then generalized.

$$W_{P \to Q} = -(U_Q - U_P) \tag{6.7}$$

where U is called the potential energy, and depends only on position.*

So far we have only defined certain new concepts. But we can re-express $W_{P \to Q}$ in another way by using Newton's laws. Thus

$$W_{P \to Q} = \int_P^Q \mathbf{F} \cdot d\mathbf{s} = \int_P^Q (m\mathbf{a}) \cdot d\mathbf{s}$$

$$= m \int_P^Q \frac{d\mathbf{v}}{dt} \cdot d\mathbf{s} = m \int_{v_P}^{v_Q} d\mathbf{v} \cdot \frac{d\mathbf{s}}{dt}$$

$$= m \int_{v_P}^{v_Q} \mathbf{v} \cdot d\mathbf{v} = \frac{1}{2} m \int_{v_P}^{v_Q} d(v^2)$$

$$= \frac{1}{2} m v_Q^2 - \frac{1}{2} m v_P^2.$$

Here in $\mathbf{F} = m\mathbf{a}$, $\mathbf{F}$ is the *resultant* force acting on the particle. In general, there may be several forces, $\mathbf{F}_1, \mathbf{F}_2, \ldots$ with $\mathbf{F} = \mathbf{F}_1 + \mathbf{F}_2 + \ldots$. In that case

$$W_{P \to Q} = \int \mathbf{F} \cdot d\mathbf{s} = \int \mathbf{F}_1 \cdot d\mathbf{s} + \int \mathbf{F}_2 \cdot d\mathbf{s} + \cdots$$

$$= W_{1, P \to Q} + W_{2, P \to Q} + \cdots$$

$$= \frac{1}{2} m v_Q^2 - \frac{1}{2} m v_P^2 \quad \text{(Newtonian).} \tag{6.8}$$

Hence the *sum* of the work done by each of the forces acting gives the *change* in the quantity $\frac{1}{2}mv^2$. In the case of conservative forces this change is again *independent* of the path between P and Q. In all cases the work done depends only on the velocity at each of the end points (in fact only on the speed). We *define* the kinetic energy by

$$\text{kinetic energy} \equiv K.E. = \frac{1}{2} m v^2 \quad \text{(Newtonian).} \tag{6.9}$$

Then for the case of conservative forces (such as gravitation or electrostatics, but not for friction) we can combine (6.8), (6.9), and (6.7) to "prove" the law of conservation of energy

$$(K.E. + U)_P = (K.E. + U)_Q$$

or

$$(K.E. + P.E.)_P = (K.E. + P.E.)_Q \tag{6.10}$$

Here U or "*P.E.*" represents the *sum* of the potential energies for each of the forces acting.

*We really also have to specify some other point, at which $U = 0$ by definition.

We do not want to discuss this law in detail, nor the generalization to include the effect of dissipative forces. It is a very powerful relation, of great use in solving actual problems. Here our purpose is to point out that we made an *arbitrary* definition of "work done by a force" which turned out to have useful properties, namely:

(i) It is always equal to the change in (Newtonian) kinetic energy $\frac{1}{2}mv^2$ of the particle on which the force acts, and this kinetic energy is a function only of the present speed of the particle, and *not* of the past motion.

(ii) In many cases it is also equal to minus the change in the potential energy U, which depends in turn only on the present position of the particle, and not on its past motion.

(iii) For those cases where (ii) is valid, we directly obtain the principle of conservation of energy. By including the work done against dissipative forces, and defining new forms of energy, such as heat, electromagnetic radiation energy density, the neutrino, and so on, this principle has become a universal physical principle of great power.

(iv) It can be proved that the classical law of conservation of energy is compatible with the classical relativity principle; that is, Eq. (6.10) is *invariant* under the Galilean transformation.

In summary, the definition of "work" is again arbitrary, but our choice should be governed by questions of usefulness. In the next section we consider the relativistic generalization of kinetic energy.

6.4   THE RELATIVISTIC DEFINITION OF ENERGY

Before we make a new definition of kinetic energy, we should ask whether the Newtonian form $\frac{1}{2}mv^2$ is still valid, either in the form $\frac{1}{2}m_0 v^2$ or in the form $\frac{1}{2}mv^2 = \frac{1}{2}m_0\gamma v^2$. To show that this is not the case, we consider whether such a definition is compatible with the basic requirement that the law of conservation of energy be invariant under a Lorentz transformation.

We apply the standard technique of looking at the same experiment from the viewpoint of two different observers. We consider two identical particles each with rest mass m_0. In Fig. 6.2(a) we show a collision as seen by an observer C, in which both momentum and energy are clearly conserved, *however* they are defined. (We look at the experiment at times sufficiently long before and after the collision so that there is no potential energy involved.)

In Fig. 6.2(b) we show the same experiment as seen by an observer

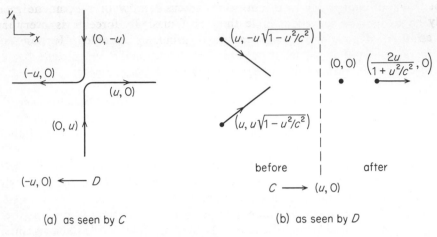

(a) as seen by C (b) as seen by D

Fig. 6.2 Two views of an elastic collision used in discussing the relativistic expression for kinetic energy.

D who is moving with constant velocity $(-u, 0)$ w.r.t. C. Applying Eq. (4.7) with $V = -u$ to obtain D's version of the velocity components, we obtain the components shown in Fig. 6.2(b). The incoming speed of each of the particles is readily seen to be $u\sqrt{2 - (u^2/c^2)}$. Let us assume that the kinetic energy T of each particle when it has a speed v is given by some *function* $T(v)$. Then we need

$$2T\left(u\sqrt{2 - \frac{u^2}{c^2}}\right) = T(0) + T\left[\frac{2u}{1 + (u^2/c^2)}\right]. \tag{6.11}$$

It is straightforward to prove that neither

$$T(v) = \frac{1}{2}m_0 v^2 \quad \text{nor} \quad T(v) = \frac{m_0 v^2}{2\sqrt{1 - (v^2/c^2)}}$$

satisfies Eq. (6.11) (cf. problem 6.3).

It is possible to analyze Eq. (6.11) by using functional analysis, and determine what function of v will satisfy it, but this is rather involved. Instead we show that the Newtonian definition of work $= \int \mathbf{F} \cdot d\mathbf{s}$, when modified by means of the relativistic expression for $\mathbf{F}$, in fact leads to an expression for kinetic energy which has all the required properties. (The derivation of the next equation requires calculus, but may be accepted on trust by those who cannot follow the computational details, and who can go on to its last line and the following paragraph.)

$$W_{P \to Q} = \int_P^Q \mathbf{F} \cdot d\mathbf{s} = \int_P^Q \left\{ \frac{d}{dt} \left[\frac{m_0 \mathbf{v}}{\sqrt{1 - (v^2/c^2)}} \right] \right\} \cdot d\mathbf{s} = \int_P^Q \left\{ \frac{d}{dt} \left[\frac{m_0 \mathbf{v}}{\sqrt{1 - (v^2/c^2)}} \right] \right\} \mathbf{v} \, dt$$

$$= \int_P^Q \left\{ d \left[\frac{m_0 \mathbf{v}}{\sqrt{1 - (v^2/c^2)}} \right] \right\} \cdot \mathbf{v} = \int_P^Q \mathbf{v} \cdot d \left[\frac{m_0 \mathbf{v}}{\sqrt{1 - (v^2/c^2)}} \right]$$

$$= \mathbf{v} \cdot \left[\frac{m_0 \mathbf{v}}{\sqrt{1 - (v^2/c^2)}} \right]_P^Q - \int_P^Q d\mathbf{v} \cdot \frac{m_0 \mathbf{v}}{\sqrt{1 - (v^2/c^2)}}$$

$$= \frac{m_0 v^2}{\sqrt{1 - (v^2/c^2)}} \bigg|_P^Q - m_0 c^2 \sqrt{1 - \frac{v^2}{c^2}} \bigg|_P^Q = \frac{m_0 c^2}{\sqrt{1 - (v^2/c^2)}} \bigg|_P^Q$$

$$= mc^2 \bigg|_P^Q . \tag{6.12}$$

(In the sixth step we made use of the general result $\int x \, dy = xy - \int y \, dx$.)

By analogy with (6.8) and (6.9), it follows that $W_{P \to Q}$ should equal the change in kinetic energy produced by the force. Notice that the expression for $W_{P \to Q}$ in (6.12) is again a function only of the speeds at P and Q. In particular, if $v_P = 0$ and $v_Q = v$, then $W_{P \to Q}$ should equal the kinetic energy $T(v)$. Thus

$$T(v) = mc^2 \bigg|_{v_P = 0}^{v_Q = v} = \frac{m_0 c^2}{\sqrt{1 - (v^2/c^2)}} - m_0 c^2. \tag{6.13}$$

This seems very different from the Newtonian result $\frac{1}{2} m v^2$, but for $v \ll c$, they agree exactly, as of course they must. For if we use the binomial theorem* in (6.13), we obtain

$$T(v) = m_0 c^2 \left[\left(1 - \frac{v^2}{c^2} \right)^{-1/2} - 1 \right]$$

$$= m_0 c^2 \left[\left(1 - \frac{1}{2} \frac{v^2}{c^2} + \frac{3}{8} \frac{v^4}{c^4} + \cdots \right) - 1 \right]$$

$$= \frac{1}{2} m_0 v^2 + 0 \left(\frac{v^4}{c^4} \right). \tag{6.14}$$

Next we ask whether the form (6.13) satisfies the condition in Eq. (6.11). It is left as problem 6.4 to prove that it does. **Hence we can define the work done by a force by Eq. (6.12), and the kinetic energy by Eq. (6.13).**

Let us look more closely at the expression mc^2. For a particle at rest this has the value $m_0 c^2$, which has the units of energy. Let us call

*That is:

$$(1 + x)^a \approx 1 + ax + \frac{1}{2} a(a - 1)x^2 + \cdots \quad \text{for } |x| < 1.$$

this the rest energy of the particle. Then $mc^2 = m_0 c^2 + T$ where T is the kinetic energy of the particle. As long as the total *rest* mass of the particles in a collision remains constant, it makes no difference whether we use the kinetic energy T or the total energy mc^2 in stating the law of conservation of energy.

But the total rest mass in a collision need not be conserved! We prove this most remarkable fact by considering yet another experiment from two points of view. This time we consider an inelastic collision in which two identical particles of *rest* mass m_0 come together and form one particle of rest mass M_0. We show one view of this experiment as seen by an observer C in Fig. 6.3(a), where the velocity com-

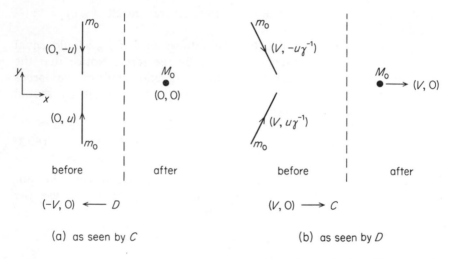

Fig. 6.3 Two views of an inelastic collision, used in discussing the creation of rest mass.

ponents before and after the collision are given. Consider the same experiment as seen by another observer D who has velocity $(-V, 0)$ w.r.t. C. We apply Eq. (4.10) with C corresponding to the primed coordinates and D to the unprimed coordinates. Then D's view of the experiment is as given in Fig. 6.3(b), where $\gamma = [1 - (V^2/c^2)]^{-1/2}$.

Let us first consider C's view. Momentum is clearly conserved, but since the collision is inelastic we do not make any assumption about the energy balance. Is momentum conserved according to D? This requires

$$2mV = M_0\gamma V, \quad \text{that is,} \quad 2m = M_0\gamma \qquad (6.15)$$

where m is the relativistic mass of each of the incident particles according to D. The speed, w, of each of these particles is given by

$$w^2 = V^2 + u^2\left(1 - \frac{V^2}{c^2}\right).$$

We note for future use that this implies that

$$1 - \frac{w^2}{c^2} = \left(1 - \frac{u^2}{c^2}\right)\left(1 - \frac{V^2}{c^2}\right). \tag{6.16}$$

Now Eq. (6.15) states that

$$\frac{2m_0}{\sqrt{1 - (w^2/c^2)}} = \frac{M_0}{\sqrt{1 - (V^2/c^2)}}.$$

But, using (6.16), this implies that

$$M_0 = \frac{2m_0}{\sqrt{1 - (u^2/c^2)}} > 2m_0. \tag{6.17}$$

Thus the *rest* mass M_0 of the final composite particle is apparently greater than the sum of the rest masses of the two incoming particles. Equivalently, this shows that

$$M_0 c^2 = \frac{2m_0 c^2}{\sqrt{1 - (u^2/c^2)}}, \tag{6.17'}$$

which says that, *according to C*, the final total energy of the stationary mass M_0 is equal to the sum of the *total* incident energies, including the incident *kinetic* energy. Thus rest mass is apparently created (i.e., $M_0 > 2m_0$), yet total energy is conserved ($Mc^2 = 2mc^2$).

Now we "know" that in such an inelastic collision, what happens is that the initial kinetic energy T becomes converted into heat energy H, with $H = T$. That is,

$$H = T = 2mc^2 - 2m_0 c^2 = 2m_0\left[\left(1 - \frac{u^2}{c^2}\right)^{-1/2} - 1\right]$$

$$= M_0 c^2 - 2m_0 c^2.$$

Thus

$$\frac{H}{c^2} = M_0 - 2m_0 = \text{"created rest mass"} = \delta m_0.$$

What this implies is that one must associate a "created" rest mass $\delta m_0 = H/c^2$ with the energy H. As long as we simply use this in the energy-balance equation, it is purely a notational shorthand. However, by the appearance of $M_0 = 2m_0 + \delta m_0$ in the *momentum*-balance equation (6.15), we are truly saying that this (rest) mass δm_0 is completely equivalent to an ordinary mass. Thus when the original heat energy $H = \delta m_0 c^2$ is moving with speed V, it carries a momentum given by $\delta p = \delta m_0 \gamma V$, just as if δm_0 were an "ordinary" rest mass.

This result is very remarkable, and Einstein himself considered it to be the most significant contribution of the theory of relativity. **In** summary: Energy and mass are convertible, according to the formula $E = mc^2$. Any form of energy, be it heat, chemical, or kinetic, has a mass associated with it of magnitude m, where $m = E/c^2$. The rest mass m_0 of a particle is to be associated with a rest energy $m_0 c^2$, so that the total energy E to be associated with a particle of rest mass m_0 and speed V is given by

$$E = mc^2 = m_0 \gamma c^2 = \frac{m_0 c^2}{\sqrt{1 - (V^2/c^2)}}.$$

(6.18)

Similarly any form of "pure" energy Q—for example, thermal or chemical energy—is to have a mass associated with it according to $Q = m_0 c^2$, or $m_0 \gamma c^2$ depending on whether the energy Q is at rest, or has a velocity V. If it is moving, it must also have a momentum $\mathbf{p} = m\mathbf{V} = m_0 \gamma \mathbf{V}$ associated with it, exactly as if $m_0 = Q/c^2$ were an ordinary mass. Similarly, therefore, this mass also has inertia, or resistance to acceleration, given by

$$\mathbf{F} = \frac{d}{dt}(m_0 \gamma \mathbf{V}).$$

In fact, this mass m_0 is even acted upon by a gravitational field, exactly as if it were an ordinary mass. Thus, for instance, two pendulums, one made of uranium, and one made of lead, would each have the same period if they had the same physical dimensions. Yet if the uranium were to fission into ultimately stable matter, the final products would have less rest mass than the original uranium. Thus some of the rest mass of the uranium is effectively the mass associated with the energy released in the fission (cf. Example 6.3 below). Yet the "mass" of uranium behaves just like the "mass" of any substance, and uranium has the usual constant acceleration g due to gravity.

The true reality of this mass is made most apparent in certain nuclear-physics and elementary-particle experiments. In such experiments it is actually possible to convert incident kinetic energy into true rest mass, as demonstrated by the production of particles which were not present in the initial state. For example, one can perform the experiment

$$p + p + \text{energy} \rightarrow p + p + \pi^\circ$$

in which a real physical pion (π°) is produced in the collision of two protons. This is discussed further in Chapter 7.

Of course, we have not really yet *proved* most of the above statements. [In fact we have not even proved that the law of conservation of (relativistic) energy is invariant under the Lorentz transformation. We do this in the next section.] Einstein's original proof was based on electromagnetic theory, and used the (classically well-known) facts that an electromagnetic wave carries energy and momentum, the energy density $\mathscr{E}$ and the momentum density $\mathscr{P}$ being related by $\mathscr{E} = \mathscr{P}c$. If we accept this fact, we can readily demonstrate that mass must be associated with energy, following a proof which Einstein himself gave.*

Consider a railway coach initially at rest on a frictionless track, as shown in Fig. 6.4. At each end of the coach there is an *identical* apparatus which consists of a rechargeable storage battery, a transmitter of electromagnetic waves, and a receiver. Each of these is assumed to be "lossless." Each complete set of apparatus is mounted on a panel which in turn is on frictionless bearings, so that, *if* the two "setups" are of equal mass, it is possible to interchange them without doing any *net* work (this will require some ancillary ideal equipment, but its nature is not important).

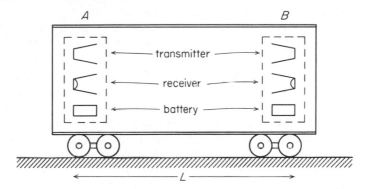

Fig. 6.4 Einstein's thought experiment, used to prove that energy has inertia.

We start with the battery at end A charged, and containing energy E, and with the other battery at end B uncharged. (But each battery has the same amount of each chemical element in it, the only difference being the way they are combined. We must include any gas in the battery system.) At end A, this energy is sent off as a sharp pulse of electromagnetic radiation towards B, carryingenergy E and momentum $P = E/c$. Since the wave has momentum P to the right, the railway coach must have momentum P to the left. Let the mass of the coach-plus-setups be M, and let the distance between the setups be L. Then the coach must have a speed $V = P/M$ to the left (where for simplicity we assume $P \ll Mc$, so that the coach is nonrelativistic). Allowing for the speed V of the coach, it takes a time $T = L/(c - V)$ for the radiation to reach the setup at B, where it is absorbed, and the energy used to charge the battery presently at the end B. At the same instant that the energy E is absorbed, so is the momentum P,

Ann. Physik, **20**, 627 (1906). This proof, however, is not his original one.

and the coach stops, *having traveled a distance $D = VT$ to the left*. Now if we assume that the masses of the two setups are still equal, we can interchange them doing no net work, and leaving the center of mass of the entire system where it already is. We are now back in the starting configuration, but with the coach having been moved D to the left. We can repeat this procedure endlessly, and apparently move the center of mass to the left *in steps* as far as we like, at no time ever exerting any external force.

But one of the more important principles of Newtonian physics (still true in relativistic mechanics) is that when there is no net external force on a system, its center of mass must *permanently* remain at rest if it is originally at rest. Hence it *must* follow that while the coach of mass M is moving to the left at speed V, the radiation traveling to the right at a speed c must be carrying mass m with it, such that $mc = MV$. (This equation looks like conservation of momentum, but really it is simply the requirement that the center of mass of M and m be at rest.) Using $MV = P = E/c$, we immediately obtain $m = E/c^2$. That is, **the radiation energy E transmitted has a mass m associated with it given by $E = mc^2$.** Further, this mass must afterwards reside in the *chemical energy* of the charged battery, when the battery has energy E. Then when we interchange the "setups" we *also* transfer this "chemical" mass m from the end B to the end A. In doing so we must necessarily give an impulse to the coach to the *right*, so that when the mass m in the battery has arrived back at the end A, the coach will again be back in its original position!*

It is a small step from chemical energy, to heat energy, and then to all forms of energy. The big step logically is that from electromagnetic energy to chemical energy. Einstein's final statement is that $E = mc^2$ refers to *all* forms of energy. In the next section we given some examples.

6.5   APPLICATIONS AND DISCUSSION OF $E = mc^2$.   TRANSFORMATION OF MOMENTUM AND ENERGY

Before discussing the further consequences of Einstein's relationship $E = mc^2$, we look at some numerical examples to see the size of the effect in particular cases.

*We have assumed that the coach is a "rigid body." Such a concept is at variance with the principle of relativity. The proof can be suitably altered to allow for this. See chap. 17 of *Physics, A New Introductory Course* (Science Teaching Center, Massachusetts Institute of Technology, 1964).

Example 6.2. The specifications of a typical 12-volt automobile battery are that it will deliver 81 amp for 20 minutes from full charge to discharge. It weighs 20 kgm when charged. How much less does it weigh when uncharged?

Answer 6.2. Total stored energy =

$$E = \left(\frac{81 \text{ coulombs}}{\text{sec}} \times \frac{60 \text{ sec}}{1 \text{ min}} \times 20 \text{ min} \right) \times 12 \text{ volts}$$

$$= 1.16 \times 10^6 \text{ joules.}$$

Therefore

$$"m" = \frac{E}{c^2} = \frac{1.16 \times 10^6 \text{ joules}}{(3 \times 10^8 \text{ m/sec})^2}$$

$$= 1.3 \times 10^{-11} \text{ kgm}$$

$$= 0.000,000,013 \text{ gm.}$$

[*Note.* The units of mc^2 are the same as those of E, since nonrelativistically $E = \frac{1}{2}mv^2$, which is (mass) × (velocity)^2, the same as mc^2. This is as it must be.]

Example 6.3. A small "tactical" atomic bomb is rated at the equivalent of 1 kiloton of T.N.T. (= 10^3 tons T.N.T.). Assume that the energy released in the detonation of 1 kgm of T.N.T. is 1000 kilocalories.* Hence determine the mass of fissionable material converted in this bomb.

Answer 6.3. The energy release is given by

$$E = 10^3 \text{ tons} \times \frac{2000 \text{ lb}}{1 \text{ ton}} \times \frac{1 \text{ kgm}}{2.2 \text{ lb}} \times \frac{1000 \text{ kcal}}{\text{kgm}} \times \frac{4200 \text{ joules}}{\text{kcal}}$$

$$= 3.82 \times 10^{12} \text{ joules}$$

$$\approx 10^6 \text{ kilowatt-hours.}$$

This is a sizable amount of energy to be released in considerably less than one second. Setting $E = mc^2$, we then find

$$m = \frac{E}{c^2} = \frac{3.82 \times 10^{12} \text{ joules}}{(3.00 \times 10^8 \text{ m/sec})^2} = 4.24 \times 10^{-5} \text{ kgm}$$

$$= 0.0424 \text{ gram} = 42.4 \text{ milligram.}$$

(In such a small bomb, the mass of fissionable material is a few kilograms, so that a few parts in 10^5 of this mass is actually converted to energy.)

In Example 6.2 the effect is far too small to measure. This is the case for all chemical effects. In Example 6.3 the effect is nearly measurable, not of course when a bomb is exploded, but indirectly in

*It actually varies between 910 and 1085 kcal, depending on the conditions of the detonation. See T. Urbanski, *The Chemistry and Technology of Explosives*, trans. I. Jęczalikowa and S. Laverton, Vol. 1 (New York: The Macmillan Company, 1964), pp. 318–319. We also assume that it is the American, or short, ton that is used as the unit.

nuclear-physics experiments. In actual fact this is not completely true, since neutrinos are emitted in fission, and their energy "escapes" from the calorimeter. However, many other cleaner nuclear reactions have been investigated (see Section 7.1 and 7.3), and in all cases the equation $E = mc^2$, together with *relativistic* equations of motion, are completely verified.

Let us return to a discussion of $E = mc^2$. We have yet to prove in general that this relationship leads to a law of conservation of energy which is invariant under the Lorentz transformation. Nor have we yet proved a similar statement about momentum. We do so now. In fact it is this analysis which makes us most certain that we *do* have the correct definitions of momentum and energy.*

We proceed by determining the transformation laws for momentum and energy under a Lorentz transformation. Our present derivation uses "brute force," and is somewhat involved, though the result will be very simple.† Equations (5.13) and (6.18) give us the momentum **p** and the energy E of a particle of rest mass m_0, when it has a velocity **v** as seen by our observer A. When seen by our second observer B who has a constant velocity **V** w.r.t. A along the x axis, the same particle will have a velocity **v'**, momentum **p'**, energy E', and the same rest mass m_0. But we *know* **v'**, since this is a kinematic quantity, and is given in Eq. (4.7). Hence we can immediately calculate **p'** and E'. Thus one readily finds

$$p'_x = \frac{m_0}{\sqrt{1 - (v'^2/c^2)}} v'_x = \frac{m_0}{\sqrt{1 - (v'^2/c^2)}} \frac{v_x - V}{1 - (v_x V/c^2)}$$

$$p'_y = \frac{m_0}{\sqrt{1 - (v'^2/c^2)}} v'_y = \frac{m_0}{\sqrt{1 - (v'^2/c^2)}} \cdot \frac{v_y \sqrt{1 - (V^2/c^2)}}{1 - (v_x V/c^2)}$$

(similarly for z), and

$$E' = \frac{m_0 c^2}{\sqrt{1 - (v'^2/c^2)}}.$$

But (now comes the brute force)

$$1 - \frac{v'^2}{c^2} = \left(1 - \frac{v_x V}{c^2}\right)^{-2} \left[\left(1 - \frac{v_x V}{c^2}\right)^2 - \frac{(v_x - V)^2}{c^2} - \left(1 - \frac{V^2}{c^2}\right) \frac{v_y^2 + v_z^2}{c^2}\right]$$

$$= \left(1 - \frac{v_x V}{c^2}\right)^{-2} \left[\left(1 - \frac{V^2}{c^2}\right)\left(1 - \frac{v^2}{c^2}\right)\right]. \tag{6.19}$$

---

*For the skeptical reader will surely agree that, after stating at great length that the definition of force is arbitrary, it is unreasonable to assume that necessarily work is indeed given by $\int \mathbf{F} \cdot d\mathbf{s}$, using our definition of **F**.

†A more elegant discussion is given in Section A.5 of Appendix A, p. 121.

[This remarkable result is the generalization of that in problem 4.3. See also Appendix A, Eq. (A.27).] Hence we now readily find (cf. problem 6.7) that

---

Transformation of momentum and energy:

$$p'_x = \gamma\left(p_x - \frac{VE}{c^2}\right)$$

$$p'_y = p_y$$

$$p'_z = p_z \qquad \text{with } \gamma = \left(1 - \frac{V^2}{c^2}\right)^{-1/2}. \qquad (6.20)$$

$$\frac{E'}{c^2} = \gamma\left(\frac{E}{c^2} - \frac{Vp_x}{c^2}\right)$$

These final equations are very simple, and tell us a most remarkable fact, namely: **the 4 quantities $(p_x, p_y, p_z, E/c^2)$ transform exactly like the basic 4 coordinates (x, y, z, t).** [Compare Eq. (6.19) with (3.13).] In fact, the reason for this is not too hard to find, and is discussed in Appendix A. Here let us simply accept Eq. (6.20).

We observe, again most remarkably considering the intermediate algebra, that the transformation of **p** and E is a *linear* transformation. Thus, let us consider two particles with momenta $\mathbf{p}_1$ and $\mathbf{p}_2$, and energies E_1 and E_2, so that the total momentum $\mathbf{P} = \mathbf{p}_1 + \mathbf{p}_2$, and the total energy $E = E_1 + E_2$. Then we can apply Eq. (6.20) to each particle individually, and hence obtain the new $\mathbf{p}'_1, E'_1$, and $\mathbf{p}'_2, E'_2$, and from these deduce $\mathbf{P}'$ and E'; but we get the same result by applying Eq. (6.20) *directly* to **P** and E (cf. problem 6.18). This is a very necessary property of any useful definition of momentum and energy.

It immediately generalizes to any number of particles, and also to the *differences* of two momenta and energies. Thus, suppose we have a process as seen by observer A in which the initial total momentum is $\mathbf{P}_{\text{before}}$, and the final momentum is $\mathbf{P}_{\text{after}}$; and let the energies be E_{before} and E_{after}. Then we can form the quantities

$$\Delta \mathbf{P} = \mathbf{P}_{\text{after}} - \mathbf{P}_{\text{before}}$$

and

$$\Delta E = E_{\text{after}} - E_{\text{before}}$$

and these will transform according to Eq. (6.20). That is, our observer B, moving at a constant velocity **V** along the x axis w.r.t. A, will determine *each* of his values of $\mathbf{P}'_{\text{before}}, \mathbf{P}'_{\text{after}}, E'_{\text{before}}, E'_{\text{after}}$, and $\Delta \mathbf{P}'$ and $\Delta E'$ according to Eq. (6.20). Thus in particular

$$\Delta P_x' = \gamma\left(\Delta P_x - \frac{V\,\Delta E}{c^2}\right)$$

$$\Delta P_y' = \Delta P_y \qquad\qquad\qquad (6.21)$$

$$\Delta P_z' = \Delta P_z$$

and

$$\frac{\Delta E'}{c^2} = \gamma\left(\frac{\Delta E}{c^2} - \frac{V\,\Delta P_x}{c^2}\right)$$

Hence *if* observer A says that momentum and energy are conserved, i.e., that $\Delta\mathbf{P} = 0$, and $\Delta E = 0$, it *immediately* follows that B will find that $\Delta\mathbf{P}' = 0$, and $\Delta E' = 0$. That is, **if energy and momentum are conserved in an experiment according to A, they are also necessarily conserved according to observer B, who is flying over the same experiment with a constant velocity V w.r.t. A.** (Of course the theory of relativity cannot in itself predict the result of A's experiment.*) Notice, however, from Eq. (6.21) that it is now impossible to have conservation of momentum but not conservation of energy, since this would not be an invariant possibility.

This crucial result shows that our relativistic definitions of energy and of momentum do indeed form a consistent whole. With this established, we have also established the *necessity* of associating a mass m with any form of energy E, according to $E = mc^2$. Similarly it now follows unambiguously that it does require an infinite amount of work to accelerate a particle with finite rest mass from rest to the speed of light. We cannot overemphasize the importance of the theorem we have just proved. Without it, our previous considerations were not complete; with it, we can proceed confidently to apply these considerations to the real world of experiment.

Let us now return to a discussion of $E = mc^2 = m_0\gamma c^2$. We have already discussed the variation of m with v in Section 5.4 and Fig. 5.3. We see that the same relativistic mass m appears in the formulas for momentum and for energy, so that it is customary to call m the relativistic mass (to be carefully distinguished from m_0, the rest mass).

If we start with a particle at rest with rest mass m_0, it takes an *infinite* amount of work to accelerate it to a speed c (when its energy and momentum would be infinite). Of course it is possible to consider a particle with m_0 imaginary, and $v^2 > c^2$, which would have finite E and p. But the properties of such a particle would be rather peculiar. In particular, we could observe it only if it were able to emit radiation which had a speed relative to itself of $\leq c$, and therefore a

---

*In actual fact the invariance principle I of p. 142 is enough in itself to prove that there exist suitable definitions of momentum and of energy which are such that they are conserved. This guaranteed that our search would be successful.

speed relative to us *also* $\leq c$. [See Section 4.3 and Eq. (4.9). But this is based on using the Lorentz transformation with $V^2 > c^2$, leading to imaginary space and time coordinates.] The interpretation of speeds greater than c seems fraught with difficulty. This is the reason that the velocity of light c is considered the ultimate, maximum attainable speed in the theory of relativity. We postulate that no *signal* (which carries energy) can have a speed greater than c in the theory, so that "hyper-radio waves" cannot exist.*

There is one interesting case when a particle can have a speed c, namely if its rest mass m_0 is zero. It is then impossible to give meaning to γ, but m can be defined by $E = mc^2$. In this case $p = mc$, and $E = pc$. The neutrino is believed to be such a particle. Of course, these relations also hold for electromagnetic radiation or light, and one often finds it useful to talk of a particle, "the photon," which is associated

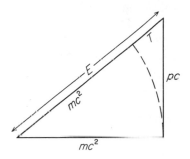

Fig. 6.5 The relationship $E^2 - p^2 c^2 = m^2 c^2$. Notice that tan $\theta = pc/E = v/c$. We have also shown $T = E - mc^2$.

with electromagnetic radiation.† These "particles" have the remarkable property that they have the *same* speed c to *all* observers. However, they do have different energies and momenta to different observers, always related by $E = pc$ (cf. problem 6.8).

Finally we observe that a remarkable identity exists between $E = mc^2$ and $p = mv$, namely

$$E^2 - p^2 c^2 = m^2 c^4 - m^2 c^2 v^2 = m^2 c^4 \left(1 - \frac{v^2}{c^2}\right) = (m_0 \gamma)^2 c^4 \gamma^{-2}$$

or

$$\boxed{E^2 - p^2 c^2 = m_0^2 c^4.} \tag{6.22}$$

*Of course, they might indeed be discovered; but that would simply mean that our theory was incorrect.

†This particle aspect of light was first proposed by Einstein, as an explanation of the photoelectric effect. We discuss it further in Section 7.4.

This relationship can be portrayed in a right-angled triangle, as shown in Fig. 6.5. At this point we remark that another useful (if self-evident) relationship is

$$Ev = c^2 p \quad \text{or} \quad v = \frac{c^2 p}{E}.$$ (6.23)

6.6   THE TRANSFORMATION OF FORCE REVISITED. LONGITUDINAL AND TRANSVERSE MASS*

We now return to the question of the transformation properties of force, already discussed in Section 6.2. That discussion was in principle enough to determine the transformation equations for the general case. However, these are very involved, which is a consequence of our definition of force as $\mathbf{F} = d\mathbf{p}/dt$, and hence we will not consider the general case† (cf. problem 6.2). We therefore will only treat a particular case: namely, when the particle on which the force acts is instantaneously at rest in the frame S', and acted upon by a force $\mathbf{F}'$. We then ask what force $\mathbf{F}$ is seen by an observer in S, who sees the particle as having a velocity $\mathbf{V}$ along the x direction.

Since $\mathbf{F}' = d\mathbf{p}'/dt'$ and $\mathbf{F} = d\mathbf{p}/dt$ we need the relationships between t' and t, and between p' and p; or rather, between dt' and dt, and between dp' and dp. The former is easy, since dt' corresponds to the proper time, so that

$$dt = \gamma \, dt', \qquad \gamma = \left(1 - \frac{V^2}{c^2}\right)^{-1/2} > 1.$$

For the momentum transformation, we use Eq. (6.20). Then we have immediately that $dp_y = dp'_y$, and $dp_z = dp'_z$. Further, we know that $(p_x, E/c^2)$ is to (x, t) as $(p'_x, E'/c^2)$ is to (x', t'), so that we have immediately the inverse equation‡

$$p_x = \gamma\left(p'_x + \frac{VE'}{c^2}\right)$$

*This section may be omitted.

†Minkowski defined a "4-force" as

$$\left(\frac{d\mathbf{p}}{d\tau}, \frac{dE/c^2}{d\tau}\right) = \left(\gamma\mathbf{F}, \frac{\gamma}{c^2}\frac{dE}{dt}\right)$$

which has very straightforward transformation properties. This is discussed further in Section A.6 of Appendix A, p. 124, where we also give the most general transformation of $\mathbf{F}$.

‡This can also be derived by solving Eq. (6.20) directly for p_x and E/c^2.

[cf. Eq. (3.13)]. Hence, by differentiating this, we obtain

$$dp_x = \gamma\left(dp'_x + \frac{V\,dE'}{c^2}\right) = \gamma\left(1 + \frac{V}{c^2}\frac{dE'}{dp'_x}\right)dp'_x.$$

But (cf. problem 6.9) it is easy to show that

$$\frac{dE}{dp_x} = \frac{c^2 p_x}{E} = v_x, \qquad \frac{dE'}{dp'_x} = v'_x,$$

where v_x and v'_x are the instantaneous x components of velocity of the particle in the frames S and S'. In our case we have stipulated that $v'_x = 0$, so that we obtain

$$dp_x = \gamma\,dp'_x.$$

Putting the above equations together, we then immediately obtain for this special case;

$$\frac{dp_x}{dt} = \frac{dp'_x}{dt'}, \quad \frac{dp_y}{dt} = \gamma^{-1}\frac{dp'_y}{dt}, \quad \frac{dp_z}{dt} = \gamma^{-1}\frac{dp'_z}{dt}.$$

Now the x direction is along the direction of **V**, so that we can denote it by the subscript ‖ (for parallel); and the y and z directions are equivalent to each other, and are perpendicular to **V**, so that we can denote both of these directions by the subscript ⊥ (for perpendicular). Hence finally we have:

> Force **F**′ acting on a particle *at rest* in S', when seen in S moving at V w.r.t. S', becomes **F**, where
> $$F_{\parallel} = F'_{\parallel}$$
> $$F_{\perp} = \gamma^{-1}F'_{\perp}, \qquad \gamma = \left(1 - \frac{V^2}{c^2}\right)^{-1/2}.$$

(6.24)

These equations should be compared with Eq. (4.29).

As a final remark, we note that there is apparently a difference between the two cases of motion of relativistic particles when a force is applied in the direction of motion, and when one is applied perpendicular to the direction of motion. These two directions are often referred to as "longitudinal" and "transverse." Owing to the nature of the relativistic equations of motion, two forces of equal magnitude, but applied in the longitudinal and in the transverse directions, give rise to accelerations of different magnitude when applied to the same particle moving with the same velocity in the two cases. This follows from the general result Eq. (6.3):

$$\mathbf{F} = m_0\gamma\mathbf{a} + \frac{m_0\mathbf{v}\gamma^3(\mathbf{a}\cdot\mathbf{v})}{c^2}.$$

(6.3)

We have already remarked that in the general case **a** need not be directed along **F**. Nonetheless, Eq. (6.3) does determine **a** uniquely in terms of **F**, for a given **v**. Let us again split **F** into two parts, $F_{\parallel}$ and $F_{\perp}$, with $F = F_{\parallel} + F_{\perp}$. Here we define $F_{\parallel}$ to be parallel to the (instantaneous) direction of **v**, and $F_{\perp}$ to be perpendicular to **v**. Similarly we write $a = a_{\parallel} + a_{\perp}$. Then Eq. (6.3) is equivalent to the two equations

$$F_{\perp} = m_0 \gamma a_{\perp}$$

and

$$F_{\parallel} = m_0 \gamma a_{\parallel} + \frac{m_0 v \gamma^3 a_{\parallel} v}{c^2} = m_0 \gamma^3 a_{\parallel}. \tag{6.25}$$

These equations indicate that the "inertia" of a relativistic particle is different in the longitudinal and transverse directions. In the very early days of experiments on fast electrons (and their identical twins, beta-rays) this effect was discovered experimentally, and played an important part in the development of a theory of the electron. The terms "longitudinal mass" and "transverse mass" were sometimes used for the quantities $m_0 \gamma^3$ and $m_0 \gamma$. However, with Einstein's formulation of the theory of relativity, this distinction became unnecessary. In fact, it is misleading to use such concepts, since they arise only because one is trying to force the correct equation $F = (d/dt)p = (d/dt)(mv)$ into the incorrect form $F \propto ma$.

6.7 SUMMARY

We have somewhat belabored the point that the definition of force is a convention. Nonetheless, the Newtonian definition is certainly the most useful one in classical physics. In relativity theory there is more than one possible definition, but in all cases the definitions must be so adjusted that the predicted motion agrees with experiment. In fact the observed motion, together with the definition, determines the force. The definition we choose is the one which leads to the simplest law of force for the motion of a charged particle in an electromagnetic field.

Since the definition of force is somewhat arbitrary, it is also somewhat arbitrary to define "work" as $\int F \cdot ds$. However, with our definition of force this quantity did possess the *essential* property that it led to a "kinetic energy," T, which depended only on the final speed of the particle and not on the details of its past motion. By considering inelastic collisions, we discovered that the total energy $E = T + m_0 c^2 = mc^2$ was conserved in such reactions. The relationship $E = mc^2$ is applicable to electromagnetic radiation even in classical physics, and Einstein made the assumption that it holds universally, and hence that energy and mass are interchangeable. For this to be the case, it is of course essential that this new form of the principle of conservation of energy be invariant under the Lorentz transformation, and we proved that this was so. At the same time we obtained a proof of the invariance of the principle of conservation of momentum. We remark that instead of the two separate Newtonian laws of conservation of mass and of conservation of energy, we now have one law of conservation of "energy-and-mass." Because of the invariance of this new "conservation of energy" we can indeed identify the E of $E = mc^2$ with energy. Thus also $m = E/c^2$ is a mass to be associated with any form of energy. The "mass" associated with forms of energy such as chemical bonding, or radioactivity, or nuclear fission (before it has taken place) has *all* the properties of mass, such as inertia, relevance to the location of the center of mass of a body, and even weight.

The relation $E = mc^2$, together with an understanding of what it truly implies, is perhaps the most profound prediction of the special theory of relativity.

PROBLEMS

(Essential problems are indicated by !. difficult problems by *.)

6.1 Consider Example 6.1, but now suppose the observer is moving upwards with a velocity V w.r.t. the apple. Working from first principles, determine the "weight" of the apple according to this observer. Compare your result with that given by Eq. (6.24). Also compare the result of Example 6.1 with this equation.

***6.2** Obtain the transformation equations for force, i.e. the relationship between the forces **F** and **F'** as seen by our standard observers A and B, for the particular case when **F** is along **V**. Work directly from the definition Eq. (6.2), and proceed by brute force. (This is *not* the best method to obtain the transformation properties of **F**. You may find the result of problem 4.3 useful.)

!6.3 Prove explicitly that

neither $T(v) = \frac{1}{2}m_0 v^2$ nor $T(v) = \frac{1}{2}mv^2 = \frac{1}{2}m_0 v^2 [1 - (v^2/c^2)]^{-1/2}$

will satisfy Eq. (6.11).

!6.4 Prove explicitly that Eq. (6.13) is compatible with Eq. (6.11).

!6.5 Prove explicitly that (relativisitic) momentum is conserved in the experiment of Fig. 6.2(b), as seen by D.

!6.6 Prove that if (x_1, y_1, z_1, t_1) and (x_2, y_2, z_2, t_2) are two events, then the form

$$c^2(t_2 - t_1)^2 - (x_2 - x_1)^2 - (y_2 - y_1)^2 - (z_2 - z_1)^2$$

is an invariant under a Lorentz transformation.

6.7 Work through the derivation of the energy-momentum transformation Eq. (6.20) in full detail, using the method of Section 6.5.

!6.8 Consider a particle with $m_0 = 0$, traveling at a speed c, and having energy E and momentum $p = E/c$. Prove that under any Lorentz transformation $p' = E'/c$. (Note that **p** and **V** need not be parallel.)

!6.9 Prove that the relativistic expressions for E and **p** lead to the result $dE/dp_x = v_x$. This is the same as the classical result. [*Hint:* Consider $E^2 = \mathbf{p}^2 c^2 + m^2 c^4$.]

*6.10 Consider a particle in the frame S which has momentum **p** at time t and is subject to a force $\mathbf{F} = d\mathbf{p}/dt$. Suppose the same particle as seen in the frame S' has momentum $\mathbf{p}'$ at time t' for the *same* space-time event (with $\mathbf{F}' = d\mathbf{p}'/dt'$). Prove directly from the Lorentz transformation equations for $(\mathbf{r}, t)$ and $(\mathbf{p}, E/c^2)$ that

$$\frac{dp_x}{dt} = \frac{dp'_x}{dt'}.$$

(This implies that $F_x = F'_x$.) [*Partial hint:* Use the result of problem 6.9.]

*6.11 Consider problem 6.10 again, for the case that the particle is instantaneously at rest in the S' frame. Prove that

$$\frac{dp_y}{dt} = \gamma^{-1} \frac{dp'_y}{dt'}.$$

[This implies that *for this case* $F_y = \gamma^{-1} F'_y$, cf. Eq. (6.24).]

!6.12 Prove the relationship $dE/dt = \mathbf{F} \cdot \mathbf{v}$. The result holds both relativistically and classically.

6.13 A particle of rest mass m moving with speed v collides with a stationary particle of mass M. If the two particles stick together, find the speed of the composite particle, and its total rest mass.

!6.14 A particle of rest mass m, velocity **u**, and *total* energy E collides with a stationary particle of mass M. Prove that the velocity of the center-of-mass (C. of M.) system (in which there is no net momentum) is given by

$$\mathbf{v} = \frac{\mathbf{p}c^2}{E + Mc^2} = \frac{m\mathbf{u}c^2}{\sqrt{1 - (u^2/c^2)}(E + Mc^2)}.$$

6.15 Consider the experiment of problem 6.14. Show that the total energy W in the C. of M. system is given by $W^2 = (E + Mc^2)^2 - p^2 c^2$. Determine W as a function of E for the two cases (a) very nonrelativistic $u \ll c$, $E = mc^2 + \frac{1}{2}mu^2$, and (b) extreme relativistic $u \approx c$, $E \gg mc^2$. [*Note.* The expression for W follows more directly from invariance arguments. Can you give these?] W may be thought of as the **total effective rest mass** of the system. Why?

6.16 In Section 5.2 we showed, by using the Newtonian definition, that the principle of conservation of momentum is invariant under the Galilean transformation. Use the same methods to show that the *classical* definition of kinetic energy leads to an energy conservation law which is invariant under the Galilean transformation.

6.17 Consider classical mechanics and the Galilean transformation. Determine the transformation laws for $\mathbf{p}$ and E for a particle of mass m. Eliminate m, so that you obtain expressions for $\mathbf{p}'$ and E' as functions of only $\mathbf{p}, E$, and $\mathbf{V}$. Note that you need to know both $\mathbf{p}$ and E in order to obtain either $\mathbf{p}'$ or E'.

!6.18 Consider a general relativistic two-body collision as seen by an observer A, in which the initial 3-momenta and energies are $\mathbf{p}_1$ and $\mathbf{p}_2$, and E_1 and E_2, respectively. After the collision let the momenta and energies be $\mathbf{p}_3$ and $\mathbf{p}_4$ and E_3 and E_4 respectively, and suppose that both momentum and energy are conserved, according to A.

(a) Explicitly transform each particle's initial and final 3-momentum and energy to the frame of reference of observer B.

(b) Prove explicitly that the total 3-momentum $\mathbf{P} = \mathbf{p}_1 + \mathbf{p}_2$ and the total energy $E = E_1 + E_2$ transform according to Eq. (6.20); i. e., prove that a compound system has a 3-momentum and energy which behave exactly like the 3-momentum and energy of a single particle.

(c) Prove explicitly that the transformation equations for $\Delta\mathbf{P}$ and ΔE given in Eq. (6.21) are valid, where $\Delta\mathbf{P}$ and ΔE represent the changes in $\mathbf{P}$ and E in a collision.

(d) Hence prove that momentum and energy are conserved according to B.

7

SOME DYNAMICAL
APPLICATIONS

In the previous two chapters we have treated the relativistic general-
izations of Newton's laws of motion, discussing mass, momentum, force,
and energy, and leading up to $E = mc^2$. In the present chapter we consider various applications of these results and compare them with experiment. In all cases that have been studied, the predictions are completely confirmed. We start by considering some examples in nuclear
physics, chosen so that all particles are nonrelativistic (have speeds
much less than that of light).*

7.1 NUCLEAR REACTIONS

Consider a "reaction" in which a particle a is fired at a stationary particle b. The simplest thing that can happen is an "elastic" collision, in which each particle comes out of the collision unaltered in
nature, with a velocity such that both total momentum and energy
are conserved. Before we can say that these are conserved, we must
of course know the masses of the particles, and measure their velocities. By using electric and magnetic fields in a mass spectrometer (see

*This is not always the case, even in nuclear physics.

the next section) it is possible to measure both of these quantities; and provided that the velocities turn out to be nonrelativistic, there is then no logical problem involved. One then does indeed find that "Newtonian" momentum and "Newtonian" kinetic energy are conserved.

As a typical example, we might fire protons (hydrogen nuclei) at Li^7 atoms in a metallic film. The collision is sufficiently violent that the effective collision is with a Li^7 nucleus, since the molecular and even electronic bonds are too weak to keep the whole Li^7 atom together. By using the methods of the next section, one is able to measure the mass of the proton to be $m_p = 1.6725 \times 10^{-24}$ gm, and that of the Li^7 nucleus to be $m_{Li^7} = 11.6470 \times 10^{-24}$ gm, being very closely seven times that of the proton. With this information one then does find that kinetic energy and momentum are conserved.

However, as well as elastic collisions, one sometimes finds that the reaction $p + Li^7 \rightarrow \alpha + \alpha$ takes place, where α denotes the He^4 nucleus.* The mass of the α particle is found to be $m_\alpha = 6.6443 \times 10^{-24}$ gm. In the experiments one finds that momentum is conserved, but that kinetic energy is apparently *created*, of constant amount $Q = 2.778 \times 10^{-5}$ ergs. On the other hand, mass is apparently destroyed, of amount

$$\Delta m = m_{Li^7} + m_p - 2m_\alpha = 3.09 \times 10^{-26} \text{ gm}.$$

But

$$c^2 \Delta m = (2.9979 \times 10^{10})^2 \times (3.09 \times 10^{-26} \text{ gm}) = 2.777 \times 10^{-5} \text{ ergs}.$$

Thus one finds nearly exact agreement between the rest mass "destroyed" Δm, and the energy created Q, given by $E = mc^2$, or $Q = c^2 \Delta m$.

The reaction $p + Li^7 \rightarrow \alpha + \alpha + Q$ is "exothermic"; that is, Q is positive, so that energy is released in the reaction. Thus in principle (if it were not for the electrostatic repulsion between the proton and the Li^7 nucleus) a proton with essentially zero velocity could interact with a stationary Li^7 nucleus to create two α particles having equal and opposite large velocities. These velocities each have magnitude given by

$$\tfrac{1}{2} m_\alpha v_0^2 = \tfrac{1}{2} Q \quad \text{or} \quad v_0 = \sqrt{Q/m_\alpha} = 2.045 \times 10^9 \text{ cm/sec}.$$

(The velocities must be equal and opposite to conserve momentum.)

However, other nuclear reactions are "endothermic," the rest mass of the final products being greater than that of the initial particles. This means that a certain input of energy is required to make the reaction "go." For example, we can have

$$\alpha + \alpha + (2.778 \times 10^{-5} \text{ erg}) \rightarrow p + Li^7.$$

*In fact this reaction was the first nuclear reaction ever studied using an "accelerator." It was investigated by Cockcroft and Walton with their original electrostatic accelerator, in 1932.

In this case an alpha particle with essentially zero velocity *cannot* interact with the stationary target α particle to form $p + Li^7$, since energy could not be balanced. One might think that if the moving α particle had kinetic energy equal to 2.778×10^{-5} erg (requiring a speed of $\sqrt{2}v_0 = 2.891 \times 10^9$ cm/sec) then one could just make a stationary $p + Li^7$. But in that case momentum would not be conserved! In actual fact the moving α must have an energy of $2 \times (2.778 \times 10^{-5}$ erg) and a speed of $v_{th} = 2v_0 = 4.090 \times 10^9$ cm/sec in order to just produce the $p + Li^7$. But then both of these are produced with *large* amounts of kinetic energy. This apparent paradox is resolved if one realizes that at this threshold α-particle energy both the proton and the Li^7 nucleus are created with the *same velocity* $\frac{1}{2}v_{th} = v_0$. Hence an observer flying over the experiment with *minus* this velocity $\frac{1}{2}v_{th} = v_0$ sees two α particles coming together each with speed $\frac{1}{2}v_{th}$, which then convert into a p and a Li^7 at *rest* w.r.t. himself. This observer is in the center-of-mass frame of the reaction (see also problem 7.1), and he observes the exact inverse reaction to that described in the previous paragraph.

Returning to $E = mc^2$, we emphasize that all the nuclear velocities encountered above were nonrelativistic, so that we could correctly use the Newtonian form of kinetic energy $\frac{1}{2}mv^2$, where m is the rest mass of the nucleus involved.* We next turn to a case where the speeds are truly relativistic.

7.2 MOTION OF CHARGED PARTICLES IN ELECTRIC AND MAGNETIC FIELDS AND THE ULTIMATE SPEED

We have asserted that the law of force governing the motion of a charged particle in both an electric and a magnetic field is given by

$$e(\mathbf{E} + \mathbf{v} \times \mathbf{B}) = \frac{d}{dt}\left(\frac{m_0}{\sqrt{1 - (v^2/c^2)}}\mathbf{v}\right). \tag{7.1}$$

Here e is the charge of the particle, m_0 its rest mass, $\mathbf{v}$ its velocity, and $\mathbf{E}$ and $\mathbf{B}$ the electric and magnetic field strengths. How can we test this law?

Consider first the case when $\mathbf{B} = 0$, and $\mathbf{E}$ is constant. Further, for simplicity we assume $\mathbf{v}$ is along $\mathbf{E}$. Then we can solve the motion as follows: the equation of motion is

*In actual fact we have found speeds of the order of $(1/7)c$ in our example. At such speeds the relativistic correction to the kinetic energy is only about one per cent, so that we are not yet really involved in a logical vicious circle of "proving" relativity by using relativity.

$$eE = \frac{d}{dt}\left(\frac{m_0}{\sqrt{1 - (v^2/c^2)}} v\right). \tag{7.2}$$

Multiply both sides by dx, note that $v = dx/dt$, and integrate w.r.t. x:

$$\int eE\, dx = eEx = \int dx \frac{d}{dt}\left(\frac{m_0 v}{\sqrt{1 - (v^2/c^2)}}\right) = \int v\, d\left(\frac{m_0 v}{\sqrt{1 - (v^2/c^2)}}\right)$$

$$= v\frac{m_0 v}{\sqrt{1 - (v^2/c^2)}} - \int dv \frac{m_0 v}{\sqrt{1 - (v^2/c^2)}}$$

$$= \frac{m_0 v^2}{\sqrt{1 - (v^2/c^2)}} - m_0 c^2 \sqrt{1 - v^2/c^2}$$

$$= \frac{m_0 c^2}{\sqrt{1 - (v^2/c^2)}} = m_0 \gamma c^2 \Big| \tag{7.3}$$

where suitable limits must be introduced.*

This equation simply says that in moving along the electric field E a distance d, the electric field provides energy eEd, which goes to increase the total relativistic energy $m_0 \gamma c^2$, according to the principle of conservation of energy. (In fact we could have written this down immediately, which shows the power of the energy conservation principle!)

The electrical energy provided by the field when the charged particle moves a distance d along the field must be independent of the velocity of the particle, or else we could extract an infinite amount of energy from the field by cyclically moving in the direction of the field at one speed and moving back again at some other speed. Thus we can measure the energy input eEd by standard electrical potentiometer determinations of the potential difference $V = Ed$. Of course this can also be compared with the change in kinetic energy given to a "heavy" slow-moving nonrelativistic particle.

We can then use the *same* field over the *same* distance to accelerate a light particle to very high velocities, measure its actual velocity, and hence test the true relationship between energy and velocity. Recently such an experiment has been performed for pedagogical purposes by W. Bertozzi.† In this experiment a known (measured) electric field acting over a distance is used to accelerate bursts (or pulses) of electrons from rest. The electrons are then timed over another known distance, so that their final velocity can be measured directly. Finally, the electrons are stopped in a target, which heats up due to the con-

---

*The fourth step in (7.3) is an application of the result $\int x\, dy = xy - \int y\, dx$.

†W. Bertozzi, *Am. J. Phys.*, **32**, 551 (1964). This experiment is shown in the film "The Ultimate Speed," made for the Physical Science Study Committee, and available from Modern Learning Aids, 3 East 54 Street, New York 10022. See also the text *P.S.S.C.: Advanced Topics Program* (Boston: D. C. Heath and Co., 1965).

version of kinetic energy into heat, and the rate of heat supply is actually *measured* by means of a calibrated thermocouple. The number of electrons in a pulse can be independently measured by measuring the total charge arriving per pulse at the target.

In this experiment one can first compare the "theoretical" energy input per electron eEd with the energy output as heat in the target per electron. One finds that they agree to within the experimental error of the heat determination, so that indeed the energy input is correctly given by eEd. One can then use this (easily measured) quantity eEd and compare it with the measured final velocity of the electrons to determine the dependence of velocity on kinetic energy. One finds that the predictions of relativity are fully confirmed. Thus, as the kinetic energy T of the electrons increases, their actual velocity approaches but never quite gets to c. On the other hand, their "classical" velocity, which is given by $\sqrt{2T/m_0} = \sqrt{2Ede/m_0}$, should reach about $10c$ at the highest electric fields used.* Furthermore, one finds that the detailed prediction of relativity, that $T = eEd = m_0c^2(\gamma - 1)$, is fully confirmed.

It is interesting to pursue this example further, since it corresponds to motion under a constant force, which classically leads to a constant acceleration eE/m_0. Equation (7.2) can be integrated w.r.t. time t directly, since the left-hand side is a constant. Hence if we consider motion starting from rest at $t = 0$, we have

$$eEt = \frac{m_0 v}{\sqrt{1 - (v^2/c^2)}},$$

or, solving for v,

$$v = \frac{(eEt)/m_0}{\sqrt{1 + [(eEt)^2/(mc)^2]}} = \frac{v_{\text{class.}}}{\sqrt{1 + (v^2_{\text{class.}}/c^2)}} \tag{7.4}$$

where

$$v_{\text{class.}} = eEt/m_0 . \tag{7.5}$$

Here $v_{\text{class.}}$ is the classical value of the velocity to be expected after a time t. We see that as long as $v_{\text{class.}} \ll c$, the relativistic result agrees with the classical result. However, v increases less slowly than $v_{\text{class.}}$ as t increases, and only approaches c as a limiting velocity.

For very large times, given by $t \gg t_0 = m_0c/(Ee)$,† we can set $v \approx c$ and $d \approx ct$. In this case even though v is essentially constant, the momentum and energy of the particle are still increasing without limit. Using Eq. (7.3) and neglecting the rest energy, we see that $mc^2 \approx Eed$

---

*Notice e/m_0 can be measured very easily for electrons by using low electric fields, which lead to "classical" velocities. Also see below.

†For an electron in a fairly weak field of 100 volts/cm, $t_0 \approx 2 \times 10^{-7}$ sec.

$\approx Ee(ct)$, and that momentum $= mv \approx mc \approx Eet$. (The momentum is necessarily given by the force multiplied by the time for which it acts.) Thus energy $\approx$ (momentum) $\times c$. (See also problem 7.2.)

At this point an apology is in order. How do we *know* that Eqs. (7.1) or (7.2) are indeed correct; in particular, should the left-hand side of (7.2) really be a constant? There are several partial answers to this question. The most direct is that all the predictions one can make agree completely with experiment.*

A more formal answer, if somewhat circular from the point of view of testing the theory of relativity, is given by electromagnetic theory. Maxwell's equations can*not* be made invariant under the Galilean transformation. However, they can be made invariant under the Lorentz transformation, provided one insists on a certain relationship between the electric and magnetic fields as seen by one observer, and as seen by another observer moving with constant velocity w.r.t. the first observer. That is, the *imposition* of Lorentz invariance forces a unique transformation law on the electric and magnetic fields. This unique transformation in turn forces upon one the use of the Lorentz force as given by the left-hand side of Eq. (7.1). Of course the reason one demands that Maxwell's equations be invariant in the first place is that they govern the propagation of light, and one wants the speed of light to be a constant to *all* observers.†

After this digression let us turn to the problem of motion of a charged particle in a constant magnetic field **B**, directed for convenience along the z axis. In this case Eq. (7.1) becomes

$$e\,\mathbf{v} \times \mathbf{B} = \frac{d\mathbf{p}}{dt} = \frac{d}{dt}\left(\frac{m_0}{\sqrt{1-(v^2/c^2)}}\,\mathbf{v}\right). \tag{7.6}$$

To solve this consider

$$\frac{d}{dt}(p^2) = 2\mathbf{p}\cdot\frac{d\mathbf{p}}{dt} = 2\mathbf{p}\cdot(e\mathbf{v} \times \mathbf{B}) = 2m_0\gamma e\mathbf{v}\cdot\mathbf{v} \times \mathbf{B} = 0.$$

Hence p is a constant of the motion, as therefore are both v and $m = m_0\gamma$.‡ Thus only the direction of **v** changes with time. Further $dp_z/dt = 0$, since $\mathbf{v} \times \mathbf{B}$ has no component along **B**. Hence v_z is a constant, and therefore so is the magnitude of the velocity component in

---

*As discussed in more detail later, the whole of high-energy elementary-particle physics is a complete verification of the theory of relativity. In particular *all* particle accelerators are designed on the basis of Eq. (7.1). Of the order of a billion dollars is invested in present accelerators, and so far no accelerator has failed to reach design performance because of violations of Eq. (7.1).

†We discuss this in more detail in Appendix C at the end of this chapter.

‡This is related to the fact that a magnetic force can do no work, since it is always perpendicular to the instantaneous velocity. Hence mc^2 is constant, and therefore so are m, γ, and v.

the xy plane $[= (v^2 - v_z^2)^{1/2}]$. Call this component velocity $\mathbf{u}$ (in the xy plane). Then $\mathbf{u}$ is constant in magnitude. Also $m(d\mathbf{u}/dt) = e\mathbf{u} \times \mathbf{B}$, so that $\mathbf{u}$, $\mathbf{B}$, and $d\mathbf{u}/dt$ are mutually perpendicular and form a right-handed system of axes. Finally the magnitude of $du/dt = euB/m = $ const. Thus, as regards the xy part of the motion, u is constant, and the acceleration is perpendicular to u, is in this plane, and is also constant. It follows that the xy motion is motion with constant speed in a circle. This circle has radius ρ such that $|du/dt| = u^2/\rho = \rho\omega^2$, the centripetal acceleration. (Here ω is the angular frequency.) Hence

$$\frac{u^2}{\rho} = \frac{euB}{m} \quad \text{or} \quad \omega = \frac{u}{\rho} = \frac{eB}{m}. \tag{7.7}$$

Thus the complete motion consists of two parts, a constant-velocity component along $\mathbf{B}$ together with a motion in the plane perpendicular to $\mathbf{B}$ in a circle with constant speed. The angular frequency around the circle is given by $\omega = eB/m = eB/(m_0\gamma)$, the radius ρ being given by $\rho = mu/(eB) = p_\perp/(eB)$. Here $p_\perp$ is the component of momentum perpendicular to $\mathbf{B}$. Notice, however, that $m = m_0\gamma$ depends on the *full* velocity, including that part along $\mathbf{B}$. The general motion is therefore a helix, as shown in Fig. 7.1.

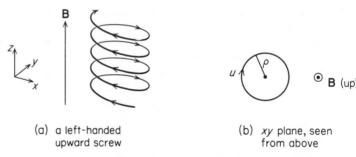

(a) a left-handed   (b) xy plane, seen
    upward screw   from above

Fig. 7.1 Helical motion of a (positively) charged particle in a uniform magnetic field.

This relativistic solution has certain similarities to the classical solution, but is more involved, since, while m is constant for a given helix, it differs from helix to helix, depending on the initial velocity. In the nonrelativistic case one has the remarkable result that ω is a constant independent of momentum or energy. This enables one to design particle accelerators using circular orbits in a magnetic field, and using a *periodic* acceleration synchronized to the *constant* orbit period $T = 2\pi/\omega$. For relativistic particles, as their energy increases, m increases and ω decreases, so that the acceleration period must be altered to follow the variation of ω. Such a technique is used in synchrotrons. For example for electrons in a "5-BeV" accelerator (see Example 7.1, below), which gives them a final energy of $10^4 m_0 c^2$, one must increase the product BT by a factor of 10^4 during a complete acceleration sequence! In actual fact both B and T are changed together to achieve this. In this case, we see from

$$\rho = \frac{p_\perp}{eB}, \quad p_\perp = eB\rho \tag{7.8}$$

that it is possible to keep the radius ρ *constant* as the particles "accelerate," by increasing B suitably, provided one starts with already relativistic particles $(E \approx 100 m_0 c^2)$ from another injector accelerator. Again we remark that the functioning of these accelerators confirms Eq. (7.1).

Example 7.1 The electron-volt. In dealing with elementary-particle processes, the kinetic energy is nearly always provided by accelerating a charge $q = \pm |e|$ in an electric field through a region of potential difference V. Here $|e|$ is the magnitude of the basic electron charge $= 1.60 \times 10^{-19}$ coulomb. Thus a useful unit of energy is *"the energy a charge $|e|$ acquires when accelerated through one volt."* This is known as an "electron-volt," abbreviated eV.

(a) How large is an electron-volt in joules?
(b) How much mass must be annihilated to produce 1 eV?
(c) The electron has a mass of $m_e = 9.11 \times 10^{-31}$ kg. To how many eV of energy is this equivalent?
(d) The proton has a mass of $m_p = 1.67 \times 10^{-27}$ kg. To how many eV of energy is this equivalent?

Answer 7.1. (a) Since 1 coulomb when accelerated through 1 volt gains an energy of 1 joule, we immediately have that

$$1 \, \text{eV} = (1.60 \times 10^{-19} \, \text{coulomb}) \times (1 \, \text{volt}) = 1.60 \times 10^{-19} \, \text{joule}.$$

(b) If $mc^2 = 1 \, \text{eV} = 1.60 \times 10^{-19}$ joule, then

$$m = \frac{1.60 \times 10^{-19} \, \text{joule}}{(3.00 \times 10^8 \, \text{m/sec})^2} = 1.78 \times 10^{-36} \, \text{kg}.$$

So 1 eV is equivalent to 1.78×10^{-36} kg.

(c) By means of the conversion factor of part (b) we immediately have

$$m_e c^2 = \frac{9.11 \times 10^{-31} \, \text{kg}}{1.78 \times 10^{-36} \, \text{kg/eV}} = 0.511 \times 10^6 \, \text{eV} = 0.511 \, \text{MeV.*}$$

Here we have introduced the unit $1 \, \textbf{MeV} = 10^6 \, \text{eV} = 1$ million eV. Another such unit is $1 \, \textbf{BeV} = 10^9 \, \text{eV} = 1$ billion eV (this is sometimes also called 1 GeV in Europe).

(d) Similarly

*Unfortunately rounding errors have been introduced, but the number 0.511 is the currently accepted value.

$$m_p c^2 = \frac{1.67 \times 10^{-27}\,\text{kg}}{1.78 \times 10^{-36}\,\text{kg/eV}} = 938\,\text{MeV}.$$

We give a table of some other elementary-particle masses in MeV in Section 7.3, p. 191.

Example 7.2. What potential difference is needed in order to accelerate a proton from rest to a speed (a) of $0.6c$? (b) of $0.8c$?

Answer 7.2. This is particularly straightforward to solve if we use the results of Example 7.1.

(a) We have

$$T_{0.6c} = mc^2 - m_0 c^2 = m_0 c^2 \left[\frac{1}{\sqrt{1 - (v^2/c^2)}} - 1 \right]$$

$$= m_0 c^2 \left(\frac{1}{\sqrt{1 - 0.36}} - 1 \right) = m_0 c^2 \left(\frac{1}{0.8} - 1 \right)$$

$$= \tfrac{1}{4} m_0 c^2 = \tfrac{1}{4}(938\,\text{MeV}) = 235\,\text{MeV}.$$

Since the proton has a charge of $+e$, we need a potential difference of 235 $\times 10^6$ volts, the proton starting at the higher potential.

(b) Similarly

$$T_{0.8c} = m_0 c^2 \left(\frac{1}{0.6} - 1 \right) = \frac{2}{3}\, m_0 c^2 = 625\,\text{MeV}.$$

Thus we need 625×10^6 volts.

Comment. We observe that

$$\frac{T_{0.8c}}{T_{0.6c}} = \frac{2/3}{1/4} = \frac{8}{3} = 2.66.$$

Classically we would have

$$\frac{T_{0.8c}}{T_{0.6c}} = \frac{(0.8)^2}{(0.6)^2} = \frac{0.64}{0.36} = 1.7\dot{7} = \frac{2}{3} \times 2.66.$$

Thus

$$\left(\frac{T_{0.8c}}{T_{0.6c}} \right)_{\text{Rel.}} = \frac{3}{2} \left(\frac{T_{0.8c}}{T_{0.6c}} \right)_{\text{Class.}}.$$

This is another indication of the fact that the relativistic expression for kinetic energy increases faster than the classical expression, as a function of v.

Example 7.3. Suppose that the proton of Example 7.2 (a) enters a region of constant magnetic field B, of magnitude 1 weber/meter^2 ($= 10^4$ gauss $= 10$ kilogauss). Assuming that it enters transverse to the field, what will be the radius of its orbit?

Answer 7.3. Using Eq. (7.8) we have

$$\rho = \frac{p}{eB}$$

with [cf. Eq. (6.23)]

$$p = \frac{Ev}{c^2} = \frac{(T + m_0 c^2)}{c} \frac{v}{c} = (235 + 938)\,\text{MeV}/c \times 0.6 = 704\,\text{MeV}/c.$$

This shows us that one allowed unit of momentum is actually MeV/c. This unit is very useful in elementary particle physics, and hence we convert the usual units for $\rho e B$ into this unit. Since $veB \sim$ force, we see that

1 meter $\times$ 1 coulomb $\times$ 1 weber/m² = 1 newton sec = 1 joule sec/meter

$$= (1\,\text{joule}) \times \frac{1}{1.60 \times 10^{-19}\,\text{joule/eV}} \times \frac{3 \times 10^8}{c}$$

$$= 1.87 \times 10^{21}\,\text{MeV}/c.$$

Here we have used the result of Example 7.1 (a). Hence

1 meter $\times$ (1.60 $\times$ 10⁻¹⁹ coulomb) $\times$ 1 weber/m²

$$= 1.87 \times 10^{21} \times 1.60 \times 10^{-19}\,\text{MeV}/c$$

$$= 299\,\text{MeV}/c.$$

This means that a particle with charge $\pm|e|$ which moves in a circle of radius 1 meter, in a magnetic field of 1 weber/m², has a momentum of 299 MeV/c. More generally, if it moves in a circle of radius ρ meters in a magnetic field of B weber/m², it has a momentum of $\rho B \times 299$ MeV/c.

In the example, $p = 704$ MeV/c, $B = 1$ weber/m² and hence

$$\rho = \frac{704}{299} = 2.36 \quad (\text{in meters}).$$

Finally, we briefly discuss the "mass-spectrometer," which is used to determine nuclear masses (cf. Section 7.1), and is based on the principles of this section. The simplest design is shown in Fig. 7.2, and consists of a source of essentially zero-velocity ions, followed by an accelerating region of longitudinal electric field, so that the particles acquire a *known* kinetic energy eV, where V is the potential difference between the source and the end of the accelerating region (V is equivalent to our previous Ed). After this the particles enter a region of

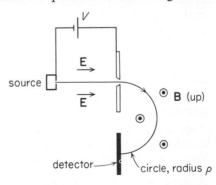

Fig. 7.2 A mass spectrometer (Dempster design).

constant magnetic field B, where they move in a circle of radius ρ, which is measured. Then from Eqs. (7.3) and (7.8),

$$eV = m_0(\gamma - 1)c^2 \quad \text{and} \quad p = m_0\gamma v = eB\rho.$$

Hence

$$\frac{(p/m_0)}{(\gamma - 1)} = \frac{\gamma v}{(\gamma - 1)} = \frac{c^2 B\rho}{V},$$

which is known. One can thus solve for v, and then use one of the two equations to determine m_0, assuming that e is known. (Mass spectrometers can determine only the ratio m_0/e.)

The "mass spectrometer" we have described here was invented by E. J. Dempster. The first mass spectrometer was invented by F. W. Aston in 1919, and used both magnetic and electric deflections. By 1926 Aston was able to measure masses to one part in 10^4. (This was sufficient for the test of $E = mc^2$ performed by Cockcroft and Walton as an extra return on their investigation of nuclear disintegration.) Present-day mass spectrometers can attain six- or even seven-figure accuracy by using comparative methods.

7.3   ELEMENTARY-PARTICLE REACTIONS

After several digressions, we now return to the application of relativistic dynamics, as demonstrated in the presently very active domain of elementary particle-physics research. We restrict ourselves to a few illustrative examples and refer the interested reader to nearly any recent issue of *Scientific American* if he wants to see the full scope of this subject.* Our illustrations are taken primarily from present-day problems and techniques. Thus we do not discuss how the masses and other properties of the older established elementary particles were originally determined. We list some of the properties of a few of these particles in Table 7.1. The theory of relativity was used extensively in the determination of their masses. In fact, it is the stock-in-trade of the elementary particle physicist, and without it he could hardly do anything. In particular, it is the use of invariance arguments and the idea of mass as given by $m^2c^4 = E^2 - p^2c^2$ that are the basis of all analysis.

*Or see for instance *The World of Elementary Particles* by K.W. Ford (New York: Blaisdell Publishing Co., 1963); *Elementary Particles* by D.H. Frisch and A.M. Thorndike (Princeton, N.J.: D. Van Nostrand Co., Inc., 1964); *Tracking Down Particles* by R.D. Hill (New York: W.A. Benjamin, Inc., 1963); or *The Fundamental Particles* by C.E. Swartz (Reading, Mass: Addison-Wesley Publishing Co., Inc., 1965). All these books are available in paperback.

Table 7.1 Properties of Some "Elementary" Particles

Name	Symbol	Mass Equivalent in MeV*	Principal Decay Mode
photon	γ	0	stable
neutrino	ν	0	stable
electron	$e^{\pm}$	0.511	stable
muon	$\mu^{\pm}$	105.7	$\mu^{\pm} \rightarrow e^{\pm} + \nu + \bar{\nu}$
pion	$\{\ \pi^{\pm}$	139.6	$\pi^{-} \rightarrow \mu^{-} + \bar{\nu},\ \pi^{+} \rightarrow \mu^{+} + \nu$
	π°	135.0	$\pi^{\circ} \rightarrow \gamma + \gamma$
proton	p	938.3	stable
neutron	n	939.6	$n \rightarrow p + e^{-} + \bar{\nu}$
hydrogen atom	H	940.1	stable
carbon atom	C	11,177.7†	stable

*Cf. Example 7.1, p. 187: 1 MeV is equivalent to 1.78×10^{-30} kg.

†By definition, a carbon *atom* has a mass of 12 atomic mass units (a.m.u.), so that 1 a.m.u. = 931.5 MeV. One a.m.u. has by definition a mass of 1 gm/N_0, where N_0 is Avogadro's number, 6.023×10^{23}. Thus 1 a.m.u. = 1.660×10^{-24} gm.

The aim of elementary particle physics is to study the kinds of "basic" particles that exist inside the nucleus, or which can be made to exist for a short time by suitably disturbing a nucleus. One wants to determine the physical properties of these particles, such as their masses, charges, and other more formal properties which belong to the subject matter of quantum mechanics; further, one wants to study whether they are stable or whether they decay into other particles, and if the latter, what their lifetimes are, and what their various decay modes are. Finally, one wants to know how these particles interact with one another—for these basic particles form the building blocks of all nuclei, and hence of all matter; their interactions are what hold all matter together. It should be admitted that, recently, Pandora's box seems to have been opened, in that the number of such "elementary particles" has increased dramatically.

Elementary (or subatomic) particles can be detected easily only if they have a charge. When charged, their motion through matter or gases can be detected by the ionization they produce. Actual tracks can thus be seen, either directly in photographic emulsion, or in "bubble chambers," "cloud chambers," or "spark chambers." In bubble chambers for example, the particles of interest travel through a liquid in the chamber, and their tracks are made visible and photographed stereographically. The details of these detectors however are not important to our present purpose (see references given in the footnote on p. 190).

An essential feature of nearly all such detectors is that the particles, when "photographed," are moving through a constant uniform magnetic field **B** of known magnitude. By measuring the radius of curvature of the tracks (in three dimensions, using stereographic photographs and electronic computers), one can determine the momenta of the particles.* Here one uses Eq. (7.8), $p_\perp = eB\rho$, and knowing the angle the track makes with $\mathbf{B}$, one can then determine $\mathbf{p}$ both in magnitude and direction.

In a typical experiment, one produces a beam of particles with an accelerator, with a fairly well-defined momentum. If possible, one tries to make the beam consist predominantly of only one kind of particle. As an example, we will consider a beam of protons (the nuclei of hydrogen atoms) having a momentum of about 400 MeV/c. One then fires this beam at a target and arranges detection equipment to determine what exactly occurred at the target.

One very useful target is a liquid hydrogen bubble chamber, since the hydrogen provides protons as targets while at the same time enabling one to detect photographically what has happened. Typically (with

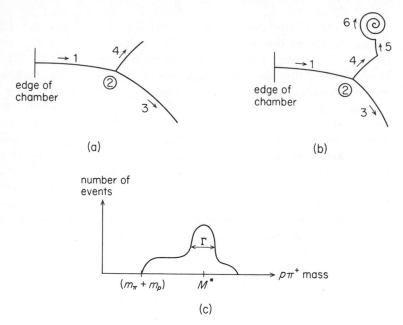

(a)   (b)

(c)

Fig. 7.3 (a) and (b): Typical elementary particle reactions as "seen" in a bubble chamber. The curvature of the tracks is caused by the magnetic field. (c) The final $p\pi^+$ mass distribution for the reaction $p + p \rightarrow p + \pi^+ + n$ (shown somewhat exaggerated).

*One assumes their charges are $+e$ or $-e$, e being the *magnitude* of the electron charge (already known).

the 400 MeV/c incident proton beam), one will then see three tracks as shown in Fig. 7.3 (a). Track 1 comes in with the beam, 2 denotes the stationary target particle, and visible tracks 3 and 4 end in the chamber; thus one can easily add the arrows which show the directions of motion. One can then assign charges $+ |e|$ to each track (based upon the direction of curvature of the tracks) and determine each particle's momentum for the various track curvatures. Note that the tracks do not increase greatly in curvature as the particles slow down and come to rest. The reason for this is quite complicated, but well understood. The particles usually do come to rest.

But what process actually occurred? Clearly the initial state contains two protons, that is $p + p$. What are the final particles, tracks 3 and 4? Unfortunately, one cannot in general determine the type of particle that makes a track, only its momentum. Thus we are forced to make a guess, and then test it, using detailed energy and momentum balance. Before resorting to this, however, one first always tests if momentum is conserved. Recall that uncharged particles can also be involved in the reaction—leaving no tracks, but carrying off momentum and energy.

Suppose we find (to within the experimental measurement uncertainty) that momentum is conserved. (Here, of course, we use Eq. (7.8), which is based upon the theory of relativity.) Furthermore, if tracks 3 and 4 simply stop in the chamber, they must correspond to stable particles, and the most likely suggestion is then that they are protons. Even if the tracks leave the chamber before stopping, as often happens, the most plausible assumption is still that the process was actually $p + p \rightarrow p + p$ (i.e., just like two billiard balls colliding). To test this hypothesis we then assume that each of the particles 1, 3, and 4 has rest mass* m_p (the known proton rest mass), as does the (invisible) target particle 2. Then, by using the relationship $E = (p^2 c^2 + m^2 c^4)^{1/2}$ for each of the initial and final particles in the collision, we can calculate the total initial energy and the total final energy, and see if they agree. If they do the hypothesis has been confirmed, and by studying the angles of the various tracks, we can then learn more about the pp interaction.

One interesting feature of this "elastic" (i.e., energy-conserving) $p + p \rightarrow p + p$ reaction is that the angle between the final tracks 3 and 4 need not be 90°. This is in contrast to the well-known classical result (see problem 7.6) that when a moving billiard ball strikes an identical ball at rest, the two balls recoil at 90° to each other, provided that kinetic energy is conserved. In relativistic dynamics, as the inci-

*Throughout the rest of this chapter, all masses m will refer to rest masses.

dent momentum increases, this angle decreases. The effect is very small for 400 MeV/c protons, and even for 6 BeV/c protons the angle is typically still 87° (even though $v \approx c$ and $\gamma \approx 6$, this is not extremely relativistic). The effect is most marked for electron-electron scattering, since electrons can readily be accelerated to extreme relativistic momenta (the important parameter is γ, see problem 7.6). Thus this effect for electrons was one of the early verifications of the increase of relativistic mass (or better, of the relativistic energy momentum relationships). Of course, the very fact that the relativistic definitions of energy and momentum were "exactly" conserved in the $p + p$ collision is another much better test of the theory.

Let us return to our collision, Fig. 7.3 (a). Suppose on the other hand that we find that momentum is apparently not conserved. We then assume that at least one other neutral particle was produced, call it X. We can immediately determine its momentum $\mathbf{p}_X$, by using $\mathbf{p}_X = \mathbf{p}_1 - \mathbf{p}_3 - \mathbf{p}_4$. However, what are particles 3 and 4? If they stop in the chamber, as shown in Fig. 7.3 (a), we again guess that they are protons with mass m_p. Since we know $\mathbf{p}_1$, $\mathbf{p}_3$, and $\mathbf{p}_4$ we can then determine E_1, E_3, and E_4 using $E^2 = \mathbf{p}^2 c^2 + m^2 c^4$. Hence we can also determine the *total* energy of X as $E_X = E_1 + m_p c^2 - E_3 - E_4$. Now, we know nothing about X, which could even consist of two, three, or more neutral particles. But we *do* know $\mathbf{p}_X$ and E_X. Hence we can construct a rest mass for X defined by $m_X c^2 = (E_X^2 - p_X^2 c^2)^{1/2}$, *even if X is a group*. We now ask whether m_X corresponds to the known mass of any already studied neutral particle. It might well be that the calculated m_X is compatible with the mass of the neutral pi-meson or pion, $\pi°$. (Recall there will always be some measurement uncertainty.) This then strongly suggests that what occurred was $\pi°$ production $p + p \rightarrow p + p + \pi°$, and we are fairly confident of this if indeed tracks 3 and 4 did stop.*

If, on the other hand, one or both of tracks 3 and 4 had left the chamber, then we would not be so sure. Rather, we would have to try other hypotheses also, even though we did have one successful fit. We might find an equally successful fit with the non-stopping track 4 assumed to be a π^+ (see Table 7.1), track 3 again assumed to be a proton. Then, if m_X—calculated using the *new* E_4—turned out to be compatible with the neutron mass m_n (see Table 7.1), we would have the new fit $p + p \rightarrow p + \pi^+ + n$. With two equally satisfactory fits, the event is ambiguous and nothing more can be done. Such is the life of the experimental elementary particle physicist.

Of course we may be lucky, and see an event as shown in Fig.

*This process $p + p \rightarrow p + p + \pi°$ is an example of the creation of rest mass, the "source" being some of the incident kinetic energy. In many elementary particle physics reactions rest mass is converted into kinetic energy, or *vice versa*.

7.3(b). Here track 4 is definitely not that of a stable proton. In fact, spiral 6 is immediately recognizable as that of a much lighter "stable" particle, the positron or positive electron, e^+.* Once we recognize 6 as a positron, then 5 nearly certainly is a mu-meson or muon, μ^+ (see Table 7.1), which decays to a positron by the process $\mu^+ \rightarrow e^+ + \nu + \bar{\nu}$ (see problem 7.11). Here ν refers to the neutrino, a neutral particle having zero rest mass, and $\bar{\nu}$ refers to its "antiparticle," the antineutrino.†

Returning to Fig. 7.3(b), if track 5 is a muon, then track 4 is nearly certainly that of a pion π^+, which decays according to $\pi^+ \rightarrow e^+ + \nu$ (really ν_e). Of course, this hypothesis must be tested in turn, by constructing $\mathbf{p}_\nu$ and E_ν of the missing neutrino on the hypothesis $4 \equiv \pi^+$, $5 \equiv \mu^+$, and then testing whether $E_\nu^2 = \mathbf{p}_\nu^2 c^2 + 0$ (see also problem 7.8).‡

If all goes well, we then "know," in Fig. 7.3(b), that track 4 is that of a π^+ and track 3 is that of a proton. We can obtain E_3 and E_4 from the measured p_3 and p_4, and then obtain the missing momentum $\mathbf{p}_X$, the missing energy E_X, and finally, the "missing mass" m_X, given by $m_X^2 c^4 = E_X^2 - \mathbf{p}_X^2 c^2$. Suppose m_X then corresponds to that of the neutron, so that we really had the chain§

$$p + p \rightarrow p + \pi^+ + n, \qquad \pi^+ \rightarrow \mu^+ + \nu, \qquad \mu^+ \rightarrow e^+ + \nu + \bar{\nu}.$$

We have succeeded in analyzing one event unambiguously. The process may have seemed involved, but in real life it is even worse, for the curvature of a track keeps changing as the particle slows down. The photographs are themselves two-dimensional views of three-dimensional tracks, and even with the aid of computers, such tedious data reduction forms a very large part of the work of high energy physicists.

*Cf. Eq. (7.8), which shows that p_6 is much smaller than any other momentum; yet the track length shows that initially it has a sizable speed. This argument is based on a detailed theory of the energy loss mechanism for charged particles, which again makes use of relativistic dynamics. Theory and experiment are always closely intertwined.

†The neutrino is a most interesting particle, which has only very recently been "detected" by its further interactions. If its rest mass is exactly zero, it must travel with speed c with respect to all frames of reference. In reality there are two types of neutrino, one associated with the muon, called ν_μ, and one associated with the electron, called ν_e. The decay is really $\mu^+ \rightarrow e^+ + \nu_e + \bar{\nu}_\mu$.

‡We remark in passing that a decay cannot only create one particle, for consider $a \rightarrow b$. Then $\mathbf{p}_a = \mathbf{p}_b$ and $E_a = E_b$. Hence, $m_a = m_b$, so a and b are the same particle. A two-body decay such as $\pi^+ \rightarrow \mu^+ + \nu$ has a very characteristic feature which is treated in problem 7.8. A three-body decay such as $\mu^+ \rightarrow e^+ + \nu + \bar{\nu}$ is less proscribed, cf. problem 7.11.

§In this chain, the first step creates rest mass from kinetic energy, and then each of the two final steps creates kinetic energy from rest mass. The overall process, $p + p \rightarrow p + n + e^+ + 2\nu + \bar{\nu}$, creates a very small amount of rest mass from kinetic energy (cf. Table 7.1).

We now come to a most important digression. When discussing the missing mass m_X, we already implied that one could compute the total effective rest mass of a system of particles by computing their total momentum $\mathbf{P}_X$, and their total energy E_X, and calculating

$$M_X c^2 = (E_X^2 - \mathbf{P}_X^2 c^2)^{1/2}$$

This generalized rest mass of a system of particles has all the properties of a true rest mass. If the same system is viewed by our two standard observers A and B, having a constant relative velocity $\mathbf{V}$ with respect to each other, then their different values for the total energy and total momentum of the system are related by the standard transformation (6.20). [See the discussion following Eq. (6.20) and also problem 6.18 (b).] Thus M_X is truly an invariant. Associated with the quantities $\mathbf{P}_X$, E_X, and M_X we can determine a velocity $\mathbf{V}_X$ of the compound system, given by

$$\mathbf{V}_X = \frac{\mathbf{P}_X c^2}{E_X}$$

[cf. Eq. (6.23)], which is often called the center of mass (or C. of M.) velocity. If we try to accelerate the system as a whole, M_X truly represents the inertial rest mass. In **all** respects, the **effective total rest mass of a system of particles acts exactly like an ordinary rest mass, and the system behaves in many respects as a particle.** This concept is very powerful, and yet is completely based on the **relativistic invariance** of the concept. As an example, in the decay $\pi^+ \to \mu^+ + \nu$ the effective total rest mass of the $(\mu^+ \nu)$ system is necessarily equal to m_π (cf. problem 7.8), whatever the initial momentum of the π^+ is.*

Let us then return to the reaction $p + p \to p + \pi^+ + n$. What can we learn about it? The total rest mass of the system $p + \pi^+ + n$ must be the same as that of the initial system $p + p$, since $\mathbf{P}_{\text{initial}} = \mathbf{P}_{\text{final}}$ and $E_{\text{initial}} = E_{\text{final}}$. Thus $M_{\text{initial}} = M_{\text{final}}$ (yet another demonstration of the usefulness of the concept of generalized rest mass†). Thus $M_{pp} = M_{p\pi n}$ is determined by the momentum of the incident p. On the other hand, in the final state $p\pi n$, there are three separate two-body subsystems, namely pn, $p\pi^+$, and $n\pi^+$. For each event, one can calculate the two-body effective masses of these three pairs. One can then study the distribution of values of these effective masses m_{pn}, $m_{p\pi}$, and $m_{n\pi}$

*Note that M_X is usually greater than the sum of the rest masses of the constituents. Only if *all* the constituents have the same *velocity* and do not interact in any way (so that there is no potential energy involved) is it true that M_X equals $\sum m_i$.

†$M_X c^2$ is also sometimes known as the total C. of M. energy, since in the C. of M. frame of the total system X under consideration, we necessarily have $\mathbf{P}_X = 0$, and therefore $E_X = M_X c^2$.

accumulated from many different individual events $p + p \rightarrow p + \pi^+ + n$ (typically, 1000 or so events), all events being selected so that the incident effective mass m_{pp} is reasonably constant. One can then make a histogram or mass distribution showing the number of events with a given value of $m_{p\pi}$. Such a histogram is shown in Fig. 7.3(c). Note that the lowest possible value of $m_{p\pi}$ is $m_p + m_\pi$. In this histogram, we observe a broad peaking around a mass M^*, superimposed on a smoother "background." What does this peak mean?

Suppose that instead of the process $p + p \rightarrow p + \pi^+ + n$, we were really observing a two-stage process $p + p \rightarrow n + N^{*++}$, $N^{*++} \rightarrow p + \pi^+$. If the N^* were a true particle with a mass M^*, then, in the second step $N^{*++} \rightarrow p + \pi^+$, the effective mass of the $p\pi^+$ combination would have to equal that of the N^*, i.e., we should have $M_{p\pi} = M^*$. This is nearly what we observe, except for the spread in the peaking and the easily understood smooth background. Notice that from the *experimental* histogram we can measure M^*, and also the "width" of the peak, called Γ. For 400 MeV/c incident protons, we would indeed find such a peak, with $M^* = 1236 \text{ MeV}/c^2$ and $\Gamma = 120 \text{ MeV}/c^2$. We have "discovered" the famous $N^*_{3,3}$ pion-nucleon resonance.

In what sense is this N^* a particle (whether elementary or not)? It is quite impossible ever to see the track of an N^* before it breaks up. This is because its lifetime $\tau \approx 5.5 \times 10^{-24}$ sec, so that even if it were traveling with $v \approx c$, and some associated γ, its track length in the laboratory would only be $\approx \gamma c \tau \approx \gamma \times (1.65 \times 10^{-13})$ cm. Here the γ allows for time dilation or length contraction, but even with a γ of 10^5 this distance is only one atomic diameter!

This should therefore be contrasted with the unstable pion or muon. The π^+ lifetime is in fact 2.55×10^{-8} sec, while that of the μ^+ is 2.2×10^{-6} sec. Thus, even with $v = 0.1c$, the π^+ can travel 75 cm, and the μ^+ 66 meters. In Fig. 7.3 (b), in which a $\pi - \mu - e$ chain is shown, the pion typically slows down and comes to rest before it decays. The relatively short μ track is due to the very rapid deceleration of the initially quite fast μ, caused by energy loss due to ionization (cf. problem 7.8). Nonetheless there is a pion track, and also a muon track. Thus, even though both the pion and the muon are unstable, they do exist as real particles with finite lifetimes.

On the other hand, for the $N^*_{3,3}$ and other more recently discovered particles, these do not even exist long enough to leave tracks, or to have their lifetimes directly measured. In fact, their lifetimes are determined only indirectly from their mass spreads, using the theory of quantum mechanics to provide the connection. The mass spread of the π^+ is about $3 \times 10^{-8} \, eV/c^2$, much too small to measure. (Recall that there must always be measurement uncertainties in any experiment.)

Thus, again we ask "In what sense is the $N_{3,3}^*$ a particle?" The answer is clear from Fig. 7.3(c). Nature does arrange that in a large fraction of the events of the process $p + p \rightarrow p + \pi^+ + n$, the $p\pi^+$ combination does get produced with a correlation between the momenta of the p and the π^+, such that the effective mass of the combination is $\approx M^*$. This *correlated* compound system is produced *as a system*, and hence it truly does exist as a physical entity, even though it immediately fragments into its components. Nonetheless, these two components were created correlated in momenta, and remain so correlated.

It therefore is useful to speak of the $N_{3,3}^*$ as a particle, since the mass M^* does have a true significance. Such a very short-lived particle is often called a "resonance" to distinguish it from longer-lived nearly stable particles. Such resonances do seem to have an equal role with that of the nearly stable and stable particles of elementary particle physics. Thus, they can be combined into groups or "multiplets" in which both stable and very unstable particles coexist on an equal basis; and this grouping is in fact *useful*, in that all members of a "multiplet" have many closely related physical properties.*

The question "What is an elementary particle?" has no easy answer. At the moment, a great deal of work is being done to attempt to learn all about the possible resonances and to understand them in some way. Certainly the ideas of the special theory of relativity are used throughout this endeavor. The topic is fascinating, but we must leave it here.

7.4 THE DOPPLER EFFECT REVISITED, AND THE PHOTON

We have already discussed the Doppler effect in Section 4.7. Here we give an alternative treatment as a preliminary to discussing the "photon," the particle associated with electromagnetic radiation.

Consider first a source of electromagnetic radiation at rest in the (x, y, z, t) frame, emitting a plane wave with the form

$$\sin(kx - \omega t) = \sin k(x - ct) = \sin 2\pi \left(\frac{x}{\lambda} - \frac{t}{T} \right). \qquad (7.9)$$

*This problem of lifetimes already exists with the π^+, π°, π^- multiplet. The π° decays into two photons; that is, $\pi^\circ \rightarrow \gamma + \gamma$, and has a lifetime of $\approx 1.8 \times 10^{-16}$ sec. On the other hand, the lifetime of the charged pions is 2.55×10^{-8} sec, which is eight orders of magnitude longer than that of the π°. Nonetheless it does turn out to be very useful experimentally to consider the π^+, π°, π^- as forming a multiplet of very similar particles. In this case all three lifetimes can be measured.

Here $\omega = 2\pi f = 2\pi/T$ is the angular frequency of the source, and $k = 2\pi/\lambda$ is called the wave number.

Suppose we have another observer at rest in the (x', y', z', t') frame, which is moving with velocity V along the Ox axis. He will see a wave of the form $\sin(k'x' - \omega't')$, where (x', t') are related to (x, t) by the Lorentz transformation, and k' and ω' are the wave number and angular frequency as seen by the second observer. How are k' and ω' related to k and ω?

We answer this by considering a single particular *event* as seen by the two observers, namely an event (x_0, t_0) such that $kx_0 - \omega t_0 = n\pi$; so that at this event there is *no* signal according to the first observer. But if there is no signal at the event, *both* observers must agree on this, so that also $k'x_0' - \omega't_0' = n\pi$. Since the relationship between (x, t) and (x', t') is linear, it follows that $kx - \omega t \equiv k'x' - \omega't'$ for all (x, t) and the related (x', t'). But we know x and t in terms of x' and t', so we have

$$k'x' - \omega't' \equiv kx - \omega t \equiv k\gamma(x' + Vt') - \omega\gamma\left(t' + \frac{Vx'}{c^2}\right)$$

$$\equiv \left[\gamma\left(k - \frac{V\omega}{c^2}\right)\right]x' - [\gamma(\omega - Vk)]t'.$$

This must hold as an algebraic *identity* for all x' and t'. Thus

$$k' = \gamma\left(k - \frac{V\omega}{c^2}\right)$$

$$\omega' = \gamma(\omega - Vk). \tag{7.10}$$

This shows how the wave appears to the observer in motion. It is easy to prove that to this observer the wave still has a speed c, since its speed is $\omega'/k' = c$ (recall $\omega/k = c$).*

Equation (7.10) shows that $(k, \omega/c^2)$ transforms as (x, t), or as $(p_x, E/c^2)$ [cf. Eq. (6.20)]. More generally (see problem 7.5) one can consider a wave of the form

$$\sin(\mathbf{k}\cdot\mathbf{r} - \omega t) \equiv \sin(k_x x + k_y y + k_z z - \omega t)$$

where $\mathbf{k} = (k_x, k_y, k_z)$, called the wave vector, has length $k = \omega/c$, and the wave travels in the direction of $\mathbf{k}$. One can then prove that $(\mathbf{k}, \omega/c^2)$ transforms exactly as $(\mathbf{r}, t)$, or as $(\mathbf{p}, E/c^2)$.

We hence have an association $\mathbf{p} \sim \mathbf{k}$ and $E \sim \omega$. Further, $\omega = kc$, from which $E = pc$. This last relationship is equivalent to the relationship $\mathscr{E} = \mathscr{P}c$ which is known to hold for the energy density and momentum density of an electromagnetic wave (see Section 6.4, page

---

*It is trivial to go from Eq. (7.10) to our previous "Doppler-shift" equation (4.23). Notice that in the present proof we did not have to introduce the somewhat artificial pulses or "clangs" of light—not that they were really necessary in Section 4.7.

167). Einstein in 1905* had asserted that the "anomalous" behavior found in the photoelectric effect could be fully understood by assuming that in some sense an electromagnetic wave consists of *particles*, called photons, traveling with the speed of light c, and *each* carrying energy $E = h\nu = \hbar\omega$, where ν is the frequency of the wave. Here h is Planck's constant, and $\hbar = h/(2\pi) = 1.05450 \times 10^{-27}$ erg sec. (This made use of the empirically known "quantization" of energy.) The consequences of this prediction were very soon confirmed by Millikan. Because of the classical relationship $\mathscr{E} = \mathscr{P}c$, this implied that the photon carries momentum $p = \hbar k$, with $p = E/c$. This last relationship corresponds precisely to the relativistic equation holding for a particle of zero rest mass, traveling (necessarily) at the speed of light.†

In the next section we treat the particle nature of the photon more fully.

7.5   THE PHOTON AS A PARTICLE

If one takes a beam of electrons and fires them at a target, X-rays are produced, which in fact consist of electromagnetic radiation—that is, light of very short wavelength. One can actually diffract X-rays on ruled gratings, and hence obtain a "monochromatic" beam of known wavelength λ (typically 10^{-3} or 10^{-4} smaller than the wavelength of visible light, i.e., $\lambda \sim 10^{-7}$ or 10^{-8} cm).

Such a beam of X-rays can then be scattered off a target, such as a thin metallic foil. Such a target contains nearly free electrons, and these should be expected to oscillate with the same frequency ν as the incident electromagnetic radiation, i.e., $\nu = c/\lambda$. As these charged electrons oscillate, they in turn will radiate with the same frequency, so that one would expect to find the X-rays scattered in all directions, but with the same frequency ν as the incident X-rays.

Experimentally this process was first investigated by A. H. Compton, who indeed found that most of the scattered X-rays had the same frequency ν; but he also found that some of the scattered X-rays had

---

Ann. Physik, **17**, 132 (1905). This is *not* the same paper as the one introducing the special theory of relativity, also written in 1905. In the same year, Einstein also wrote a most important paper on Brownian motion and the kinetic theory of gases, from which one was able to obtain Avogadro's number. This gave great impetus to the atomic view of matter.

†The relationship $p = \hbar k = h/\lambda$ was generalized by de Broglie in 1924 so as to associate a wave with wavelength $\lambda = h/p$ to *any* particle having a momentum p. This was the foundation of wave mechanics, and was first confirmed experimentally by Davisson and Germer, who observed interferencce effects in electron scattering. De Broglie's reasoning was indeed based on relativistic invariance.

a lower frequency v', which was a function of the angle θ through which they were scattered (see Fig. 7.4a). This result is completely paradoxical from the point of view of classical physics, which treats the X-rays as a wave motion having a time dependence associated with the frequency v.

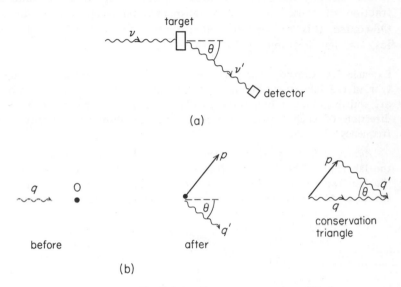

(a)

before   after

(b)

Fig. 7.4 (a) Compton scattering; (b) the momenta involved.

On the other hand the Compton effect is perfectly understandable from the viewpoint of relativity and quantum theory, if we once admit that the photon is a *particle*, with an energy $E \doteq hv$. We use the symbol γ for the photon. In an elastic collision $\gamma + e \rightarrow \gamma + e$ with the initial electron at rest, it is perfectly reasonable for the energy of the scattered γ to be different from that of the incident γ. In fact, denoting the momentum of the incident γ by $q = E/c = hv/c = h/\lambda$, and that of the scattered γ by $q' = hv'/c = h/\lambda'$, we then *know* that the momentum of the scattered electron is $\mathbf{p} = \mathbf{q} - \mathbf{q}'$ [cf. Fig. 7.4(b)]. But by energy conservation

$$hv = hv' + (\sqrt{p^2c^2 + m^2c^4} - mc^2)$$

where m is the rest mass of the electron. Since $p^2 = q^2 + q'^2 - 2qq' \cos\theta$, one readily finds that (cf. problem 7.13)

$$\frac{h}{mc^2}(1 - \cos\theta) = \frac{1}{v'} - \frac{1}{v} = \frac{1}{c}(\lambda' - \lambda). \qquad (7.11)$$

This equation is found to agree exactly with experiment.* Notice that in the derivation we have assumed that the photons do travel with the speed of light c, so that $E = pc$.

If one were to explain this particle nature of X-rays as completely distinct from any electromagnetic wave, then classical physics (or rather the physicists) would find it just as hard to understand the diffraction of these particles by a spectrometer-type diffraction grating. Of course, this wave-particle duality is a feature of quantum mechanics, and has nothing to do with relativity.

Example 7.4. Consider the decay $\pi^\circ \to 2\gamma$, where the initial pion has velocity **u** in the laboratory. Suppose that in the C. of M. frame the two photons are emitted along a line perpendicular to the direction of **u**. What is the direction of each emitted photon in the lab frame, its momentum, and its frequency?

Answer 7.4. We show the decay in Fig. 7.5, both in the C. of M., and in the lab frame. The C. of M. frame has a velocity **u** w.r.t. the lab frame, and the lab frame has a velocity $-\mathbf{u}$ w.r.t. the C. of M. frame. Suppose that in the C. of M. frame each photon has a momentum q, and hence an energy

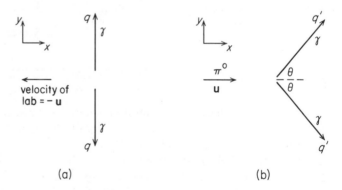

Fig. 7.5 The decay $\pi^\circ \to 2\gamma$: (a) in the C. of M. frame; (b) in the laboratory frame.

cq. Then necessarily $m_\pi c^2 = 2cq$, or $q = (1/2)m_\pi c$. Thus the momentum of one of the photons in the C. of M. frame is given by $\mathbf{q} = (0, q, 0)_{\text{C.M.}}$ where the x and y axes are as indicated in the figure; and its energy is given by $E = cq$. Hence in the lab frame these become transformed to

$$\mathbf{q}' = \left(\frac{\gamma u(cq)}{c^2}, \, q, \, 0\right)_{\text{lab}} \quad \text{and} \quad E' = \gamma(cq),$$

*Now the surprise is that one does observe some scattered photons having the original v. These were scattered off the atom as a whole, so that m becomes the mass of the atom. Properly even in this case there is a small frequency shift.

where we have used Eq. (6.20) with $V = -u$ (since the primed coordinates refer to the lab frame). Here $\gamma = [1 - (u^2/c^2)]^{-1/2}$. If we rewrite these as

$$\mathbf{q}' = (q' \cos \theta, q' \sin \theta, 0) \quad \text{and} \quad E'$$

we see that

$$q'^2 = \left(\frac{\gamma^2 u^2}{c^2} + 1\right) q^2 = \gamma^2 q^2$$

or

$$q' = \gamma q.$$

Also

$$\sin \theta = \frac{q}{q'} = \gamma^{-1} < 1$$

and (necessarily, for otherwise we would have a contradiction with $q' = \gamma q$)

$$E' = cq'.$$

Hence

$$\theta = \sin^{-1} \sqrt{1 - (u^2/c^2)}$$

$$q' = \frac{1}{\sqrt{1 - (u^2/c^2)}} \frac{1}{2} m_\pi c$$

and

$$\nu' = \frac{cq'}{h}.$$

With this example, we end our discussion of applications of the Special Theory of Relativity. We have not tried to be complete in any sense. A very large part of modern physics rests upon the framework of the Special Theory of Relativity, and one of the few solid cornerstones of the theory of elementary particles *is* the necessity of invariance of any theory under the Lorentz transformation.

In the following final chapter, we very briefly indicate that there are further realms of questioning and understanding to be discovered beyond the Special Theory of Relativity.

PROBLEMS

(Essential problems are indicated by !, difficult problems by *.)

7.1 Consider a nuclear-physics "endothermic" reaction $A + B \rightarrow C + D$, with $c^2(m_C + m_D - m_A - m_B) = Q > 0$. Since $Q > 0$ (the meaning of "endothermic") some *minimum* kinetic energy T_0 must be given to A in order that the reaction can "go." (We assume that the target B is at rest.) Assume that all velocities are *nonrelativistic*, and evaluate T_0. Perform the calculation in two ways:

(a) in the laboratory frame; (b) in the C. of M. frame (cf. problem 6.14). [*Hint*: What are the minimum possible kinetic energies of C and D in the C. of M. frame?]

*7.2 Consider in more detail the constant-force motion governed by Eqs. (7.2) and (7.4), in the long time limit. Determine the asymptotic approach of v to c, correct to powers of $1/t^2$, and use this to determine the energy and momentum to order $1/t$.

*7.3 Consider a charged particle moving at high velocity $\approx c$ along the x axis, which enters a region of constant electric field E directed along the y direction. Determine its momentum as a function of time. Hence using $E^2 = m^2c^4 + p^2c^2$, and $Ev = pc^2$, determine its velocity components as a function of time. Discuss your results, commenting in particular on v_x.

7.4 Through what electric potential must a proton be accelerated to attain the speed of light according to Newtonian mechanics? What speed does it actually attain? If it is accelerated through ten times this potential, what is its speed? What is its relativistic (total) mass for each of these cases?

*7.5 Consider a general electromagnetic wave $\sin(\mathbf{k} \cdot \mathbf{r} - \omega t)$, traveling in the direction $\mathbf{k}$, with frequency $\nu = \omega/(2\pi)$ and wavelength $\lambda = 2\pi/k$. Proceed as in Section 7.4, and show that $(\mathbf{k}, \omega/c^2)$ transforms exactly like $(\mathbf{r}, t)$. Hence determine how the direction $\mathbf{k}$ and the frequency ν transform under a Lorentz transformation. Compare your results with the treatment of aberration (Section 4.6), and the Doppler effect (Section 4.7, but there only given for the longitudinal and transverse cases). The two effects are necessarily related, cf. p. 98.

7.6 Consider a collision between two identical particles, each having a rest mass m_0, and one being initially at rest. Suppose that the two final velocities make angles θ and ϕ with the incident velocity $\mathbf{v}$. Obtain a general relationship between θ, ϕ, v, and m_0 for the two cases: (a) $v \ll c$, that is, "classical" or nonrelativistic; (b) v comparable with c.

7.7 Consider an elastic scattering $\pi^+ + p \rightarrow \pi^+ + p$ which is being used to determine the mass of the pion. An incident pion of measured momentum $q = 1.313 \, \mathrm{BeV}/c = 1.313 \times 10^9 \, \mathrm{eV}/c$ strikes a proton at rest. Each particle recoils at a direction of 45° with the incident beam direction, and each is observed to have the same momentum of $q/\sqrt{2}$. What is the π^+ mass, given that $m_p = 938 \, \mathrm{MeV}/c^2$? [*Note*: This problem is very artificial since one could not hope to obtain m_π accurately once one allowed for measurement uncertainties. Why is this?]

7.8 (a) Consider the π^- decay at rest $\pi^- \rightarrow \mu^- + \bar{\nu}$. Obtain algebraic expressions for the kinetic energies of the μ meson and of the anti-neutrino, and show that these are equal to 4.1 MeV and 29.8 MeV, respectively; i.e., 6.6×10^{-13} joule and 47.7×10^{-13} joule. What is the speed of the μ^-? Of the $\bar{\nu}$?

(b) Consider the $\pi^- \rightarrow \mu^- + \bar{\nu}$ decay in flight in the laboratory, with measured momenta $\mathbf{p}_\pi$ and $\mathbf{p}_\mu$, and calculated energies E_π and E_μ. Transform these momenta and energies to the π^- rest frame by using the appropriate velocity $\mathbf{V}$ of the Lorentz transformation, given by $\mathbf{V} = -\mathbf{p}_\pi c^2/E_\pi$. Obtain the rest frame muon *kinetic* energy in terms only of laboratory quantities.

(c) Set the rest frame muon kinetic energy obtained in part (b) equal to the algebraic expression obtained in part (a). Show that the resulting constraint on the laboratory momenta and energies is exactly equivalent to that which says $m_\nu^2 c^4 = (E_\pi - E_\mu)^2 - (\mathbf{p}_\pi - \mathbf{p}_\mu)^2 c^2 = 0$. This last equation again shows the power of invariance arguments, since it can be evaluated in *any* frame of reference, including that of the laboratory.

7.9 Consider the production process $p + p \to \pi^+ + n + p$. Find the laboratory threshold kinetic energy T for the incident proton which is needed for the process to "go." [*Hint*: Transform to the C. of M. frame, cf. problems 6.14 and 6.15.]

7.10 A photon collides with a proton at rest to form a π°-meson by the reaction $\gamma + p \to \pi^\circ + p$. Find the threshold energy of the photon (and hence the photon frequency) needed for the process to occur. What is then the speed of the π° in the lab? Of the final p? [*Hint:* Transform to the C. of M. frame.]

7.11 Consider the process $\mu^+ \to e^+ + \nu + \bar{\nu}$, where ν and $\bar{\nu}$ are neutral and have zero rest mass. Determine the maximum and minimum kinetic energies that the electron can have in the rest frame of the decay (i.e., the frame in which the μ^+ is at rest). Contrast this result with that of problem 7.8.

7.12 Consider the process $e + p \to e + p$, where the initial proton is at rest, and the direction of the incident e is known, but *not* its momentum. The momentum of the final p is measured to be q, in a direction making an angle θ with the incident direction. Further, the direction of the final e is observed to make an angle of ϕ with the incident direction (in the opposite sense to θ), but suppose that its momentum can*not* be measured. Show how to obtain the incident beam momentum. What is its value? (This type of problem often arises in bubble-chamber physics. In such a case one has only *just* sufficient information to "solve" the motion. It is really desirable to measure too much information, in order to obtain a "self-consistency" check.) *Note:* Naturally the directions of the incident e, and of the final e and p lie in a plane. Why?

7.13 Work through the complete derivation of the Compton effect, and obtain Eq. (7.11).

APPENDIX C

RELATIVITY AND ELECTROMAGNETISM

C.1 INTRODUCTION

Our treatment of the special theory of relativity has been based on a discussion of space and time, and on mechanics. However the historical development relied heavily upon Maxwell's Equations of Electromagnetism.* The connection between electromagnetism and the special theory of relativity is very close. In particular, the basic signal velocity c, the velocity of light, is in fact the velocity of electromagnetic radiation. The existence of electromagnetic radiation having the velocity c is a prediction of Maxwell's equations, and these equations can indeed be made invariant under the Lorentz transformation, once one suitably defines how electric and magnetic fields are to transform. This means that if one imposes the First Relativity Postulate upon Maxwell's equations, one can determine the relationship between electric and magnetic fields as seen by an observer in a frame S, and as seen by an observer in a frame S', where S' and S have a constant relative velocity.

Actually, the theory of relativity has even greater impact on electromagnetism than the above. For one can prove, starting *only* from Coulomb's law and the special theory of relativity:

(i) that magnetic fields must exist and be produced by currents,

(ii) that they obey all the standard "magnetic" equations of electromagnetism,

(iii) that in a combination of electric and magnetic fields the force on a charged particle is given by the Lorentz force $\mathbf{F} = q(\mathbf{E} + \mathbf{v} \times \mathbf{B})$, and,

(iv) that Faraday's law of electromagnetic induction must hold.

*Eor example, Einstein's first paper on the subject was called "On the Electrodynamics of Moving Bodies." We gave a translation of the first five sections as Appendix B; three of the remaining five sections deal directly with Maxwell's equations.

The list (i)–(iv) implies that Coulomb's law, together with the special theory of relativity, is equivalent to the complete structure of electromagnetism as given by Maxwell's equations. Once again, this was not the historical development!

In this appendix, we wish to indicate briefly how the existence of magnetic fields can be demonstrated as a consequence of the special theory of relativity. Our treatment will not be complete, since this is not our purpose. It leans heavily on the beautiful treatment of electromagnetism, starting from the special theory of relativity, given by Edward M. Purcell in *Electricity and Magnetism: Berkeley Physics Course,* Vol. 2 (New York: McGraw-Hill Book Company, 1963, 1964, 1965). We refer the reader to this work for clarification of those points that we only sketch lightly—or worse still, discuss not at all.

C.2 GAUSS' THEOREM, AND THE DEFINITION OF CHARGE

We start with electro*statics*, Coulomb's law, and Gauss' theorem. By definition, the force on a particle of charge q which is at *rest* in an electro*static* field $\mathbf{E}$ is given by

$$\boxed{\begin{array}{l} \text{charge at rest:} \\ \mathbf{F} = q\mathbf{E}. \end{array}} \tag{C.1}$$

Futhermore, Gauss' theorem tells us that

$$\boxed{\int\limits_{\text{closed surface}} \mathbf{E}\cdot d\mathbf{S} = \frac{1}{\epsilon_0}\, Q_{\text{enclosed}}.} \tag{C.2}$$

Suppose now that our charged particle is *moving* through the electric field $\mathbf{E}$ produced by other charges at rest. We *cannot* assume immediately that $\mathbf{F} = q\mathbf{E}$ (though this will turn out to be true). In fact, we cannot even be sure that the charge of a moving particle is the same as its charge when at rest. We first need an operational definition of charge for moving bodies. This is provided by Gauss' thorem, which enables us to obtain the net charge inside a closed surface by measuring the electric field everywhere on the surface. This measurement can be done using *stationary* test charges. We use Gauss' theorem to *define* the net charge of a system, independently of whether parts of that system are in motion. Of course, for this to be reasonable, we must show experimentally that the surface flux integral is independent of the particular surface taken, provided all such surfaces include the same charges.

With this operational definition of charge, we can then experimentally demonstrate that the charge of a moving particle is the *same* as when the particle is at rest. In other words, charge is *invariant* with respect to motion, and hence charge is invariant under a Lorentz transformation.

C.3 THE TRANSFORMATION OF THE ELECTRIC FIELD

With this knowledge, and Gauss' theorem, we can now determine the transformation properties of the electric field $\mathbf{E}$ under a Lorentz transformation. More precisely, consider observers A and B in their frames S and S', and consider a particular space-time event $P \equiv (\mathbf{r}, t)_A \equiv (\mathbf{r}', t')_B$. A measures the electric field *at this event*—that is, A measures $\mathbf{E}(\mathbf{r}, t)$. Similarly B in his frame measures the electric field *at the same event* $\mathbf{E}'(\mathbf{r}', t')$. How are $\mathbf{E}$ and $\mathbf{E}'$ related?

We answer this question by considering a special charge configu-

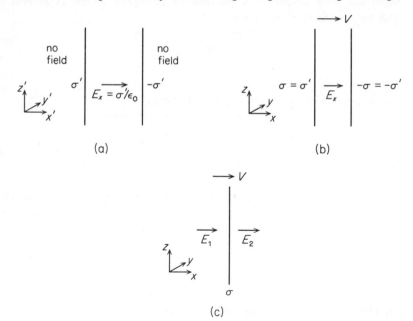

(a)

(b)

(c)

Fig. C.1 (a) A parallel-plate capacitor as seen by B; (b) the same capacitor as seen by A, according to whom the capacitor has velocity V; (c) a single charged plate moving with velocity V as seen by A.

ration. Suppose B sees an infinite parallel-plate condenser at rest in S', with surface charge densities σ' and $-\sigma'$, and an internal electric field $E' = \sigma'/\epsilon_0$. Suppose first that the plates are parallel to the $y'z'$ plane, so that E' is along the Ox' direction [see Fig. C.1(a)]. A then sees this parallel-plate capacitor moving with velocity V along the Ox direction. A and B measure different spacings of the plates, on account of the Lorentz-Fitzgerald contraction, but they each measure the *same* surface charge densities, so that $\sigma = \sigma'$. What electric field does A see? [See Fig. C.1(b).]

We can answer this by using the principle of superposition. In Fig. C.1(c) we show a single such plate moving with velocity V and having a charge density σ. By symmetry and Gauss' theorem, the electric field must be along Ox and must have values E_1 and E_2 on the two sides of the plate as shown, such that $E_2 = E_1 + \sigma/\epsilon_0$. A similar single plate with charge density $-\sigma$ must then have fields $-E_1$ and $-E_2$ on the two sides. Then, by superposition, in Fig. C.1(b) the electric field in the leftmost region must be $E_1 + (-E_1) = 0$, in the central region it must be $E_2 + (-E_1) = \sigma/\epsilon_0$, and in the rightmost region it must be $E_2 + (-E_2) = 0$. Hence A sees the *standard* capacitor field $E = \sigma/\epsilon_0$ between the plates, and $E = E'$ (recall $\sigma' = \sigma$). Since this electric field was parallel to V we have really only demonstrated that $E_{\parallel} = E'_{\parallel}$ (and so far only for a particular experimental setup).

We next consider a capacitor whose plates are parallel to the $x'y'$ plane, at rest w.r.t. B as shown in Fig. C.2(a), and as seen by A in Fig. C.2(b). Now as a consequence of the x length contraction w.r.t. x', we see that $\sigma \propto Q/l_x = Q/(\gamma^{-1}l'_x) \propto \gamma\sigma'$, that is, $\sigma = \gamma\sigma' > \sigma'$. When we turn to the electric field as seen by A, we are apparently in difficulty, since V gives us a new direction in the problem. Thus for a single charged plate moving at velocity V in its plane as seen by A, the field could have the somewhat startling form shown in Fig. C.2(c), where E_1 and E_2 are mirror images of each other. But this, together with superposition, is enough to show that in the case of Fig. C.2(b), E can only have a z component E_z, and further, that a nonzero E_z exists only between the plates. Then by applying Gauss' theorem to Fig. C.2(b), we immediately obtain $E_z = \sigma/\epsilon_0 = \gamma(\sigma'/\epsilon_0) = \gamma E'_z$. Clearly this can be generalized to $E_{\perp} = \gamma E'_{\perp}$.

These results have been obtained by considering very special geometries. Nonetheless, if we believe in the basic *field* nature of electromagnetism, we imply that the *local* value of the electric field has a true existence, *independent* of the particular source arrangement which produced this local field. Once this is admitted, the transformation equations for E must be independent of the particular source arrangement, but can depend only on E. Furthermore, the principle of superposition must apply.

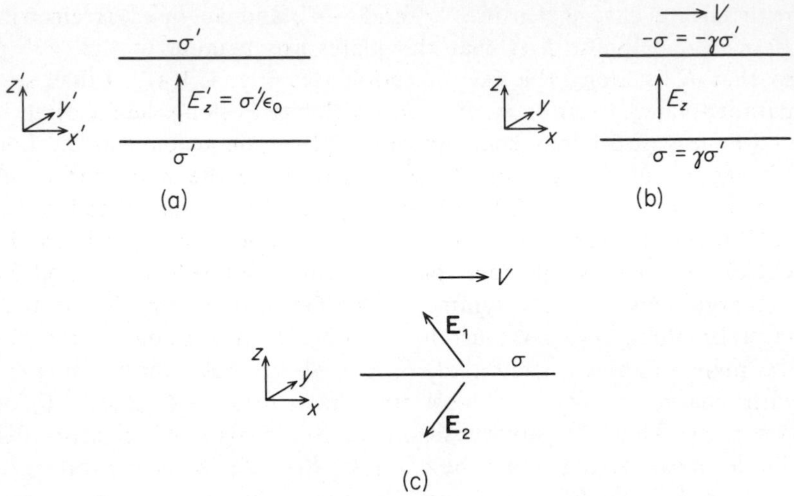

Fig. C.2 (a) A parallel-plate capacitor as seen by B; (b) the same capacitor as seen by A, according to whom the capacitor has velocity V; (c) a single charged plate moving with velocity V as seen by A.

Hence we can now write the *general* transformation law as

$$\boxed{\begin{array}{l} \text{For } E' \text{ due to charges } at\ rest \text{ w.r.t. } S', \text{ then} \\[4pt] E_{\parallel} = E'_{\parallel} \\[4pt] E_{\perp} = \gamma E'_{\perp}, \quad \gamma = \left(1 - \dfrac{V^2}{c^2}\right)^{-1/2} \\[4pt] \text{evaluated at the same space-time point.} \end{array}} \qquad \text{(C.3)}$$

C.4 THE ELECTRIC FIELD DUE TO A MOVING POINT CHARGE

We apply this result to the field due to a point charge Q moving with constant velocity V along the Ox direction. In Fig. C.3(a) we show a charge Q at rest at B's spatial origin, together with the Coulomb field due to that charge as seen by B. Then at the spatial point $(x', 0, z')$, we have that

$$(x', 0, z'): \quad E'_x = \frac{Q}{4\pi\epsilon_0} \frac{\cos\theta'}{r'^2} = \frac{Q}{4\pi\epsilon_0} \frac{x'}{(x'^2 + z'^2)^{3/2}}$$

$$E'_z = \frac{Q}{4\pi\epsilon_0} \frac{\sin\theta'}{r'^2} = \frac{Q}{4\pi\epsilon_0} \frac{z'}{(x'^2 + z'^2)^{3/2}} \tag{C.4}$$

where these are independent of t'. We now look at the same experiment from A's point of view, at the instant that the charge is at A's spatial origin, i.e., at $t = 0$. Furthermore we consider the point $(x, 0, z)$ such that $(x, 0, z, t=0)_A \equiv (x', 0, z', t')_B$ where $(x', 0, z')$ is the spatial point according to B already considered in Eq. (C.4). That is,

$$x' = \gamma(x - Vt) = \gamma x, \qquad z' = z.$$

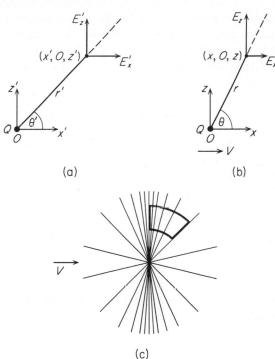

(a)   (b)

(c)

Fig. C.3 (a) The Coulomb field of a point charge Q at rest at B's spatial origin; (b) the same field, as seen by A, for whom the charge has a velocity V (the figure is drawn for that instant, according to A, at which the charge is at A's spatial origin); (c) the general pattern of field lines produced by a moving charge (a closed path having non-vanishing $\int \mathbf{E} \cdot d\mathbf{l}$ is also shown).

Then for this event as seen by A, we must have

$$E_x = E'_x = \frac{Q}{4\pi\epsilon_0}\frac{x'}{(x'^2 + z'^2)^{3/2}} = \frac{Q}{4\pi\epsilon_0}\frac{\gamma x}{[(\gamma x)^2 + z^2]^{3/2}}$$

$$E_z = \gamma E'_z = \gamma\frac{Q}{4\pi\epsilon_0}\frac{z'}{(x'^2 + z'^2)^{3/2}} = \frac{Q}{4\pi\epsilon_0}\frac{\gamma z}{[(\gamma x)^2 + z^2]^{3/2}}.$$

(C.5)

Notice that because of the γ in $E_z = \gamma E'_z$, we find that $E_x/E_z = x/z$. Hence, as seen by A, the electric field at the event $(x, 0, z, 0)_A$ due to a charge Q *instantaneously* at the origin is directed along the radius connecting the origin to the point of observation.

This is *most* remarkable, since it says that, according to A, at $t = 0$ the electric field at all points is directed along the line joining the observation point to the *instantaneous* position of charge Q. This looks dangerously like instantaneous transmission of the information of the position of the charge! But it isn't, since the charge has been moving with constant velocity **V** along a trajectory such that it will arrive at A's spatial origin at $t = 0$. This is the information that is really used at the event $(x, 0, z, 0)_A$. This information was actually sent out from that particular earlier event K on Q's trajectory such that it would reach the event $(x, 0, z, 0)_A$ by traveling from the earlier event K at the speed of light. The motion of Q after the event K cannot affect the field seen at the event $(x, 0, z, 0)_A$. We cannot go into this question further here, but it leads to the prediction of electromagnetic waves (cf. Purcell, *loc. cit.*).

Returning to Eq. (C.5), we see that while **E** is radial, its magnitude is not given by the simple $1/r^2$ law. If we set $x = r\cos\theta$, $z = r\sin\theta$, we see that

$$E_r = \left[\frac{Q}{4\pi\epsilon_0}\frac{1}{r^2}\right] \times \frac{1 - (V^2/c^2)}{[1 - (V^2\sin^2\theta/c^2)]^{3/2}}, \qquad E_\theta = 0 \qquad (C.6)$$

so that the strength of the field is greatest at $\theta = \pi/2$. We show this field pattern schematically in Fig. C.3(c). The lines of force have become "compressed" into the plane transverse to the velocity **V**. We remark that for the field pattern given by Eq. (C.6), the line integral $\int \mathbf{E} \cdot d\mathbf{l} \neq 0$. [For consider the path made up of parts of radii and arcs of circles as shown in Fig. C.3(c).] This is most remarkable, but after all this is *not* electrostatics. We will shortly show that there is a (changing) magnetic field associated with this moving charge, and hence, by Faraday's law we would not expect $\int \mathbf{E} \cdot d\mathbf{l}$ to vanish.

C.5   THE FORCE ON A MOVING CHARGE

Equations (C.1) and (C.5) can be combined to tell us the force exerted upon a stationary charge due to another charge moving at constant velocity. We can now apply the first relativity postulate to determine the force exerted upon a moving charge due to stationary charges. We know, from Section 6.6 [particularly Eq. (6.24)], that the force must transform according to

particle at rest in S':

$$F_{\parallel} = F'_{\parallel}, \qquad F_{\perp} = \gamma^{-1} F'_{\perp}. \tag{C.7}$$

But $\mathbf{F}' = q\mathbf{E}'$. Furthermore, we can rewrite Eq. (C.3) as:

For $\mathbf{E}$ due to charges at rest in S, then:

$$E_{\parallel} = E'_{\parallel}, \qquad E_{\perp} = \gamma^{-1} E'_{\perp}. \tag{C.8}$$

Using $\mathbf{F}' = q\mathbf{E}'$, we then immediately obtain

Force on q moving in S due to charges at rest in S:
$$\mathbf{F} = q\mathbf{E}. \tag{C.9}$$

This result is the *generalization* of Eq. (C.2), but at first sight it may seem trivial (since so familiar). However, there was no obvious need for Eq. (C.2) to generalize to Eq. (C.9). Equation (C.9) does hold experimentally, as we have discussed in Chapter 7 (in particular Section 7.2). This may properly be considered as a verification of charge invariance, upon which all our present discussion has been based.

C.6 THE MAGNETIC FIELD

We finally consider the force between two moving charges. We will obtain this force by use of the First Relativity Postulate, and our previous results based solely upon Coulomb's law. Our result will be expressible as due to a "magnetic field," this magnetic field obeying all the usual equations. In fact it is just the usual magnetic field. We will hence have proved that the magnetic field is a necessary consequence of Coulomb's law and the Special Theory of Relativity. Since this is our aim, we consider a rather special system of charges, which is really a model of a current in a straight wire.

We consider an infinite set of point charges uniformly spaced along the x axis, so that in *their* rest frame the charge density per unit length of the x axis is given by λ. We now go to the "laboratory frame" shown in Fig. C.4(a), in which this uniform line of charges moves along the x axis with a constant velocity v. In this frame, by the Lorentz-Fitzgerald contraction, the effective charge density and the effective current are given by:

$$\lambda_l = \lambda \left(1 - \frac{v^2}{c^2}\right)^{-1/2} \quad \text{and} \quad I_l = v\lambda_l, \tag{C.10}$$

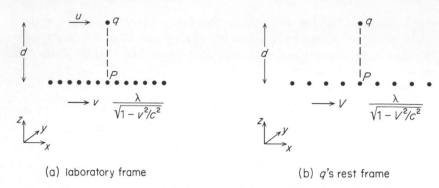

(a) laboratory frame   (b) q's rest frame

Fig. C.4 A point charge q and a line of charges in relative motion as seen (a) in the laboratory frame and (b) in the rest frame of the charge q.

where the suffix l denotes "lab". In this frame there is also another charge q, moving with constant velocity u parallel to the x axis, but distant d from this axis. We ask, "What is the force on q?"

We answer this question by going to the rest frame of q, shown in Fig. C.4(b). In this rest frame (called "r"), the line of charges has a velocity and charge density given by:

$$V = \frac{v - u}{1 - (vu/c^2)} \quad \text{and} \quad \lambda_r = \frac{\lambda}{\sqrt{1 - (V^2/c^2)}}. \qquad (C.11)$$

The force on q in its rest frame is given by $q\mathbf{E}^{(r)}$, where $\mathbf{E}^{(r)}$ is the electric field at q due to the *moving* line of charges. But what is the direction of $\mathbf{E}^{(r)}$ in this frame? This can be answered by transforming to the rest frame of the line of charges. In this frame $E_x = 0$. Hence, using Eq. (C.2), with $E'_\parallel = E_x = 0$, we see that $E_x^{(r)} = 0$. Thus the electric field $\mathbf{E}^{(r)}$ in the rest frame of the charge q [Fig. C.4(b)] lies only in the yz plane, and by symmetry must be directed "radially" outwards from the line of charges.

Now that we know the direction of $\mathbf{E}^{(r)}$, we can immediately use Gauss' theorem to tell us that $\mathbf{E}^{(r)}$ at q has magnitude given by $\lambda_r/(2\pi d\epsilon_0)$. Hence in the q rest frame the force on q is given by

$$F^{(r)} = qE^{(r)} = \frac{q\lambda}{2\pi d\epsilon_0\sqrt{1 - (V^2/c^2)}}, \quad \text{along } Pq. \qquad (C.12)$$

This force is perpendicular to u, and is the force on q in its rest frame. Hence we can use Eq. (C.7) to obtain the force on q in the lab frame. From Eq. (C.7), we finally have

$F_l = $ force on q in lab frame is directed along Pq, and

$$= \sqrt{1 - (u^2/c^2)}\, F^{(r)} = \sqrt{1 - (u^2/c^2)} \left(\frac{q\lambda}{2\pi d\epsilon_0\sqrt{1 - (V^2/c^2)}} \right). \qquad (C.13)$$

But (cf. problem 4.3) one can readily show, using Eq. (C.11), that

$$1 - \frac{V^2}{c^2} = \frac{[1 - (u^2/c^2)][1 - (v^2/c^2)]}{[1 - (vu/c^2)]^2} .$$

Putting everything together, one "easily" finds that

$$F_l = \frac{\lambda_l q}{2\pi d\epsilon_0}\left(1 - \frac{vu}{c^2}\right). \tag{C.14}$$

Now $\lambda_l/(2\pi d\epsilon_0) = E_l$ [cf. the equation for $E^{(r)}$ due to the moving line of charges]. Further, $\lambda_l v = I_l$. Let us define

$$c^2 \epsilon_0 = \frac{1}{\mu_0} \quad \text{and} \quad B_l = \frac{\mu_0 I_l}{(2\pi d)} . \tag{C.15}$$

Then Eq. (C.14) can be written

$$F_l = q(E_l + uB_l)$$

or

$$\mathbf{F}_l = q(\mathbf{E}_l + \mathbf{u} \times \mathbf{B}_l) \tag{C.16}$$

where we assume that $\mathbf{B}_l$ goes in circles looping I_l in a clockwise sense.

Clearly this analysis does not prove Eq. (C.16) in general. However, we have shown that when both q and the source of $\mathbf{E}$ are moving, *the force on q is not completely given by $q\mathbf{E}$*, and that some extra force is *uniquely* specified by the First Relativity Postulate. If we had considered the most general direction for $\mathbf{u}$, we would have been compelled to arrive at the Lorentz force Eq. (C.16).

From this point of view $\mathbf{B}$ is an "auxiliary construct." By using superposition, nearly all problems can be reduced to that of two point charges in relative motion. One can then always go to the frame in which the "source" charge is at rest. In this frame Coulomb's law contains all of electromagnetism. However, rather than going to this frame, the First Relativity Postulate enables us to work in any frame. In such a general frame, the force between the two charges can be written as the sum of an electric force $q\mathbf{E}$ and a "magnetic" force $q\mathbf{v} \times \mathbf{B}$. But $\mathbf{B}$ is an auxiliary construct, since it can always be obtained from $\mathbf{E}$ in the source rest frame. In fact, $\mathbf{B}$ is simply given by

$$\mathbf{B} = \mathbf{V} \times \frac{\mathbf{E}}{c^2} \tag{C.17}$$

where $\mathbf{V}$ is the velocity of the source charge in the lab frame. From this point of view, it is clear that μ_0 *must* be related to ϵ_0 and c.

We do not expect to have convinced the reader of this "auxiliary" nature of $\mathbf{B}$. Furthermore, we have yet to prove that our $\mathbf{B}$ satisfies Maxwell's equations. Once we have done this, our $\mathbf{B}$ must necessarily be identical to the usual $\mathbf{B}$. Nonetheless, our statements are correct. This should not be taken to mean that $\mathbf{B}$ is a fraud. In a general frame, it is certainly easiest to work with $\mathbf{E}$ and $\mathbf{B}$, on an equal footing. The point is that $\mathbf{E}$ and $\mathbf{B}$ are related. There are not two separate subjects, "electricity" and "magnetism," but only one: "electromagnetism."*

For more details of this relativistic view of electromagnetism we refer the reader to Purcell, *loc. cit.* This view does not overthrow the "classical" point of view, but illuminates it. That the classical viewpoint requires "illumination" can be illustrated by the famous experiment of Trouton and Noble† which was performed before the development of the special theory of relativity. Consider two equal and opposite charges at the ends of a rod suspended by a torsion fiber (cf. Fig. C.5). Sup-

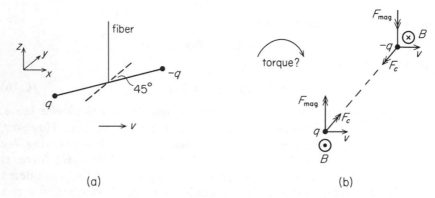

(a)   (b)

Fig. C.5 The Trouton and Noble experiment: (a) general 3-dimensional view; (b) top view, showing the various forces acting.

pose the system is moving at an angle of 45° to the rod with velocity **v**. Then each charge sets up a magnetic field at the location of the other charge, and magnetic forces are set up, such that a magnetic torque acts on the system. The Coulomb force is along the line joining the charges, and so should exert no torque (cf. Section C.4.). Does the system rotate? If yes, we have a way of detecting absolute motion. The experiment was unable to detect absolute motion (fortunately, from the point of view of the theory of relativity). The resolution of this result is quite complex within the framework of the (correct) equations of electromagnetism. The torque *does* exist, but causes *no rotation.*‡ The easy resolution is via the First Relativity Postulate. Since the system certainly will not rotate in the frame in which v is zero, it cannot rotate in any frame!

*In fact, Faraday's law is most readily understood in terms of $\mathbf{F} = q\mathbf{v} \times \mathbf{B}$! One then introduces an "auxiliary" **E** according to $\mathbf{F} = q\mathbf{E}$.

†F. T. Trouton and H. R. Noble, *Proc. Roy. Soc.*, **72**, 132 (1903).

‡The resolution of this "paradox" is beyond the scope of this book. It requires a full relativistic study of the mechanics of solid bodies. In fact, the concept of a "rigid" body is in contradiction with the theory of relativity (cf. Example 3.4).

8

THE GENERAL THEORY
OF RELATIVITY

Throughout our discussion, we have only considered observers in *constant* relative motion w.r.t. each other. What about observers who accelerate w.r.t. each other? Of course, there is no difficulty with the special theory of relativity when considering the accelerated motion of a particle, as seen by an observer who is at rest in an inertial frame. What is not specified by the special theory is how an observer sets up a *consistent* space-time frame of reference when he himself is accelerating. Thus in the discussion of the twin paradox in Section 4.8, *A* could discuss the complete motion of *B*, even though this included accelerations; but *B* was unable to describe *A*'s motion consistently as long as *B* tried to consider himself at rest. This is because *B* was not in the same inertial frame throughout the motion.

Thus another question has to do with our restriction to inertial frames. By definition, in Newtonian physics, an inertial frame is one in which a body moves with constant velocity as long as it is not under the influence of any net external force. But how do we know when there is no net external force? By considering the example of the fictitious centrifugal force in a rotating frame of reference, one sees that an inertial frame is really defined as any frame in which $\mathbf{F} = m\mathbf{a}$ holds, where $\mathbf{F}$ includes only real forces, as opposed to "fictitious" forces. This definition transfers straightforwardly to the special theory of relativity.

But is this distinction into real and fictitious forces so self-evident? In particular, is gravitation a real force?

Having raised the topic of gravitation, we remark on the fact that there are two different definitions of mass. The inertial mass m_i appears in $F = m_i a$ and its relativistic generalization. The gravitational mass m_g appears in $F_g = m_g m_g'/r^2$, the law of Newtonian gravitation.* Galileo's famous (if apocryphal) experiment at the leaning tower of Pisa already demonstated that $m_i \propto m_g$, since all bodies fall with the same "acceleration due to gravity."† Very careful experiments, originally performed in the 1890's and 1900's by R. von Eötvös, and more recently to higher accuracy by R. H. Dicke, have shown that m_i/m_g is a universal constant for each of the many substances tested, to an accuracy of a few parts in 10^{11}. (One can then set this constant $=1$ by suitably defining G.) Why should this be so, when the very concept of mass itself is so hard to define?

These questions were studied in detail by the philosophically minded physicist E. Mach.‡ Another question he posed has to do with absolute rotation. Newton had stated that absolute rotation could be detected. Thus he asserted that if a bucket of water were at rest w.r.t. a frame of reference in absolute rotation, the surface of the water would take on a parabolic shape. Mach asked, "What was it with respect to which the frame was in absolute rotation?" He went on to answer that the "absolute frame" was determined by the positions of all the masses in the universe, in particular the "fixed stars." Thus Mach said that in an empty universe, the concept of absolute rotation was meaningless. Similarly there could be no "twin paradox" in an empty universe. Mach's ideas have been summarized in "Mach's Principle," which can be stated as: "The inertia of an object is caused by the mutual effect upon it of all the other bodies in the universe."§ This principle has not

---

*Actually here we can also differentiate between the mass which is the source of the gravitational force, and the mass upon which it acts. Newton's third law enables one to "prove" that these masses must be proportional, but Newton's third law itself runs into difficulties if applied to forces which act at a distance.

†G. Feinberg [*Am. J. Phys.*, **33**, 501 (1965)] has computed the surprisingly large effect of air resistance which Galileo would have encountered if he had actually performed the experiment. See also the references given by Feinberg.

‡The same Mach whose name is a unit for air speed in this supersonic jet age.

§We remark that this idea has a most profound consequence, totally at variance with the day-to-day working philosophy of the practicing physicist. This is that very distant matter exerts a fundamental influence on the results of small-scale experiments performed in the laboratory. Since this influence is constant, the working physicist can and does proceed by ignoring the possibility! Thus he *assumes* that the effect is independent of direction. (The universe does in fact seem to be uniform in all directions.)

been proved, but it is attractive to many physicists. It asserts that m_i is due to m_g, but does not go on to explain the proportionality.

Mach's principle greatly influenced Einstein, who however still wanted to demonstrate that the relationship $m_i \propto m_g$ was not only an accident. If not an accident, this relationship must be built into the very framework of the theory. Hence Einstein proceeded to build it in, not by postulating this particular relationship, but by *postulating* another principle, the "Principle of Equivalence," which principle automatically leads to $m_i \propto m_g$. (He proposed this idea in 1911.) We can illustrate the principle of equivalence very readily. Consider an experimentalist in a large laboratory with no windows. The laboratory is situated on the surface of the earth, and the physicist soon discovers the constant force of gravity mg. Now imagine the whole laboratory accelerated downwards at a constant rate $\frac{1}{3}g$. The physicist has no way of distinguishing this from the possibility that his laboratory has been transferred to the surface of some other planet where the acceleration due to gravity is $\frac{2}{3}g$, his laboratory being at rest w.r.t. this surface. For in each case the acceleration of a freely falling body will be measured by the physicist to be equal to $\frac{2}{3}g$. But notice how in these two viewpoints the roles of gravitational mass and inertial mass become intertwined.

Einstein asserted that in a local sense (i. e., in a small region such as the windowless laboratory) it is impossible to distinguish between the effects of a gravitational field, and the effects of being in an accelerated frame of reference. In other words, being in a gravitational field is locally equivalent to being in an accelerated frame of reference. (The restriction to a local region is needed because if the gravitational field varies in direction or magnitude from place to place, then the equivalent acceleration also varies. Thus we need a different accelerated coordinate system for each region.)

This principle of equivalence is in itself a very powerful theorem, but must not be confused with the full General Theory of Relativity. Before discussing the latter, we turn to some applications of this principle.

Consider two observers A and B in a region of constant downward gravitational field g, A being a height d above B, as shown in Fig. 8.1(a). In Fig. 8.1(b) an equivalent viewpoint is shown in which there is no gravitational field, but A and B each have constant upward acceleration $a = g$. Suppose A emits a pulse of light having a frequency v. What frequency does B observe? We answer this in the second viewpoint of Fig. 8.1(b). It takes the light a time $t = d/c$ to travel from A to B. (Here we have neglected a small correction of order gd/c^2.) Suppose the light was emitted when A had an upward velocity v. Then it reaches B when B has an upward velocity $v + at = v + gd/c$, so that

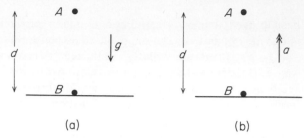

Fig. 8.1 The gravitational red shift: (a) an experimental setup with two observers, A and B, at rest in a constant *down*ward gravitational field g; (b) the "equivalent" viewpoint in which both A and B are accelerating *up*wards with a constant acceleration $a = g$, in a field free region.

the *effective* relative motion of the source A and the receiver B is given by gd/c (independent of v). Hence there will be a Doppler shift, with B receiving a frequency v' given by

$$\frac{v'}{v} = \sqrt{\frac{c + (gd/c)}{c - (gd/c)}} \approx 1 + gd/c^2 \qquad (8.1)$$

[cf. Eq. (4.25)]. This result must also hold in the equivalent experiment of Fig. 8.1(a). Thus **in falling a distance d in a gravitational field g, light must increase in frequency according to Eq. (8.1)**. This result also has a profound effect on the concept of time, and of ideal clocks. For if A emits n wavelengths of light per unit time, then B must surely receive the *same* number n of wavelengths per unit time. Yet $v' \neq v$, so it follows that the unit of time differs for A and B (cf. p. 223).

This "gravitational red-shift" effect can also be deduced very readily from the photon theory of light. For if A emits a photon of frequency v, the photon has an energy hv, and hence a mass $m = hv/c^2$. In falling it then gains an amount of energy mgd, the gravitational potential energy. Thus $hv' = hv + mgd = hv + hvgd/c^2$, the same as Eq. (8.1). This experiment has actually been carried out.* The distance d was ≈ 22 meters, but was effectively doubled by repeating the experiment with A and B interchanged. Thus the predicted effect is given by

$$\frac{\Delta v}{v} = \frac{v' - v}{v} \approx 2 \times 2.46 \times 10^{-16}.$$

They obtained $\dfrac{(\Delta v)_{\text{expt}}}{(\Delta v)_{\text{theory}}} = +1.05 \pm 0.10.$†

*R. V. Pound and G. A. Rebka, Jr., *Phys. Rev. Letters*, **4**, 337 (1960). This experiment used the Mössbauer effect in Fe⁵⁷.

†The whole effect could be simulated by a temperature difference of 1°C between A and B. This was very carefully monitored. More recently, in a refinement of the experiment, R. V. Pound and J. L. Snider [*Phys. Rev.*, **140**, B788 (1965)] have obtained $(\Delta v)_{\text{expt}}/(\Delta v)_{\text{theory}} = 0.9990 \pm 0.0076$. They estimate that any systematic error is smaller than or equal to $+0.0100$. In general, all tests of general relativity involve very small effects, and so are very hard to perform.

A similar effect is predicted for the light emitted from the surface of a star, and observed on earth. This effect depends on the difference in gravitational potential between the source and the observer. This "gravitational red-shift" has possibly been detected from the surface of the sun, but the interpretation is ambiguous. This is because it is always superimposed on much larger Doppler shifts, caused by the velocity of the star or (as in the case of the sun) the convective mass motion of the various parts of the star which are emitting the radiation.

Notice that by using the principle of equivalence we are able to calculate the effect of a *constant, uniform* gravitational field in an experiment, if we *already* know the prediction of the special theory of relativity in an "equivalent" experiment.* Thus the twin paradox can also be discussed in the *noninertial* frame of the traveler B, if one superposes a gravitational field which acts only during the time that B is accelerating. During this time, A's clock will undergo a gravitational "speeding up," of just such an amount that when this gravitational aging is allowed for, A is again found to be older than B, even though A is now effectively the traveler. However, such a discussion of the twin paradox is really empty, since it relies on the principle of equivalence, and hence necessarily must obtain the *same* result as given by the special theory of relativity. As previously emphasized, A is truly in an inertial frame throughout the motion, while B definitely changes inertial frames. Once this is understood, the detailed calculation of the relative aging of the twins is properly within the scope of the *special* theory of relativity. What is outside the scope of this theory is what determines that B is not in an inertial frame. Even though the special theory cannot answer this, we do unambiguously know that B is the traveler, since he *feels* the accelerations.

While the principle of equivalence essentially postulates that $m_i \propto m_g$, and while it does discuss the effect of gravitational fields in certain cases, it does not provide a complete theory of gravitation. Now Newtonian gravitation is an action-at-a-distance theory, in which the effect of moving the source of a gravitational field is detected *immediately* by the body upon which it acts. Thus Newtonian gravitational signals travel with an infinite speed. It follows that Newton's theory of gravitation is in contradiction with the special theory of relativity (cf. Section 4.5 and Example 4.5). Thus it is necessary to develop a new theory of gravitation.

Furthermore, the special theory of relativity only discusses the equivalence of two observers who have constant relative velocities. It would clearly be desirable to have a theory in which *all* observers are

---

*The restriction to a uniform field is the same restriction as the restriction to a local region in the Principle of Equivalence.

equivalent. (Of course they may give different interpretations to the same experiment.)

Einstein in 1916, in his General Theory of Relativity, proposed a theory which incorporated the principle of equivalence, made *all* observers equal, and also incorporated a specific theory of gravitation in which gravitational effects propagate at the speed of light.

Einstein's General Theory of Relativity is not the only such theory which has been proposed. Other such theories contain different specific theories of gravitation and theories of the source of gravitational fields. These theories are, of course, extremely hard to test experimentally. Einstein himself proposed three tests of *his* General Theory. We give these now:

(i) Owing to a modification of Newton's law of gravitation $F = Gm_1 m_2/r^2$, the orbits of the planets should not be exact ellipses, but instead each nearly elliptical orbit should be slightly displaced with respect to the previous orbit. They are not ellipses in any case, owing to the influence of the other planets (the three-body problem), but this effect can be calculated using Newtonian theory. A very small discrepancy remains in the case of the orbit of Mercury. This is the planet closest to the sun, and hence most likely to be affected by Einstein's modification to Newton's law, The prediction and the experimental observation agree very well. This effect is known as the "precession of the perihelion of Mercury."* Similar effects have also been observed for Venus and for the Earth though these are much smaller, and so even harder to measure accurately. The agreement with the Einstein prediction for all three planets makes this one of the best tests of this particular aspect of the Einstein theory. In particular, since the predictions agree so well for three planets, it is hard to conceive of another explanation (for instance an oblateness of the sun) which which do as well.†

(ii) Einstein's second test was the deflection of light in a gravitational field. If we believe that light consists of particles with mass, then a beam of light should be deflected by a (very strong) gravitational field. This effect can be calculated classically, and the "mass" of the light cancels out of the calculation (Why?). However, one should use the relativistic equations of motion, and in fact the full General Theory. One then obtains a predicted result twice as great as

---

*The magnitude of the effect is about 43″ of arc per century, which corresponds to one complete precession of the orbit every three million years. It is remarkable that either theory or experiment can deal with such small effects.

†For an up-to-date summary, see paper 1, "Experiments on Gravitation," by B. Berotti, D. Brill, and R. Krotkov, in *Gravitation: An Introduction to Current Research*, ed. L. Witten (New York: John Wiley & Sons, Inc., 1962). This paper also discusses the other Einstein tests.

the "Newtonian" result (the latter was first calculated by Soldner in 1801). The experiment is very difficult, and is performed by observing stars very near the edge of the sun at the time of a total eclipse, and then again six months later when the sun is no longer there (it will then be night time). The apparent positions of the stars in the two cases should differ by an amount of 1.75 seconds of arc.* Control techniques are used in which one also photographs star fields away from the sun at the two times. Nonetheless the experiments are very exacting, and while the Newtonian prediction is certainly too small, and the experiments are reasonably compatible with the Einstein prediction, yet the agreement is not perfect. Recently there has been work on the possibility of detecting this effect without waiting for a solar eclipse. Another variant of this test which uses microwave and radar techniques was proposed by I. I. Shapiro in 1965. This experiment may well be performed by 1968.

While this effect is plausible on the "particle" theory of light, yet it has startling consequences upon the wave theory of light. For any refraction of light observed in a particular space-time frame of reference, must imply that the velocity of light is not constant in that frame. Thus the second relativity postulate of the Special Theory is restricted to a four-coordinate system in which there is *no* gravitational field. (We know that we can always find such a system at a *point*.) Similarly the ideal clocks which are considered in the Special Theory must all be in a gravitationally field-free region. We remark that the "reason" that light must be deflected in a gravitational field can already be seen from the principle of equivalence. For in an accelerating frame of reference a "true" straight-line path is necessarily curved. However this explanation only predicts half of the full effect. The principle of equivalence is *not* enough to explain the effect fully.

(iii) Einstein's third test was the solar gravitational red-shift, which we have already discussed. The test cannot be made, and in any case is only a test of the principle of equivalence, already verified in the Pound-Rebka experiment.

In summary, the status of the various experimental results is such that they are compatible with many different "gravitational theories" which have been proposed. Einstein's own "General Theory" is only one such theory, and is not particularly singled out, except by its formal simplicity.†

There is presently a great deal of interest and research into general

---

*A *very* small angle, roughly that subtended by a dime (or a sixpence) at a distance of 2 kilometers.

†An excellent summary of all the present experiments and their implications for the various theories is given in *The Theoretical Significance of Experimental Relativity*, R. H. Dicke (New York: Gordon and Breach, 1964).

theories of gravitation and cosmology, and the last word has certainly not been written.* One of the more exciting predictions of Einstein's theory is the *possible* existence of gravitational waves, which travel with the speed of light. A search is presently under way to detect such waves.

With this, we end our discussion of Einstein's two great theories of relativity. The Special Theory by itself is a remarkable work, which has withstood all the attacks of time unscathed since 1905. The General Theory is even more daring, and though it suffers from having few laboratory-type experimental tests, it has great consequences for astrophysics and cosmology. Finally, we remark that the elementary-particle physicist in particular may be making a great error in ignoring the influence of gravitation in his theories. If inertia and mass are ultimately due to the fixed stars, how can this "simplifying" assumption be correct? It is fitting to close this book with a question.

*Thus, for instance, there is presently disagreement concerning the exact aspect of the General Theory which would be tested by Shapiro's experiment. Does it, or does it not, give more information than is provided by the deflection-of-light experiment? (This footnote, written in 1966, may soon be out of date.)

A PARTIAL BIBLIOGRAPHY

HISTORICAL AND PHILOSOPHICAL

Einstein, A., and L. Infeld, *The Evolution of Physics*. New York: Simon and Schuster, Inc., 1938.

Holton, G., "On the Origins of the Special Theory of Relativity," *Am. J. Phys.*, **28**, 627 (1960).

Lanczos, Cornelius, *Albert Einstein and the Cosmic World Order*. New York: John Wiley & Sons, Inc., 1965. A somewhat panegyric but very interesting nonmathematical account of the significance of Einstein.

Schilpp, P. S., ed., *Albert Einstein: Philosopher-Scientist*, 2 vols. New York: Tudor Publishing Co., 1951; paperback, Harper Torchbooks, 1959.

Scribner, C., Jr., "Poincaré's Role in Relativity," *Am. J. Phys.*, **32**, 672 (1964). See also H. M. Schwartz, *Am. J. Phys.*, **33**, 170 (1965).

Shankland, R. S., "Conversations with Albert Einstein," *Am. J. Phys.*, **31**, 47 (1963) [but see also *ibid.*, **32**, 16 (1964)].

A comprehensive list of other historical references is given by G. Holton in "Resource Letter SRT-1 on Special Relativity Theory," *Am. J. Phys.*, **30**, 462 (1962).

TEXTBOOKS

Born, Max, *Einstein's Theory of Relativity*, revised edition prepared with the collaboration of Günther Leibfried and Walter Biem. New York: Dover Publications, Inc., 1962. A very good account both of the early "ether" theories and of Einstein's Special and General Theories of Relativity. Highly recommended.

Durell, Clement V., *Readable Relativity*. London: G. Bell & Sons, Ltd., 1926; softcover reprint by Harper & Row, 1960. An indeed very readable account of relativistic kinematics, at about the level of this book.

Einstein, A., *Relativity, the Special and the General Theory*. London: Methuen & Co., Ltd., 1920; reprinted as a University Paperback, 1960. Not really a textbook; quite difficult in places.

Landau, L. D., and G. Rumer, *What is Relativity?*, trans. N. Kemmer. Edinburgh: Oliver and Boyd, 1960. A lighthearted Russian presentation with witty illustrations; paperback.

Rindler, W., *Special Relativity*. Edinburgh: Oliver and Boyd, 1960. A good intermediate-level text.

Rosser, W. G. V., *An Introduction to the Theory of Relativity*. London: Butterworth & Co., Ltd., 1964. A detailed, intermediate-level text.

BOOKS REFERRED TO IN THE TEXT

Bohm, D., *Special Theory of Relativity*. New York: W. A. Benjamin, 1965, paperback.

Bondi, H., *Relativity and Common Sense*. Garden City, N. Y.: Doubleday & Co., Inc., 1964, paperback.

Feynman, R. P., R. B. Leighton, and M. Sands, *The Feynman Lectures on Physics*. Reading, Mass.: Addison-Wesley Publishing Co., Inc., 1963.

Lorentz, H. A., A. Einstein, H. Minkowski, and H. Weyl, *The Principle of Relativity—a Collection of Original Memoirs*, trans. W. Perrett and G. B. Jeffery. London: Methuen & Co., Ltd., 1923; paperback reprint, Dover Publications, 1958.

Special Relativity Theory, selected reprints published for A.A.P.T. American Institute of Physics, 335 E. 45th Street, New York 17, N. Y. 1962.

OTHER TEXTS TREATING RELATIVITY AT THE LEVEL OF
THE PRESENT BOOK

Atkins, C. R., *Physics*. New York: John Wiley & Sons, Inc., 1965. The section on the twin paradox is very misleading.

Kittel, C., W. D. Knight, and M. A. Ruderman, *Mechanics*; *Berkeley Physics Course Vol. 1*. New York: McGraw-Hill Book Company, 1965.

Smith, J. H., *Introduction to Special Relativity*. New York: W. A. Benjamin, 1965, paperback.

Taylor, E. F., and J. A. Wheeler, *Space Time Physics*. San Francisco: W. H. Freeman, 1966.

Young, H. D., *Fundamentals of Mechanics and Heat*. New York: McGraw-Hill Book Company, 1964.

A novel diagrammatic way of presenting the content of the Lorentz transformation has been developed by R. W. Brehme, *Am. J. Phys.*, 30, 489 (1962). It has been described and used in the textbook *University Physics*, by F. W. Sears and M. W. Zemansky (Reading, Mass.: Addison-Wesley Publishing Co., Inc., 1963).

INDEX